D0203276

Desert Biomes

GREENWOOD GUIDES TO
BIOMES OF THE WORLD

Introduction to Biomes
Susan L. Woodward

Tropical Forest Biomes
Barbara A. Holzman

Temperate Forest Biomes
Bernd H. Kuennecke

Grassland Biomes
Susan L. Woodward

Desert Biomes
Joyce A. Quinn

Arctic and Alpine Biomes
Joyce A. Quinn

Freshwater Aquatic Biomes
Richard A. Roth

Marine Biomes
Susan L. Woodward

Desert BIOMES

Joyce A. Quinn

Greenwood Guides to Biomes of the World

Susan L. Woodward, General Editor

GREENWOOD PRESS
Westport, Connecticut • London

Library of Congress Cataloging-in-Publication Data

Quinn, Joyce Ann.
Desert biomes / Joyce A. Quinn.
p. cm.—(Greenwood guides to biomes of the world)
Includes bibliographical references and index.
ISBN 978-0-313-33840-3 (set : alk. paper)—ISBN 978-0-313-34016-1 (vol. : alk. paper)
1. Desert ecology. 2. Deserts. I. Title.
QH541.5.D4Q56 2009
577.54—dc22 2008027509

British Library Cataloguing in Publication Data is available.

Library of Congress Catalog Card Number: 2008027509
ISBN: 978-0-313-34016-1 (vol.)
978-0-313-33840-3 (set)

First published in 2009

Greenwood Press, 88 Post Road West, Westport, CT 06881
An imprint of Greenwood Publishing Group, Inc.
www.greenwood.com

Printed in the United States of America

The paper used in this book complies with the Permanent Paper Standard issued by the National Information Standards Organization (Z39.48–1984).

10 9 8 7 6 5 4 3 2 1

Contents

Preface

As this book and the length of the species lists testify, deserts are not barren, lifeless places. Because many deserts developed in isolation from one another, unique plants and animals evolved, often, however with similar adaptations to environmental conditions of heat, aridity, and salinity. While the most severe climates, such as the majority of the Sahara Desert, are devoid of plant and animal life, others, such as parts of the Sonoran Desert in North America or the Monte Desert in South America, often appear crowded with plants. Some plants, such as cardon cacti in Baja California or dragon's blood trees on the island of Socotra, are large and imposing. In contrast, many so-called stone plants in the Succulent Karoo of South Africa are so tiny they must be viewed on hands and knees. Animal species, both large and small, are present but infrequently seen because most are nocturnal or crepuscular, avoiding midday heat. Animal populations are low because of scarce resources.

Although I have traveled to and experienced many deserts in North America, Asia, and Africa firsthand, research for this volume was a learning experience. For example, I now realize that the interesting 6 in (15 cm) plant that I coddle in my greenhouse can reach a height of 15 ft (4.5 m) in the rocky hills of Namibia. With a better grasp of conditions in their natural environments, I now view my plants with greater respect and also can care for them more appropriately. When we say that deserts have "harsh" environmental conditions, we consider them from a human standpoint. Just as a maple tree or magnolia tree would be ill-suited to grow in a desert, a rainy climate such as a mid-latitude forest would be "harsh" to a desert-adapted plant or animal. Simply stated, water your cactus too much and it will die.

Many humans live in regions that are considered arid or semi-arid, sometimes of necessity, sometimes just because we like the sunshine and rainless days. Scarce water supplies in those regions would be better utilized if residents were aware of the environmental requirements of landscape plants. The variety of shapes, colors, textures, and flowers of plants from the world's deserts provide great selections for drought-tolerant landscaping.

Deserts are fragile environments. Plants often take several years to grow and mature. Sparse and unreliable rainfall, intense heat or cold, and poor soils may mean that a damaged area may never fully recover. Animals that depend on plants for food or cover are also negatively affected.

Deserts are defined by little rainfall, but not all have consistent high temperatures. The first chapter explains elements, such as temperature, precipitation, and adaptations, common to all deserts of the world. Differences in climate, vegetation, and animal life are elaborated on in subsequent chapters where selected geographic regions are described.

Textual material is illustrated with numerous maps, diagrams, photographs, and line drawings. The intended audience is not only advanced middle school and high school students, but also university undergraduates and anyone else who is interested in the natural environment of deserts.

I would like to thank Kevin Downing of Greenwood Press for his insights and constant support in the completion of this project. Jeff Dixon did a masterful job of deciphering my sketches to produce meaningful illustrations. Bernd Kuennecke of Radford University's Geography Department prepared the maps of the worldwide distribution of desert regions. Several people generously provided pictures for the book, while others read drafts and offered suggestions. Special mention is made of Björn Jordan, who cleared up my confusion about Old World desert rodents. I am deeply indebted to all individuals who enabled me to finalize this volume. Any errors, however, are solely my own.

How to Use This Book

The book is arranged with a general introduction to desert biomes and a chapter each on the Warm Deserts Biome, Cold Deserts Biome, and West-Coast Fog Deserts Biome. The introduction describes unifying characteristics, such as the physical environment of the biome and plant and animal adaptations. Subsequent chapters begin with a general overview at a global scale and descriptions of features specific to that biome. Regional descriptions are organized by the continents on which they appear. Each chapter and each regional description can more or less stand on its own, but the reader will find it instructive to investigate the introductory chapter and the introductory sections in the later chapters. More in-depth coverage of topics perhaps not so thoroughly developed in the regional discussions usually appears in the introductions.

The use of Latin or scientific names for species has been kept to a minimum in the text. However, the scientific name of each plant or animal for which a common name is given in a chapter appears in an appendix to that chapter. A glossary at the end of the book gives definitions of selected terms used throughout the volume. The bibliography lists the works consulted by the author and is arranged by biome and the regional expressions of that biome.

All biomes overlap to some degree with others, so you may wish to refer to other books among Greenwood Guides to the Biomes of the World. The volume entitled *Introduction to Biomes* presents simplified descriptions of all the major biomes. It also discusses the major concepts that inform scientists in their study and understanding of biomes and describes and explains, at a global scale, the environmental factors and processes that serve to differentiate the world's biomes.

The Use of Scientific Names

Good reasons exist for knowing the scientific or Latin names of organisms, even if at first they seem strange and cumbersome. Scientific names are agreed on by international committees and, with few exceptions, are used throughout the world. So everyone knows exactly which species or group of species everyone else is talking about. This is not true for common names, which vary from place to place and language to language. Another problem with common names is that in many instances European colonists saw resemblances between new species they encountered in the Americas or elsewhere and those familiar to them at home. So they gave the foreign plant or animal the same name as the Old World species. The common American Robin is a "robin" because it has a red breast like the English or European Robin and not because the two are closely related. In fact, if one checks the scientific names, one finds that the American Robin is *Turdus migratorius* and the English Robin is *Erithacus rubecula.* And they have not merely been put into different genera (*Turdus* versus *Erithacus*) by taxonomists, but into different families. The American Robin is a thrush (family Turdidae), and the English Robin is an Old World flycatcher (family Muscicapidae). Sometimes that matters. Comparing the two birds is really comparing apples to oranges. They are different creatures, a fact masked by their common names.

Scientific names can be secret treasures when it comes to unraveling the puzzles of species distributions. The more different two species are in their taxonomic relationships, the farther apart in time they are from a common ancestor. So two species placed in the same genus are somewhat like two brothers having the same father—they are closely related and of the same generation. Two genera in the same family might be thought of as two cousins—they have the same grandfather, but different fathers. Their common ancestral roots are separated farther by time. The important thing in the study of biomes is that distance measured by time often means distance measured by separation in space as well. It is widely held that new species come about when a population becomes isolated in one way or another from the rest of its kind and adapts to a different environment. The scientific classification into genera, families, orders, and so forth reflects how long ago a population went its separate way in an evolutionary sense and usually points to some past environmental changes that created barriers to the exchange of genes among all members of a species. It hints at the movements of species and both ancient and recent connections or barriers. So if you find two species in the same genus or two genera in the same family that occur on different continents today, this tells you that their "fathers" or "grandfathers" not so long ago lived in close contact, either because the continents were connected by suitable habitat or because some members of the ancestral group were able to overcome a barrier and settle in a new location. The greater the degree of taxonomic separation (for example, different families existing in different geographic areas), the longer the time back to a common ancestor and the longer ago the physical separation of the species. Evolutionary history and Earth history are hidden in a name. Thus, taxonomic classification can be important.

Most readers, of course, won't want or need to consider the deep past. So, as much as possible, Latin names for species do not appear in the text. Only when a common English language name is not available, as often is true for plants and animals from other parts of the world, is the scientific name provided. The names of families and, sometimes, orders appear because they are such strong indicators of long isolation and separate evolution. Scientific names do appear in chapter appendixes. Anyone looking for more information on a particular type of organism is cautioned to use the Latin name in your literature or Internet search to ensure that you are dealing with the correct plant or animal. Anyone comparing the plants and animals of two different biomes or of two different regional expressions of the same biome should likewise consult the list of scientific names to be sure a "robin" in one place is the same as a "robin" in another.

1

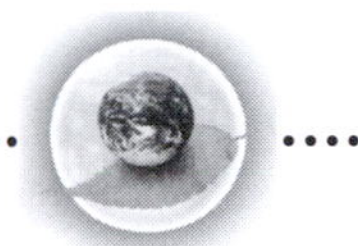

Introduction to Desert Biomes

The term desert has many connotations. Many people think a desert is a barren wasteland of sand dunes with no water and no life. That definition, however, defines very few deserts. Deserts are regions where life is sparse but not nonexistent. Deserts can be caused by climate conditions, soil excesses or deficiencies, or human activities. An overabundance of one element, such as sodium, in the soil may retard plant growth so severely that the region becomes barren. Overgrazing of grassland or cutting of timber may cause water erosion to devastate an area, leaving a lifeless landscape. Cities have been called urban deserts. This volume is devoted to climatic desert biomes with unique assemblages of plants and animals adapted to arid conditions, sometimes hot, sometimes cold, depending on the location.

No universally accepted definition exists of what constitutes a climatic desert. It can be defined on the basis of lack of rainfall, but scientists disagree as to whether that should be as little as 5 in (125 mm) or as much as 15 in (380 mm). Koeppen's climate classification system places the boundary between humid and semiarid climates where evaporation is equal to precipitation. It arbitrarily places the boundary between semiarid and arid climates where evaporation is twice as much as precipitation. Terminology can further confuse the issue—desert, semidesert, subdesert, steppe—none have a precise definition. The broad definition of desert centers on the fact that the potential for evapotranspiration (the combined process of evaporation and transpiration) is more than precipitation. This means that if it were available, more water could be evaporated or used by plants than the region receives as rainfall or snowfall. Unlike a wet climate where precipitation exceeds evapotranspiration and the excess runs off as rivers and streams, this deficit of water results in dry river channels and lack of consistent water flow. Because potential evapotranspiration (PET) depends largely on temperature (at higher temperatures, more water can evaporate), it is misleading to state that a desert receives a certain amount of precipitation. A region like southern Arizona with about 10 in (250 mm) of yearly rainfall is a desert because temperatures and evaporation are high. Deserts, however, are not always hot. Cooler locations like Mongolia are deserts because they receive even less rainfall. The seasonality of precipitation, whether it rains predominantly in cooler winter or in hotter summer, is an important factor in the relationship of PET to precipitation. Winter rainfall is more useful to plants and animals because less evaporates, while summer rainfall may evaporate without being used at all. Therefore, if two regions both receive the same amount of yearly precipitation, the one with summer rather than winter precipitation is more arid.

Just as the term desert has several definitions, the deserts of the world can be subdivided in several ways (see Figure 1.1). This volume will describe three major types—warm, cold, and west-coast fog (see Table 1.1). Warm (or hot) deserts lie predominantly in the subtropical latitudes and are characterized by temperatures that rarely fall below freezing. Cold deserts in mid-latitudes have temperature extremes, hot in summer and below freezing in winter. In the Northern Hemisphere, both warm and cold deserts are more extensive and more extreme due to larger landmasses. Deserts in the Southern Hemisphere are more restricted in area. For the same reason, the larger continents of Asia and Africa have larger and drier deserts than North America does. West-coast fog deserts are found in tropical or subtropical regions but are limited to the west coasts of continents. Some small, local deserts will be addressed in this chapter because their plant and animal assemblages are unique. Rainshadow location also may contribute to desert conditions in any type of desert.

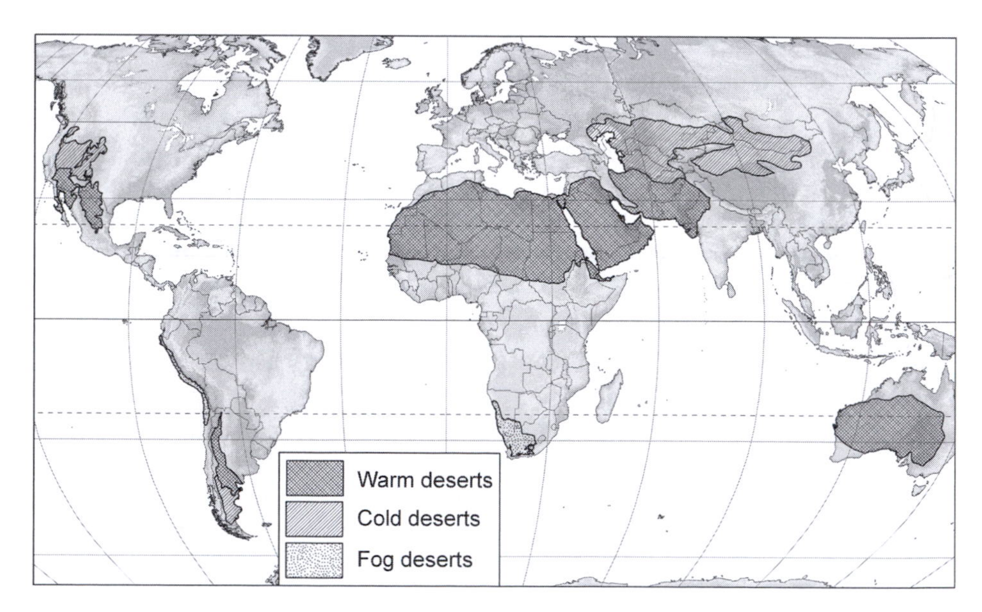

Figure 1.1 Deserts have a wide distribution throughout the world, both in tropical and mid-latitude locations. *(Map by Bernd Kuennecke.)*

Table 1.1 Physical Environment of Warm Deserts, Cold Deserts, and West-Coast Fog Deserts

	Warm Deserts	Cold Deserts	West-Coast Fog Deserts
Location	Tropic and subtropics (10°–35° N & S); west side of continents	Middle latitudes (35°–50° N); interior of large continents or rainshadow of major mountain ranges	Tropics (10°–35° N & S); narrow strip along west coasts
Temperature controls	Tropical latitude; low elevations; intense solar radiation	Mid-latitude seasonality enhanced by continentality; intermediate elevations	Cold coastal current moderates tropical temperatures
Mean summer temperature	85°–95° F (29.5°–35° C)	70°–80° F (21°–27° C)	65°–75° F (18°–24° C)
Mean winter temperature	45°–60° F (7°–15.5° C)	20°–40° F (−7°–4.5° C)	50°–65° F (10°–18° C)
Extreme high temperature	110°–120° F (43°–49° C)	100°–110° F (38°–43° C)	90°–100° F (32°–38° C)
Extreme low temperature	20°–30° F (−1° to −6.5° C)	−15° to −40° F (−26° to −40° C)	30°–45° F (−1° to 7° C)
Precipitation controls	Subtropical high-pressure dominant	Continental or rain-shadow location; cyclonic storms with dry airmasses	Subtropical high-pressure dominant; cold current stabilizes air
Annual precipitation	0–10 in (0–250 mm); rain only	0–10 in (0–250 mm); rain in summer, snow in winter	0.5–5 in (13–125 mm); rain in winter, fog in summer
Seasonality of precipitation	Summer, winter, or sporadic	Cyclonic storms in winter; convectional storms in summer	Winter
Soils	Calcification, salinization, aridisol, azonal, salt pans, rocky, sandy, little humus	Calcification, salinization, aridisol, azonal, salt pans, rocky, sandy, little humus	Calcification, salinization, aridisol, azonal, salt pans, rocky, sandy, little humus

Polar Deserts

Antarctica and parts of the northern Arctic are often called deserts because they support very little life. However, their environments are very different from mid- to low-latitude deserts caused by lack of precipitation, and they should not be placed into the same category. Precipitation is low, but cold temperatures limit evaporation, and plants and animals have distinct adaptations to those cold, dry conditions. See *Arctic and Alpine Biomes* in this series.

Adiabatic Process

Physics is important in determining whether it rains or is dry. In the adiabatic process, air will cool due to expansion and warm due to compression, but no energy is gained or lost. The change in temperature is due only to change in volume, caused by expansion or compression. Release air from a bicycle tire, where it has been compressed to keep the tire inflated, and it feels cool as it comes out. Pump the air back in and the tire becomes warm. As air rises in the atmosphere, it expands and therefore cools. Depending on other conditions such as the relative humidity, the cooling air may form clouds. Conversely, as air sinks, it warms by compression, and no clouds can form.

Physical Environment

Climate

Precipitation. Low rainfall can be caused by three factors. Meteorological high pressure, meaning that the air is heavy and is sinking, increases the temperature of the air and prevents the formation of clouds. The higher temperatures lower the relative humidity which both prevents cloud development and increases evaporation. Paradoxically, then, the warm air becomes light and unstable, wanting to rise, but the stronger high pressure above keeps a lid on the rising air. At times when conditions are right, warm moist air may rise, cool, and form clouds. Because it is warm and the relative humidity is very low, this unstable air usually has to rise very high to produce a thunderstorm cloud. Sometimes dark streaks of rain can be seen coming down from the bottom of a big desert cloud, but they do not reach the surface and nothing is getting wet. The rain evaporates into the dry desert air before reaching the surface, a phenomenon called virga. Regions on the lee sides of mountain ranges are in the rainshadow of prevailing winds (see Figure 1.2). Winds approaching the windward side must rise. The rising air cools as it expands,

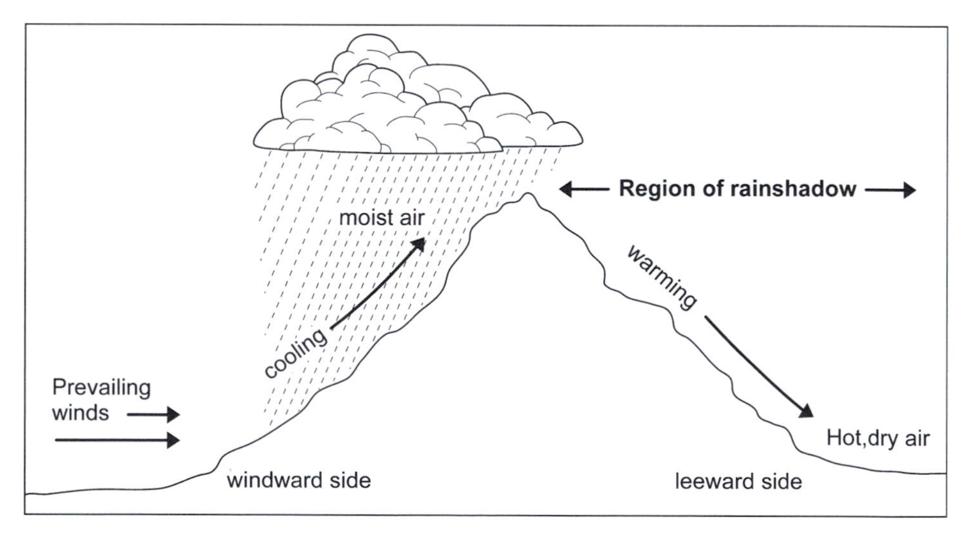

Figure 1.2 The windward side of a mountain is usually rainy, while the lee side, or rainshadow, is dry. *(Illustration by Jeff Dixon.)*

and if cooled enough, clouds will develop. On the lee side, the air sinks back down, and like the high pressure, warms and prevents cloud formation. The dry lee side is called a rainshadow. Direction of the wind determines which side of the mountains is wet and which side is dry. In coastal locations with a cold ocean current along shore, the water both cools and stabilizes the air. As the cooler air blows over the adjacent land, the stable air sinks because it is heavy, again preventing cloud formation and precipitation. Many deserts are affected by more than one of these drying effects. Annual averages of precipitation calculated for a 30-year period are only approximations of what to expect in any given year. Rainfall is sporadic and unpredictable. Sometimes rain may not fall for months or years; at other times isolated torrential downpours may occur. In very general terms, annual precipitation as rain or snow is less than 10 in (250 mm).

Dust Devils

Dust devils may resemble little tornadoes, but these small whirlwinds are very different. Irregularities on the desert floor result in spots that are hotter than those nearby. The high temperatures create a localized low pressure, causing the air to rise in a tight spiral that is visible because of sand and smaller soil particles picked up by the wind. Dust devils usually are short-lived, lasting only a few minutes.

Temperature. Desert temperatures are variable, with extremes of both heat and cold depending on the type of desert. Warm deserts in subtropical latitudes are warm to hot all year, 50°–110° F (10–43° C), and rarely experience temperatures below freezing. Cold deserts in the mid-latitudes have temperature extremes. Long sunny days in summer can raise the temperature to 90°–110° F (32°–43° C). Short winter days and polar airmasses in winter cause freezing to occur nightly, and temperatures may not rise appreciably during the day. Winter months average close to or well below freezing, with lower temperatures in more continental locations. Even though they are subtropical in latitude, West-coast fog deserts have moderate temperatures all year, 50°–75° F (10°–24° C), because of the moderating effect of the oceans. Inland areas of West-coast deserts experience more extreme temperatures, with cooler winters and hotter summers.

Climate data usually provide only the average temperatures, whether they are daily, monthly, or annual, masking many important variations. The average temperature of the day is calculated by adding the highest and lowest temperatures and dividing by two. Diurnal temperature changes, how temperature varies during the day, are often more important to plants and animals

Continental versus Maritime

Why is it cool in summer next to a lake or ocean, or even around a swimming pool? It takes a long time for temperature of water to increase or decrease. In summer, water absorbs and stores heat, leaving less energy to warm the air, so areas adjacent to water are cooler than inland. In winter, water slowly releases that stored energy, warming the land around it. In contrast, land heats and cools more quickly, and the larger the continental area, the bigger the extremes in air temperature will be. A region influenced by water, called maritime, will have moderate seasonal temperature changes. A region without the influence of water, called continental, will experience colder winters and warmer summers.

than the average temperature. If the highest temperature reached during the day is 120° F (49° C) and the lowest, 70° F (21° C), the average is 95° F (35° C). That means that a plant or animal must be able to survive, or avoid, not only 95° F (35° C) but anything between 120° F (49° C) and 70° F (21° C) (see the section Common Adaptations). The same logic applies to monthly and annual temperatures. Average annual temperatures, however, are especially misleading. Walvis Bay in Namibia (Africa) and Barstow in California (North America) both have an average annual temperature of 60°–65° F (15.5°–18.5° C), a figure which tells you nothing about temperature variation throughout the year. The average temperatures of the warmest and coldest months at Walvis Bay are 66° F (19° C) and 52° F (11° C), respectively. In Barstow, the warmest month averages 102° F (39° C), while the coldest month averages 31° F (−0.6° C). Extremes are even more variable.

Geology and Soils

Local distribution of plants and animals in a desert is related to the various types of local environments. Rocky soils have a tendency to hold more water and support a greater variety of life. Salty or sandy locations have a limited number of plants and animals adapted to those conditions. Therefore, a desert landscape exhibits a mosaic of biotic communities based on landform, rock, and soil characteristics.

In spite of the fact that deserts are defined as areas with little moisture, and most of the time desert stream channels are dry, running water is the dominant erosional process. Depending on world location, dry water courses are called washes, wadis, or arroyos. Many desert areas are characterized by interior drainage. Rainfall never reaches the ocean; instead, it drains to the "interior" of the landscape between higher mountain areas. Consequently, sediment (sand and gravel) carried by the streams is deposited not in the ocean but on the land wherever the water either percolated into the ground or evaporated. Desert landscapes are often characterized by abrupt changes from steep mountains or cliffs to gently sloping plains or flats (see Figure 1.3). During sporadic and torrential rainfall events, rapidly flowing streams in the mountains pick up and carry a lot of sediment. As the streams flow out of the canyons at the steep mountain front, the more gentle gradient causes the water to quickly lose speed. As it slows, it loses its ability to carry sediment, which is then deposited in a long, gentle slope at the base of the mountain. The larger particles, maybe even large boulders, are dropped first, the finer material in succession farther down the slope. This long gentle slope of sediment is an alluvial fan. Coalesced alluvial fans are called bajadas. Springs may develop at the base of the alluvial fan as the water percolating through the layers of alluvium reemerges at the surface. If surface or underground water reaches the low point in the valley, it may create a temporary lake only a few inches deep. As the water evaporates, the salts that would be taken to the ocean by exterior drainage accumulate instead on the surface. These usually dry lakebeds are called playas. The surface can be clay or layers of salt. The most common salts are ordinary table salt (sodium chloride) and calcium carbonate.

Figure 1.3 Alluvial fans develop at the base of steep mountains in desert areas because slower velocity forces the stream to deposit its sediment. *(Photo by author. Illustration by Jeff Dixon.)*

Wind plays a role in erosion and deposition, but it is usually localized and minor (see Figure 1.4). The tiniest specks of clay and silt, that is, dust, can be swept to 10,000 ft (3,000 m) or above, but even strong winds are incapable of carrying sand very high. Thus, the concept of cliffs being sand-blasted is a myth. In general, sand can be suspended only about 5 ft (1.5 m) off the ground; therefore, wind erosion is limited in extent. Although the stereotypical desert landscape is nothing but a vast expanse of sand, in reality, sand dunes occupy only 20 percent of all desert areas. Areas of shifting sand dunes in the Sahara Desert are called ergs. The most common result of wind erosion is desert pavement. Wind picks up and carries the finer surface particles—sand and silt—in a process called deflation. Over many years the larger pebble- and cobble-size rocks left behind settle into the vacated spaces and become tightly packed. The surface then resembles a cobblestone street. In some countries in North Africa, the stony surface is called a reg. Although hard enough to walk on without disturbing the pebbly mosaic, the surface layer can be broken by repeated use or vehicle traffic. When desert pavement is disturbed and the unprotected subsurface exposed, erosion can proceed unchecked as water courses develop and enlarge.

On a solid surface, all the fine particles may be completely eliminated by the wind, leaving only bare rock called a hammada. Sand periodically blown from adjacent regions, or from hollows in the rock surface where the sand would accumulate during calm periods, may sand-blast and sculpt the bare rock into fantastic

Figure 1.4 Two major desert landscapes: (a) Sand dunes, sometimes called ergs. *(Photo courtesy of Kh. Terbish.)* (b) Desert pavement, sometimes called regs. *(Photo by author.)*

shapes called yardangs (see Plate I). An individual rock, large or small that has been sculpted by the wind is called a ventifact, meaning "made by wind."

Desert biomes are characterized by rocky outcrops and rocky, sandy, alkaline, or saline soils. Soils have little humus content because plant litter is sparse. The scarcity of water limits chemical reactions that in wetter climates would alter the substrate and create a true soil with distinct horizons (layers) exhibiting specific characteristics such as texture and nutrient content. The lack of humus also retards water absorption and retention. However, wherever burrowing animals disturb the crust and turn over the soil, more water soaks in. Because most water evaporates before it has a chance to penetrate deeply into the soil, little to no leaching takes place, the process by which nutrients are distributed to different horizons. The U.S. Soil Conservation Service classifies desert soils as aridisols, reflecting the lack of water.

Calcium carbonate may accumulate on the surface or at shallow depth. When rainwater percolates partway into the soil, the calcium carbonate that was dissolved in the water crystallizes and accumulates at the level where the water

Tea Kettles

The white, crusty substance that accumulates in tea kettles is calcium carbonate, also known as lime. The dissolved calcium solidifies as the water evaporates. Lime will form faster if the water is 'hard,' meaning that it contains a lot of dissolved minerals. The same process occurs in desert soils, although at a much slower rate.

evaporates. The calcium may appear as isolated white nodules or as a thick continuous layer called hardpan, caliche, or calcrete. Although usually a few inches to a few feet, caliche has been measured up to 300 ft (90 m) thick. It is as hard and impermeable to water as concrete. Water and roots cannot penetrate caliche, and over time so much salt may build up in the overlying soil that the area will support no plant life. Agriculturalists sometimes resort to dynamite blasting to break holes in caliche. Other areas that are extremely alkaline or have a salt crust on the surface are intermittent lakebeds or playas. Salt-loving plants may grow around the perimeters of these salt flats, but nothing grows in the middle.

Dune areas often have more moisture because the coarse texture and wide pore spaces between grains inhibit percolation, preventing the water from being pulled up to the surface to evaporate. Plants with deep roots that extend to the moist, deeper sand layers have a more reliable water supply.

Plants adjacent to drainage channels have access to more moisture than would be indicated by precipitation alone because water accumulates there, either in intermittent flows on the surface during or after an intense storm, or as groundwater beneath the surface. Riparian vegetation, meaning the plants along water courses, has different adaptations to desert conditions than those plants dependent solely on local precipitation.

Vegetation bordering rivers like the Nile through the Sahara or the Colorado through the American Southwest are not truly desert plants. These rivers originate in wetter climates and carry water through the deserts. Although levels fluctuate with seasons and snowmelt, the constant supply of water negates the need for plants to conserve water by special adaptations. The same is true for plants growing in desert oases, areas that have a water source like a spring or groundwater and are not dependent on local precipitation. Plants such as palm trees that inhabit oases are not truly desert plants because they are not adapted to aridity.

Common Adaptations

Few species, genera, or even families of plants or animals, are common to all deserts on all continents. Each continent has a unique biota, indicating that it evolved from adjacent more humid habitats. Even though most desert plants and animals did not spread from desert to desert, many desert growthforms have similar adaptation mechanisms. The term convergent evolution refers to the phenomenon that plants (or animals) can produce similar adaptations in response to the environment without being taxonomically related (see Figure 1.5). Cactaceae and Euphorbiaceae are two families of plants that are often confused. Euphorbia plants sold in nursery outlets are often labeled as cactus. The confusion stems from the fact that some of the plants look alike. Not botanically related, both families originated under similar desert conditions and evolved similar mechanisms of drought-tolerance. Both families contain many stem succulents, have plants with few to no leaves, and may have a

Figure 1.5 Convergent evolution is illustrated by (a) organ pipe cactus in Arizona that resembles (b) Euphorbia in southwestern Africa. (c) Joshua trees in California are similar in growthform to (d) tree aloes in southern Africa. *(Photos by author.)*

taproot (see the section Plant Adaptations). Cacti are native only to the Americas. Euphorbias are more widespread, but many succulent types are native to Africa and Asia. Succulent euphorbias are generally less spiny than cacti and may have residual leaves that are shed with drought. An additional defense mechanism of euphorbia is toxic sap, a milky white substance that at a minimum can cause irritation, at most blindness. Poinsettia, the common Christmas plant, is a Euphorbia known for its toxic qualities. Large leaf succulents are also prevalent in some warm deserts. The agaves, yuccas, and similar plants common to warm deserts of the Americas are replaced by aloes in Africa. The growthform is similar, rosettes of large succulent leaves, sometimes growing to tree height.

Convergent evolution also occurs in animals (see Figure 1.6). Unrelated kangaroo rats in North American deserts and jerboas in the Sahara have similar physiology and appearance. The equivalent of jackrabbits in North America is the unrelated Patagonian hares or maras in South America. The kit fox, common to North American deserts, is similar in appearance and habit to the fennec fox in

Figure 1.6 Animal examples of convergent evolution include (a) jackrabbit in North America compared with (b) mara in South America. (c) Kit fox in North America resembles (d) fennec fox in northern Africa. *(Courtesy of Shutterstock. Copyright: (a) IRC; (b) Nick Biemans; (c) Hagit Berkovich; (d) 3483253554.)*

North Africa. Many unrelated lizards on different continents have adapted to digging into cooler sand by using their feet or heads.

All life in deserts must contend with or adapt to three major environmental conditions—aridity, heat, and salinity. Plants and animals living with low water supply and high temperatures face a paradox. Water is necessary to keep cells in plants turgid. Without enough water, cells collapse and the plant wilts. However, plants must lose water in the transpiration process. Animals must be able to maintain their body moisture, but evaporative cooling may be necessary to lower body temperature. The adaptive problem is to balance the need for water with the need to use it. Even cold deserts have extreme temperature conditions in the summer, and both plants and animals have developed mechanisms, behavior, or growthform to control their internal temperatures. Plants and animals also have several means of avoiding intense solar radiation and heat. Animals particularly have to control body temperature. High temperatures increase aridity and water loss, so it is difficult to totally separate adaptations of heat avoidance. Because of the scarcity of water in deserts, salts that would normally be diluted with abundant water accumulate, either in the soil or in or on plants. Plants growing in those soils or animals feeding on salty plants must have a way to eliminate excess salt.

Plant Adaptations

Many plants live in deserts, but it is only xerophytes that can withstand and live under long-term dry conditions (see Table 1.2). Plants that grow along water courses with access to more water or plants that complete their life cycle during a short wet season do have adaptations that allow them to live in the desert, but they are not considered true xerophytes. Some xerophytes can lose up to 75 percent of their water content for a short time. An extreme, euxerophytes, can lose up to 94 percent of their water and survive. An example is the resurrection plant, a club moss from the Chihuahuan Desert. Although desiccated, it revives within hours of receiving rain. Several plants have more than one type of adaptation.

Succulence

Succulence, a plant's ability to store moisture to be used during dry periods, is the most easily recognizable adaptation to a desert climate. The moisture can be stored in various organs in the plant—stem, leaf, base, root, or bulb—and plants may have more than one type of succulence (see Figure 1.7). Cacti are examples of stem succulents. Cactus pads or the cactus body are actually the stems of the plant, and they contract or expand according to the availability of water. Thick or fleshy leaves, such as in agaves or aloes, may also store moisture. When the base or root of the plant swells with moisture, it is called caudiciform because of the enlarged plant part, the caudex or base, either above or below ground. *Cyphostemma* and *Pachypodium* from southwestern Africa are examples. Several plants, such as lilies, store moisture in the root as a bulb.

The extreme opposite of succulence is almost complete desiccation. Cyanobiosis, literally meaning hidden life, enables some cyanobacteria, algae, nematodes, and lichens to exist in a dehydrated state. The tiny or microscopic organisms have the ability to become almost totally dry, retaining only 1–5 percent of their body mass as water. With sufficient rainfall, they rehydrate and become active in a few hours, returning to a desiccated state when the soil dries. They are most often found on clay or silty soils where millions of them together may form a slight crust.

Leaves and Photosynthesis

Because plants use water during transpiration, alterations in leaf size or texture limit the amount of water lost. Smaller leaves minimize evaporation. The prevalence of tiny, compound leaves such as in paloverde and acacia prevent wilting. The parts of the leaf farthest from veins are the first to suffer from insufficient water. By breaking a large leaf into a compound one, those areas are eliminated. Some leaves like creosote bush are thick with a waxy coating. Firm leaves with strong tissue do not rely on water to remain turgid. By maintaining their shape instead of wilting when dry, damage to tissue is reduced. Plant stems or caudices may also be waxy, such as in *Cyphostemma.* In cacti, leaves have been replaced by spines. Cacti do not need leaves because photosynthesis takes place through the green stem or body of the plant. Another response to conserving water is to be

Table 1.2 Examples of Plant Adaptations

Adaptation	Plants
Stem succulent	*Aloe dichotoma*
	Cactaceae
	Euphorbia
	Hoodia
	Pachypodium
	Stapelia
Leaf succulent	*Agave*
	Aloe
	Crassula
	Hechtia
	Kalanchoe
	Lithops
Basal succulent (caudiciform)	*Adenium*
	Bursera
	Commiphora
	Cyphostemma
	Pachypodium
	Tylecodon
Small leaves	*Acacia*
	Alluaudia
	Calligonum
	Cercidium
	Haloxylon
	Larrea
	Olneya tesota
	Prosopis
Few or no leaves; green stem	*Adenium*
	Cactaceae
	Cercidium
	Euphorbia
	Stapelia
	Moringa
Waxy coating or hard cuticle	*Adenium*
	Jatropha
	Artemisia
	Cactaceae
	Larrea
	Simmondsia chinensis
Drought-deciduous	*Alluaudia*
	Didelta spinosa
	Fouqueria
	Othonna
	Pachypodium
	Pelargonium
Phreatophytes	*Acacia*
	Populus
	Prosopis
	Salix
	Tamarix
Hydraulic lift	*Agropyron desertorum*
	Ambrosia dumosa
	Artemisia
	Larrea
	Sarcobatus vermiculatus
Taproots (not phreatophytes)	*Ammodendron*
	Artemisia
	Carnegia gigantea
	Haloxylon
	Larrea
	Pachycereus pringlei
	Trichocereus
Shallow roots	*Artemisia*
	Carnegia gigantea
	Larrea
	Mesembryanthemaceae
Seed scarification	*Atriplex confertifolia*
	Cercidium
	Prosopis
Halophytes	*Anabasis*
	Atriplex
	Frankenia palmeri
	Halocnemum
	Reaumuria
	Suaeda
	Tamarix
	Zygophyllum
C_4 or CAM	Aizoaceae
	Alluaudia
	Artemisia
	Cactaceae
	Crassulaceae
Avoidance	Annuals
Toxins and Allelopathy	*Larrea*
	Mesembryanthemaceae
	Opuntia (Cholla)

Note: CAM = Crassulacean acid metabolism.

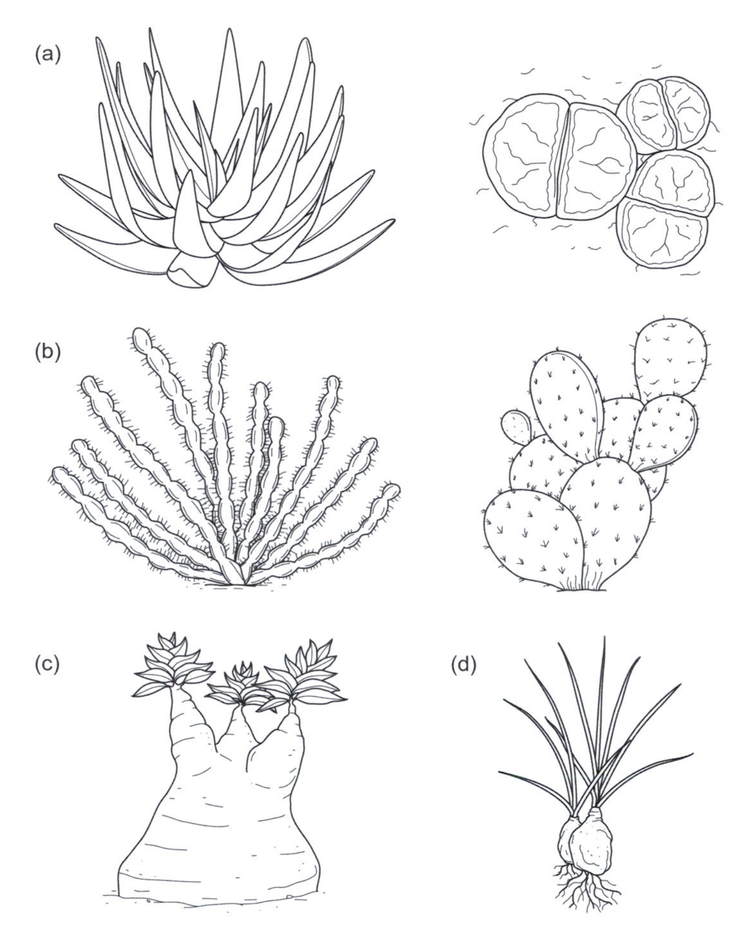

Figure 1.7 Plants adapt to dry climates with different types of succulence. (a) Leaf succulents can be either large, up to several feet or meters, or very small, less than 1 in (2.5 cm). (b) Stem succulents are typified by difference types of euphorbia or cacti. (c) Basal succulents, also called caudiciform, store moisture in a large base or caudex. (d) Roots or bulbs store moisture and energy below ground. *(Illustration by Jeff Dixon.)*

drought-deciduous. The ocotillo of the Sonoran and Chihuahuan deserts grows new leaves whenever sufficient rain falls, but it drops its leaves during drought. It can do so several times a year. Many desert plants, even if they are not drought-deciduous, respond to rainfall by quickly producing new growth.

Light colored hairs and/or salt crusts on leaves increase the albedo (reflectivity) of plants and reflect more of the sun's energy. Some plants orient their leaves so that the narrow edge faces the sun. Desert holly holds its leaves so it receives more direct rays during the cooler morning and evening hours but avoids them at mid-day. Leaves of annuals, however, are oriented to maximize radiation interception because they need to photosynthesize quickly before conditions deteriorate. Cacti seem to be at a disadvantage because of their large surface area, but light-colored spines both increase albedo and provide shade. Some mature cactus can withstand a body temperature of 140° F (60° C). Young plants cannot withstand this temperature, however, and require shade. Often they are found growing in the shade of a nurse plant such as creosote bush.

Water evaporates through stomata, the openings in the leaf through which gas exchange takes place in photosynthesis. In some desert plants, stomata may be on the underside of the leaf, or recessed and protected from drying winds. Hairs may occur on the leaf or around stomata, which reduce the air flow and help maintain a higher humidity near the leaf, which in turn decreases evaporation. Several grasses fold or roll their leaves, hiding stomata and reducing transpiration considerably. Many desert plants close their stomata during the day in response to high temperatures, thereby preventing a high evaporation rate. The plants open their stomata at night when it is cooler. A negative side effect of this adaptation is that the plants do not benefit from the cooling due to evaporation during the heat of the day.

Roots

Root systems range from storage units (caudices or bulbs) to long taproots or extensive lateral roots, with some plants utilizing a combination. Most plants have a

C_4 and CAM Plants

In its simplest form, photosynthesis combines carbon dioxide (CO_2), water, and light to make carbohydrates and oxygen. The carbon and water combine and oxygen is released. The carbon-based molecules (carbohydrates) are then converted to sugar. Normally a 3-carbon molecule is created, especially in plants at higher and cooler latitudes. Plants that use this method are called C_3. Although efficient, a drawback of this method is that when temperatures are high, plants close their stomata and no more CO_2 enters. When the leaf runs out of CO_2, photosynthesis stops and the plant may go dormant or die. Many plants that evolved in tropical areas are adapted to higher temperatures and use a slightly different method. These plants, called C_4, create a 4-carbon molecule. That allows plants to use lower levels of CO_2 in the leaf so the plant can stay green when it is hot. Fewer than 1 percent of plants worldwide are C_4, but the percentage is higher in deserts.

Crassulacean acid metabolism (CAM), a third method of photosynthesis utilized by many plants in hot, dry climates, involves storing the CO_2 for later use. To limit water loss, CAM plants open their stomata at night when temperatures are lower and relative humidity is higher. CO_2 enters, and the plant temporarily binds it to organic acids in the leaf. During the next day when the stomata are closed, CO_2 is released from the acid molecules and photosynthesis takes place in sunlight. The CAM method is highly efficient for the amount of water used, but only for a short time. Therefore, plants use CAM only when needed, in times of drought. Otherwise, they use the C_3 or C_4 method. CAM plants, which are usually succulents, are slow growing and unusual.

taproot of some sort combined with more shallow lateral roots. Most taproots reach only the deeper, moister layers of soil, not the water table. Plants with roots that do tap the water table along stream beds, in dune areas, or near springs are called phreatophytes. Taproots vary from a single stout root to a brush of several smaller roots. They may extend 40–60 ft (12–18 m) or more into the soil. Roots of mesquite have been measured to 160 ft (49 m). For many plants, the taproot is the first vegetative part, growing quickly after germination to provide the plant with a deeper water source after the surface soil has dried.

Larger or older plants grow a series of lateral roots for two reasons—additional support and access to water in a wider surface area. Lateral roots run 2–6 in (5–15 cm) beneath the surface and are quick to take advantage of short rains that do not penetrate far into the soil. Generally, little competition exists among plants for soil water. Each species grows its taproots to a different depth and extends its laterals within a different depth. As a result, each species takes water from only one or two soil levels and does not interfere with other species' roots. More roots occur around rocks because the rocky areas have more available moisture than fine substrate does. Within hours after rain, some cacti produce fine water-absorbing roots, which then die when the soil dries.

In a process called hydraulic life, taproots may transfer water from deeper soil levels to shallower areas more available for plants. Water normally moves through plants from areas of more moisture to areas of less moisture. Water is picked up from moist soil and moves through the plant to the leaves where it exits into drier air. At night when stomata are closed, the plant cells become well hydrated from this flow of water. However, if the soil is dry, water moves from the roots of the plant into the soil. Deeper roots take up water during the day, which then gets redeposited in the surface soil at night where it is conveniently available to be used the next day. Plants that typically use this method are sagebrush, crested wheatgrass, creosote, and white bursage.

Seed Germination

Many plants have rigid requirements for germination of their seeds, ensuring that the seedling will have a better chance of survival. The most obvious requirement is moisture, but temperature and other factors are equally important. Some shrubs such as creosote bush need high temperatures and a least 1 in (2.5 cm) of rainfall. Ocotillo needs several good rains at one- to two-week intervals.

Some seeds have a coating that must be removed either chemically or physically, called scarification, for germination to take place. A common example is the paloverde trees that grow along washes. These seeds need the abrasive action of being tumbled along a streambed to remove the coating. The stream action ensures that the seed is in the correct habitat with enough water and a chance of survival after germination. Other scarification techniques may be chemical or fungal action. A fungal growth on shadscale in the spring prepares the seed during a warm, wet time beneficial to germination. Some seeds have chemical inhibitors that need enough water to wash them away. It has been speculated that the increase of mesquite in the Sonoran Desert is due to seed scarification. Cattle browse the mesquite and deposit the seeds after passing them through their digestive tracts. The seedling then has a ready source of nutrients.

Many desert plants survive by avoiding heat and drought. Annuals are ephemeral, meaning that they last only a brief time. Displays of desert wildflowers are examples of ephemerals. The seeds lie dormant in the soil for years until enough rain falls at the right time to ensure that plants will have enough moisture to complete their life cycles and set seed for the next time. The right time depends on the desert's precipitation regime. In deserts that receive predominantly winter precipitation, annuals grow and bloom in late winter and early spring under cooler conditions. In summer-rain deserts, annuals bloom in the summer when temperatures are higher. All the seeds of a species do not germinate in the same year. If they did, the species easily could become extinct if favorable conditions declined before the plants had time to set seed for future years. Only 13 percent of species worldwide are annuals compared with 40 percent of desert species, indicating that drought-avoidance is a significant coping mechanism. Although seemingly barren to the naked eye, desert soils often are flush with seeds. Measurements indicate that desert bajadas have 370 to 18,500 seeds per square foot (4,000 to 200,000 seeds per square meter), a factor explaining the prominence of seed-eating rodents in desert areas.

Salt Content or Toxic Elements

Because many desert habitats have a high salt content in the soil, especially in the playas and salt flats, plants that live there must be adapted to those conditions. Halophytes are plants that are tolerant of excess salt. Water moves from low to high salt concentrations. Under normal conditions, soils have a low salt content, which allows easy movement of water from the soil into a plant. However, if the soil is saltier than the plant, the plant is unable to get the water it needs and actually would lose moisture to the soil. Halophytes such as saltbush have an exceptionally high salt content in their tissues, saltier than the soils in which the plants grow and even saltier than the ocean. That excess salt allows water to move from the soil into the plant, in spite of the high salt content of the soil. As water evaporates from the plant's stomata, crystallized salt remains on the leaves, giving the plant a dusty gray look. An additional benefit of salty tissues is that the plant is unpalatable to most animals even though its moisture-containing leaves may be tempting. With a few exceptions, most animals must avoid salty plants because they cannot get enough water to flush excess salt from their systems.

Many desert plants contain elements that are toxic, either to animals that might want to eat the plant or to other plants in the vicinity. Allelopathy refers to the habit of some plants to exude toxins that prevent germination of seeds around its base, therefore ensuring that the plant will not have to share meager rainfall. The even spacing of creosote bush on desert bajadas is a good example of allelopathy.

Cholla cactus produces oxalic acid, a highly toxic compound used as a fungicide and a bleaching agent in woodworking.

Animal Adaptations

Many animals have unique adaptations to aridity, heat, and salinity, while others have none. Morphological adaptations that limit heat gain or water loss relate to size or shape. Physiological adaptations involve alterations in bodily functions that allow the animal to survive low water availability, high heat, or excessive salt. Animals that have few or no morphological or physiological adaptations rely on behavior to avoid extreme conditions. It is often difficult to totally separate adaptations into these categories (see Table 1.3).

Table 1.3 Examples of Animal Adaptations

Adaptation	Animals
Little need for free water; water comes from food or metabolic processes	Chuckwalla Hill kangaroo Ibex Jerboas Kangaroo rats Gemsbok Rufous-crowned Emu-wren Spinifex hopping mouse Woodrat
Concentrated feces and urine	Antelope squirrel Camel Gazelle Kangaroos Kangaroo rats Mulgara Gemsbok Spinifex hopping mouse Springbok
No or little sweating	Armadillo Birds Camel Canines Felines Gemsbok Reptiles Rodents
Withstand loss of body weight in water	Desert bighorn sheep Burro California Quail Camel Chuckwalla Onager Gemsbok
Aestivation or avoidance	Australian frogs Crustaceans (e.g., fairy shrimp) Couch's spadefoot toad Desert tortoise Iranian ground squirrel Pocket mouse
Move long distance to water	Camel Coyote Desert elephant Gazelle Onager Gemsbok Ostrich Sandgrouse
Long appendages or ears	Bat-eared fox Cape hare Fennec fox Jackrabbit Kit fox Patagonian hare

(*Continued*)

Table 1.3. (*Continued*)

Adaptation	Animals	Adaptation	Animals
Insulation	Birds	Burrowing	Antelope squirrel
	Furred animals		Armadillo
High body temperatures	Armadillo		Fennec fox
	Birds		Gerbils
	Iguana		Ground squirrels
	Gemsbok		Hamsters
Vasodilation	Birds		Jerboas
	Camel		Kit fox
	Gemsbok		Meerkat
	Reptiles		Mongoose
Nocturnal or crepuscular	Aardwolf		Porcupine
	African wild cat		Shrews
	Antelope squirrel		Spinifex hopping mouse
	Bat-eared fox		Tuco-tuco
	Brown hyena		*Uma* lizards
	Caracal		Vlei rat
	Fennec fox	Salt tolerance	Black-backed jackal
	Ground squirrels		Chisel-tooth rat
	Jackrabbit		Gerbil mouse
	Javelina		Gemsbok
	Kangaroo rats		Plains vizcacha rat
	Kit fox		Roadrunner
	Patagonian hare		Sand rat
	Sand cat		Zebra Finch
	Woodrat		

The ratio of surface area to body mass is especially significant in regulating an animal's temperature and water balance. A lower ratio (small surface area compared with large body) in large animals is beneficial. Less surface area absorbs less heat. A small animal has a larger ratio (more surface area compared with small body mass) and is at a disadvantage. The larger relative surface area will absorb more energy and the temperature of the smaller body will rise too quickly. Like small rocks compared with one large rock, small animals heat up faster and have to be more tolerant of high body temperatures, require more water to cool down, or have to be able to avoid the heat. The same rationale applies to water loss. Large animals also lose less water relative to their body mass.

Aridity

Water accounts for 60–80 percent of an animal's body weight, and the ratio of water loss to body weight is critical to survival. Water loss must be balanced by water intake. Water is gained by drinking, from food, and by metabolic generation. Some animals require free water (water to drink), while others get what they need from food or manufacture it in their bodies (metabolic water). Water is lost primarily in evaporation from breathing and perspiration and in body waste (urine and feces).

Metabolic Water

Metabolic water is created from oxidation of nutrients in food. When food is digested, sugar is broken down. The hydrogen and oxygen that are released combine to create water within the animal. Different foods generate different amounts of water, fat being the highest. Oxidation of 1 g of fat results in 1.1 g of water. Carbohydrate and protein produce only 0.6 and 0.4 g, respectively. Even though prey contains a lot of free water and generates a lot of metabolized water from protein and fat, water is also required to metabolize that food. Getting oxygen requires respiration, a process that causes moisture loss, and moisture is also lost in body waste. Usually, metabolic water creation results in no net gain of water.

Physiological. Animals have several physiological adaptations to conserve water in desert environments. Some animals will drink water if it is available, but others will not. Desert bighorn sheep in North America can go three to five days without drinking. Feral burros, which compete with bighorn, can go a week with no ill effects. Amphibians like toads and frogs do not drink but get water through their skin; therefore, they are usually restricted to a wet environment when active. Some insects like the desert cockroach and pinacate beetle can absorb water vapor, not liquid, directly from the air or from humid sand.

Many animals obtain water from food, that is, from the bodies of animals or juicy plants they eat, either directly or through metabolic processes. Most animals depend on a combination of these sources. Although most birds need to drink, some get enough water from their food. Gambel Quail in North America get sufficient water from eating leaves, buds, mistletoe berries, and cactus fruit. Even seemingly dry seeds with only 10 percent water content may provide enough moisture. Kangaroo rats and pocket mice in North America and jerboas and gerbils in the Sahara exist on a diet of dry seeds and never need to drink free water. All their requirements are met via metabolic water. However, North American woodrats and Saharan jirds both require moist food. Carnivores get moisture from body fluids of their prey. Prey animals are usually two-thirds water, and the percentage remains constant, unlike plants that become drier in summer. Usually the amount of water gained from prey balances with the amount the predator loses. The North American sparrow hawk, for example, gets enough water from its prey, providing it rests in the shade during the heat of the day.

In addition to obtaining water, it is important to limit water loss. Normally, water is excreted with body waste in feces and urine. Many desert animals, however, have concentrated urine. Fecal pellets also have less water content, as low as 36 percent compared with a typical 75 percent for nondesert organisms. The kidneys of kangaroo rats are five times more powerful than those of humans and can concentrate waste with much less water. Several rodents, such as kangaroo rats, also eat some of their fecal pellets, recapturing lost nutrients and moisture. By withdrawing most of the water, birds concentrate urea into uric acid, producing a white pasty substance rather than a liquid. Reptiles excrete a similar pasty composition of uric acid instead of liquid urine.

Moisture may be lost through the skin, such as in sweating for humans. Arthropods (insects and arachnoids) have a waxy exoskeleton which, like hairs on plant leaves, increases the thickness of the humid layer of air over the organism and decreases evaporation. When they are aestivating, the skin of frogs and toads can become impermeable to and drastically impede water loss. Reptiles are even more waterproof, as are some birds and mammals. Poorwills and cactus mice have skins nearly as impermeable to moisture loss as that of reptiles. Some species change according to conditions. The sculptured scorpion in the Sonoran Desert has an outer covering that is less permeable during the hot, dry summer than it is in the cooler, wetter winter. For mammals, birds, and some reptiles, much moisture is also lost through panting, a means of evaporative cooling.

Many desert animals, however, have an extreme tolerance to lack of body water. The water content in their bodies fluctuates according to environmental conditions. Some mammals and insects can withstand up to 30 percent loss of body weight due to dehydration. Some desert birds and reptiles tolerate 30–50 percent loss, and a few reptiles can survive more than 50 percent drop in weight due to water loss. The weight is replenished when the animals drink water. In contrast, a domestic dog's tolerance to dehydration is low, and it will die with only 10–15 percent weight loss. Because water is taken from the blood in most animals, decreased plasma volume will cause circulatory failure.

Birds' tolerance to dehydration is variable. A House Finch dies at 27 percent loss of body weight, but a California Quail survives with a 50 percent loss, although that loss may not be all water. In springtime, chuckwallas in the Mojave Desert eat succulent, hydrated green plants that grow in response to winter rains. The lizards become fat with stored water. In late spring, they are reduced to eating dry vegetation, and in midsummer they do not eat at all. They never drink water, even if it is available, and by fall have lost 37 percent of their body weight.

Just as annual plants complete their life during a short, favorable time period, so do some animals. This adaptation is not specific to deserts. All organisms time egg-laying or reproduction to favorable environmental conditions. Small and short-lived pools of water briefly support a lot of small life—eggs and larvae of flies and mosquitoes, and crustaceans such as fairy shrimp and water fleas. Although not limited to deserts, parthenogenesis, asexual reproduction, is an adaptation that may be beneficial in environments that require fast response to take advantage of conditions. Desert mites, brine shrimp, copepods, and whiptail lizards are examples. Some females in the population reproduce without male help, but they can only produce females like themselves. Parthenogenesis may be a quick way to increase the population of species.

Behavioral. Similar to how animals in cold climates hibernate to escape unfavorable conditions, some animals in deserts aestivate when water and food sources are scarce. In aestivation and hibernation, both responses to unfavorable conditions, animals go into a dormant state. Similarities include a drop in metabolic rates, such as heartbeat and respiration, resulting in a decrease in energy use that allows the animal to survive on stored reserves. Animals in cold climates go into hibernation in response to cooling temperatures. However, an explanation of what triggers aestivation is more complex. It might be a direct response to high temperatures, or more likely an indirect response when food and water become too scarce. Onset of aestivation for many rodents in desert areas coincides with a rapid drying of vegetation. During aestivation, all body functions including those that use water—respiration, urine and feces formation—slow. Also, because the entrances to burrows are usually sealed, relative humidity within the burrow is high, close to 100 percent, further decreasing water loss. Because ground squirrels and pocket mice are diurnal, many aestivate to escape unfavorable conditions. Many amphibians also aestivate.

Animals that need to drink free water must move long distances to find it. Birds and large mammals, rather than small animals, have that ability. White-winged Doves, which spend summers in the Sonoran Desert, must drink twice a day. Unlike rodents that may have a mobility of only a 100 yd (900 m) radius, birds can fly for several miles and can migrate to avoid the worst conditions. They fly to and take advantage of the sporadic and widely spaced thunderstorms in the desert. Large animals can also travel several miles, and coyotes may dig 3 ft (1 m) into arroyos seeking water. Many animals or insects that do not fly do not need to drink free water.

Heat

Whether they are ectothermic (cold blooded) or endothermic (warm blooded), animals must control their body temperature and not become too cold or too hot. Adaptive mechanisms to heat are to (1) avoid it, generally by burrowing or being nocturnal, (2) tolerate it by withstanding an increased body temperature, or (3) cool by evaporation.

Morphological. Albedo refers to the reflectivity of an object. Light colors reflect rather than absorb sunlight, like wearing a white shirt in summer compared with a black shirt. Color is often used for protection or camouflage, and insects and reptiles are well known for approximating the color of their environment. Some animals can change color according to the temperature or humidity. Certain lizards may be dark toned in the morning when they need to absorb solar radiation and warm up, but may change to a lighter tone in the afternoon when more absorption would be detrimental. Color is a complex issue for many reasons, however, not just related to albedo.

Many animals in hot, dry climates have long appendages like ears or legs. Black-tailed jackrabbit ears are very large and thin. The network of blood vessels close to the surface of the skin increases blood flow and allows excess heat to be radiated away from the body (see Figure 1.6). The large ears in the kit fox in North America or the fennec fox in Africa also serve to discharge heat.

One would not think that a fur coat in the desert would be beneficial. Experiments have shown, however, that thick fur is even better than thin fur. Fur absorbs radiation at its outer surface and serves as insulation between the body and the air, keeping the animal's skin and core cooler. It is similar to a human wearing loose clothing rather than going shirtless and in shorts. Because ground temperature and fur temperature may be the same (158° F, 70° C), little heat is transferred from ground to animal because the temperature difference is minor. However, the temperature difference between the hot fur (158° F, 70° C) and cooler air (104° F, 40° C) is so great that heat is readily radiated or conducted from the fur into the air, thereby keeping the animal's skin temperature at 100° F (38° C). Bare human skin at 95° F (35° C) not only absorbs solar radiation directly but also gains heat from both the 104° F (40° C) air and the 158° F (70° C) ground. Like fur, clothing creates an insulating air space that keeps the skin relatively cooler. However, clothing is not as efficient in insulating as animal fur is, and because the human is absorbing more heat, he or she requires more water for evaporative cooling through perspiration.

Physiological. A major characteristic of endothermic animals is that they maintain a constant body core temperature (see Table 1.4). In humans, this is 98.6° F (37° C). However, many desert-living animals can tolerate a moderate increase in core temperature and survive. The antelope ground squirrel's temperature ranges 100°–109° F (38°–43° C), and the black-tailed jackrabbit can have a core temperature as high as 111° F (44° C), but only for short periods during the day. If the core temperature of an animal rises above a certain point (distinct for each species), the body's cooling mechanisms break down. In humans, this stage is called heatstroke, characterized by hot, flushed, dry skin because sweating and evaporation have ceased. With no natural cooling, core temperature rapidly rises and, unless checked by exterior means of cooling, death results. Mammals and birds have

Table 1.4 Typical Body Temperatures

Animal	Normal Temperature Range
Humans	98.6° F (37° C)
Antelope ground squirrels	100°–109° F (38°–43° C)
Birds	104°–108° F (40°–42° C)
Desert iguanas	111°–115° F (44°–46° C)
Snakes	109°–111° F (43°–44° C)

Evaporative Cooling

Have you ever come out of a swimming pool on a hot summer day and shivered because you were cold? The water droplets on your body were evaporating. To do so, they needed energy and took that heat energy from you. The same concept applies when your dog pants. The water evaporating from his tongue takes heat from the animal. Some houses in hot climates depend on evaporative coolers for air conditioning. Air blown through a water-soaked pad becomes cool as the water evaporates. Evaporation of moisture is a common cooling mechanism.

several means of regulating body temperature, the most common being evaporation of some sort. In a desert environment, water is scarce and evaporative cooling may not be possible.

Body temperatures for most mammals average 100° F (38° C) with little tolerance for much increase in core temperature. Birds (not just desert birds) average 104°–108° F (40°–42° C), and many survive temperatures up to 115° F (46° C) for short times. In general, when birds are exposed to high temperatures, their body temperature rises. This higher body temperature helps to lose heat by radiation and conduction rather than by evaporation. Birds are not restricted to the ground, so even with body temperatures of 104°–108° F (40°–42° C) they can lose heat to the relatively cooler air above. Bare legs and thinly feathered undersides of wings also dissipate heat. When resting, desert birds can often be seen with their wings hanging loosely away from their body, a position that increases air circulation and cooling.

Because lizards, snakes, and tortoises are small animals with a small range of movement, they must be adapted to local conditions. Although they can be active within a wide range of body temperatures, 86°–113° F (30°–45° C) depending on the species, most lizards try to maintain their body temperature within a narrow range. The desert iguana of the American southwest has a high normal body temperature, 111°–115° F (44°–46° C), not far below its lethal limit of 116.5° F (47° C). Lizards that live in the warmest deserts have a high lethal temperature, 118°–120° F (48°–49° C), perhaps because they are active during the day. Snakes generally have a lower lethal limit, 109°–111° F (43°–44° C), perhaps because many are nocturnal and not exposed to daytime highs. The first reaction to potential overheating for reptiles is to escape to the shade or go underground.

Although few desert animals sweat, many desert creatures have unique ways of cooling by evaporation. The desert cicada has pores for evaporative cooling and "sweats" when it gets too hot. Most mammals, birds, and reptiles depend instead on evaporation during respiration. Several insects breathe through their skin, but the pores penetrate deep into the body to limit exposure to dry air. This adaptation is similar to recessed stomata in plants.

The major method of evaporative cooling for canines is panting. Evaporation takes place from the long, wet tongue as the animal takes 300–400 shallow breaths per minute. Normal respiration is only 10–40 breaths per minute. Like sweating, this method works well when the relative humidity is low, but it is less effective with high humidity. If the air is humid, little evaporation and, thus, little cooling can take place. Panting is advantageous because salt loss is minimal, compared with sweating, and the motion provides increased air movement over the wet surface. Canines do, however, sweat, not as a general cooling mechanism but to locally cool the skin when it gets too hot. Since reptiles have no sweat glands, the only evaporative cooling is through respiration. Many lizards do a type of panting. They open their mouths wide in a panting gesture but without the rapid respiration. Birds also have no sweat glands, but they lose water through respiration. When body temperature becomes too high, the respiration rate increases to a type of shallow panting. Flapping of loose skin on the throat, called gular fluttering, increases air flow through their mouths and thus provides cooling.

Desert tortoises have frothy saliva and also urinate on themselves to cool off. Western box turtles in the Chihuahuan Desert have large bladders, maybe to store liquid for evaporative cooling.

To keep body core temperatures within an appropriate range, many reptiles, birds, and mammals use vasodilation. Blood vessels in the skin will dilate, causing more blood flow to extremities and radiation of excess heat. This is an important mechanism in camels' ability to survive in extreme environments. Birds also increase heat loss from their legs in this way. Gemsbok in South Africa can dissipate heat from the base of their brain, keeping the head cool.

Behavioral. Many desert dwellers have no special adaptations to desert heat and must avoid extreme conditions of aridity and heat by their behavior. The most common response is to be nocturnal, active only at night. Nocturnal activity is more prevalent in deserts than it is in any other ecosystem. Crepuscular animals are active near dawn and at dusk, also avoiding the heat of the day.

Many types of mammals, invertebrates, amphibians, and reptiles burrow into the soil seeking cooler conditions. At noon, temperatures 6 in (15 cm) deep may be 36° F (20° C) cooler than on the surface. At 20 in (50 cm), little to no daily temperature change occurs; the temperature stays at the daily mean. At deeper levels, the ambient temperature is closer to the annual mean, with little variation not only from day to night but also from summer to winter. Most burrows are 8–28 in (20–70 cm) below the surface. Animals that burrow into cooler soil or are nocturnal have no need to adapt to high temperatures, but they must avoid hot conditions. Merriam's kangaroo rat has a normal body temperature of 96.8°–100.4° F (36°–38° C) and cannot sweat or pant if it becomes hotter. The rat can temporarily survive higher body temperatures in an emergency if it cannot find safety in its burrow, but a body temperature of 104° F (40° C) is lethal if it lasts for several hours. At an air temperature of 109° F (43° C), kangaroo rats will die within 30 minutes, with 10 percent of their body weight lost through evaporation. Many rodents, including ground squirrels and jerboas, will spread saliva on their chins and throats in an attempt to cool off, but the animal cannot do this for long before running out of water.

Animals (mammals, birds, or reptiles) active during the day are called diurnal, but they avoid long exposure to the sun by seeking frequent shade. Because of their small size and surface-to-body-mass ratio, most birds and rodents have similar problems of heat regulation. They must avoid exposure to sun and heat. They may also orient their bodies to minimize sun absorption, such as the ground squirrel providing its own shade by arching its tail over its back. Large animals do not have the option of burrowing and must spend time in the shade.

Invertebrates, amphibians, and reptiles are ectothermic, using environmental conditions for thermal regulation, and must depend on microclimates to maintain safe body temperatures. Because their internal temperatures would rise to lethal levels, they cannot tolerate desert heat and must find shade or cooler soil. Temperature regulation of reptiles depends primarily on conduction to or from the ground and radiation from the sun. Conduction of heat to or from the surrounding air is minor. Depending on the temperature of the surface, the reptile will either gain or lose heat. Because they are small animals, they heat up quickly and use behavioral adaptations to moderate heat gain. On cool mornings a lizard might lie flat on a warm rock in full sunlight, absorbing heat from the surface and from solar radiation. Radiation from the sun is always a gain in heat. By going from sun to shade or by changing the orientation of its body to the sun, the lizard can partly control absorption of radiation. In the hot afternoon, the same lizard might run on its hind legs, minimizing contact with and therefore heat gain from a hot surface. The lizard may stop and by using its abdomen and forelegs dig a shallow depression into the sand to get direct contact with cooler layers beneath. Some lizards may dig completely into cooler sand and disappear from sight. Fringe-toed lizards have an additional adaptation to sand. Their nasal passages are configured so sand does not get inside.

Surface temperatures can be much higher than the air temperature at 6 ft (2 m). This is apparent to anyone who has walked over a sandy beach in bare feet. Therefore, depending on the air temperature, many animals either try to minimize or maximize contact with the surface. Lizards sometimes lift their feet one at a time to cool off. Insects stand tall on their legs, keeping their bodies away from the surface. The sidewinder rattlesnake's method of locomotion lifts its body away from the sand. Conversely, the antelope ground squirrel will sprawl flat on its body in the shade, legs spread out, to lose body heat to the relatively cool ground.

Salinity

Few animals are adapted to ingesting excess salt, but unique exceptions exist. Salt is often concentrated in desert environments because of the lack of water to dilute it. Although most animals avoid salty soil and food, some mammals, birds, and reptiles can drink water that is brackish or even saltier than sea water. At least two rodents routinely eat nothing but the succulent leaves of saltbush, using modified teeth or mouth bristles to strip off the salty crust. Most desert lizards excrete salt via glands in their noses. The salt crystallizes as it oozes out, and the lizard often sneezes to expel it. Roadrunners also have nasal salt glands to rid themselves of excess salt.

The Ideal Desert Dweller

Found in all North American deserts, the kangaroo rat (*Dipodomys* spp.) has a combination of adaptive mechanisms that make it ideally adapted to desert conditions. Most deserts have a rodent with similar adaptations. Active at night, it spends the day in the cool of its burrow. In summer when air temperature is 113° F (45° C) and soil surface is 167° F (75° C), the temperature 3 ft (1 m) into the soil is only 86° F (30° C). Similar temperature conditions are found in the Sahara and other warm deserts. The kangaroo rat never needs to drink water and eats dry seeds, a high-energy food, even when green vegetation is available. The soil contains thousands of small seeds, and the rat can smell tiny seeds that are buried as much as 8 in (20 cm) below the surface. Using its small front paws, the rodent winnows the soil for seeds, storing them in a mouth pouch before taking them back to its burrow. During the day, the rat seals the opening to its burrow, creating a barrier to the dry desert air outside. The rat's respirations increase the humidity inside the burrow, and in this small microclimate, the stored seeds absorb moisture. Seeds in dry air have 10 percent water content, but in the higher relative humidity of the burrows, it is doubled to 20 percent. When the rat eventually eats the seeds, the moisture lost through respiration is then reclaimed.

Poisonous Species

Several desert species use poisons, toxins, or just unpleasant taste or odor to either subdue prey or repel predators (see Plate II). Pinacate bugs are beetles that secrete a substance that repels enemies. Velvet ants, actually a type of wasp, sting. Vinegaroons, called whip-tailed scorpions, are not scorpions at all. They have no sting and rely on the secretion of a repellant. Large and small scorpions inject varying amounts of venom. Tarantulas have an undeserved bad reputation. Their hair is prickly and unpleasant to touch, and their bite, only after much provocation, is only mildly poisonous. The tarantula hawk is a wasp that paralyzes the tarantula without killing it. By laying her eggs in the nest with the immobile tarantula, the insect ensures that her larvae will have fresh food when the eggs hatch. Several snakes such as coral snake, rattlesnake, and cobra inject venom through their fangs when they strike.

Although not as conspicuous as birds, reptiles, or mammals, the most abundant animals in terms of biomass are ants and termites. Termites are especially abundant in the warm Chihuahuan and Sonoran deserts. Harvester ants store thousands of seeds. Honeypot ants have a unique way of storing food for dry periods. Certain individuals, called

Venomous or Not?

Except for the coral snake, all poisonous snakes in the United States are pit vipers such as rattlesnakes. Pit vipers have a deep pit or indentation between the nostrils and eyes. Nonvenomous snakes do not. The pupils of pit vipers are narrow slits, contrasted with round pupils of other snakes. The head of a pit viper has a triangular shape that is distinct from the body, while nonpoisonous snakes have rounded heads that are a continuation of the body. Some nonpoisonous snakes, however, mimic the pit vipers by temporarily flattening and broadening their heads as a defensive action. Arizona coral snakes can be recognized by the brightly colored red, white, and black bands. Some nonpoisonous snakes have similar color, but the bands are in a different order.

replete, store liquid food in a distended abdomen. They literally hang out in the nest and allow others to feed off them when food is scarce.

Just as plants that are not truly desert adapted grow along permanent streams in desert areas, some animals that are not truly desert animals live within desert boundaries. Hippopotamus in the Nile River can hardly be described as desert dwellers. To be considered a desert animal, it must have some method by which it copes with the desert environment—aridity, heat, and salinity.

Floristic Realms and Dominant Plant Families

Deserts are found in five of the six world's floristic realms—Holarctic, Neotropical, Palaeotropical, Cape, and Australian. Antarctic is the exception. Deserts that straddle floristic realm boundaries have floras with a mixed origin. Goosefoot (Chenopodiaceae) is the most common family in desert floras. It is dominant in the mid-latitude Asian deserts and is also important in the Sahara, Australian, North American, and South American deserts. However, it is almost absent from the Thar Desert and southwestern Africa. Mustard, pink, and buckwheat families are widespread in the Holarctic. Mustards are most abundant in the Sahara, while pinks are abundant in central Asia. Buckwheat is represented by different genera in Asian and North American deserts. Mesembryanthemum and lily are important families in southern Africa. The isolation of Australia is reflected in its flora. *Casuarina,* myrtle, and some *Protea* originated there. The Sonoran, Chihuahuan, Thar, South American, and southern African deserts have many tropical affinities, that is, tropical plants adapted to arid conditions. Examples are milkweed in southern Africa, morning glory and squash in the Thar, and mallow in general. Figworts are also important in both southern Africa and the Thar. Cacti are unique to North and South America. Pineapple and oxalis families are also common in South American deserts.

Further Readings

Books

MacMahon, James A. 1985. *The Audubon Society Nature Guides: Deserts.* New York: Alfred A. Knopf.

National Geographic Society. 1982. *The Desert Realm.* Washington, DC: National Geographic Society.

Internet Sources

The Animal Spot. n.d. "Desert Animals." http://www.desertanimals.net/guide.html.

Boyce Thompson Arboretum. n.d. "Desert Plants." http://ag.arizona.edu/desertplants/contact.html.

DesertUSA. n.d. "Exploring the Southwest." http://www.desertusa.com.

World Wildlife Fund. n.d. "Terrestrial Biomes." http://www.worldwildlife.org/wildworld/profiles.

2

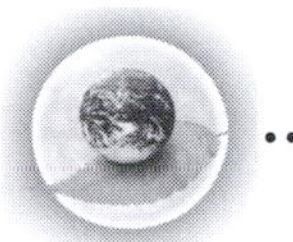

Warm Deserts

Warm, or hot, deserts are located in the Tropics or Subtropics, generally between 10° and 35° latitude, both north and south of the Equator. They are concentrated on the western sides of landmasses where the subtropical high-pressure cells and cold ocean currents are dominant. With low humidity and high evaporation potential, dew and fog are uncommon.

Climate

Temperature

Warm deserts have a continental temperature regime, with hot summers and cool winters (see Figure 2.1). Daytime temperatures in summer average above 100° F (38° C) and extremes may be 120°–130° F (49°–54° C). At night, temperatures drop to 70° F (21° C). Average temperatures mask this day-to-night variation. For example, the average July temperature for Yuma, Arizona, in the Sonoran Desert in North America is 90° F (32° C). Winter temperatures are lower but still warm, 60°–70° F (16°–21° C) during the day and 40°–50° F (4°–10° C) at night. The common belief that temperatures always drop below freezing at night is wrong. It does happen, but it is unusual. However, after 130° F (54° C) during the day, the 60° F (33° C) drop in temperature may make 70° F (21° C) seem chilly. At higher elevation, however, night temperatures often do drop below freezing. Those daytime figures represent the temperature of the air. A person, plant, or animal exposed to the sun will feel much warmer because of direct absorption of solar radiation.

Tropics

When many people hear the word Tropics, they think of a warm sandy beach with palm trees. The term actually refers to both the latitudes of the Tropic of Cancer at 23½° N and the Tropic of Capricorn at 23½° S and to the latitudes in between. It does not refer to a specific climate. Several climates, such as desert, grassland, and rainforest, occur in tropical regions. Even alpine environments can be found on high mountains within the Tropics. The Tropics is the only region on Earth where the sun can be directly overhead (i.e., making a 90° angle with the surface) sometime during the year, a factor that contributes to its high temperatures. The term Subtropics refers to latitudes just outside the Tropics, a few degrees north and south.

Many factors make these deserts hot. Because of the low latitude, the sun is either directly overhead or close to being so. When the sun is high in the sky, its energy is concentrated in a smaller area compared with a lower sun that spreads the energy over a larger area. Clear skies with little cloud cover and humidity allow the sun's rays to penetrate the atmosphere and be more easily absorbed at the surface. The energy is then reradiated upward where it warms the air. Evaporation is

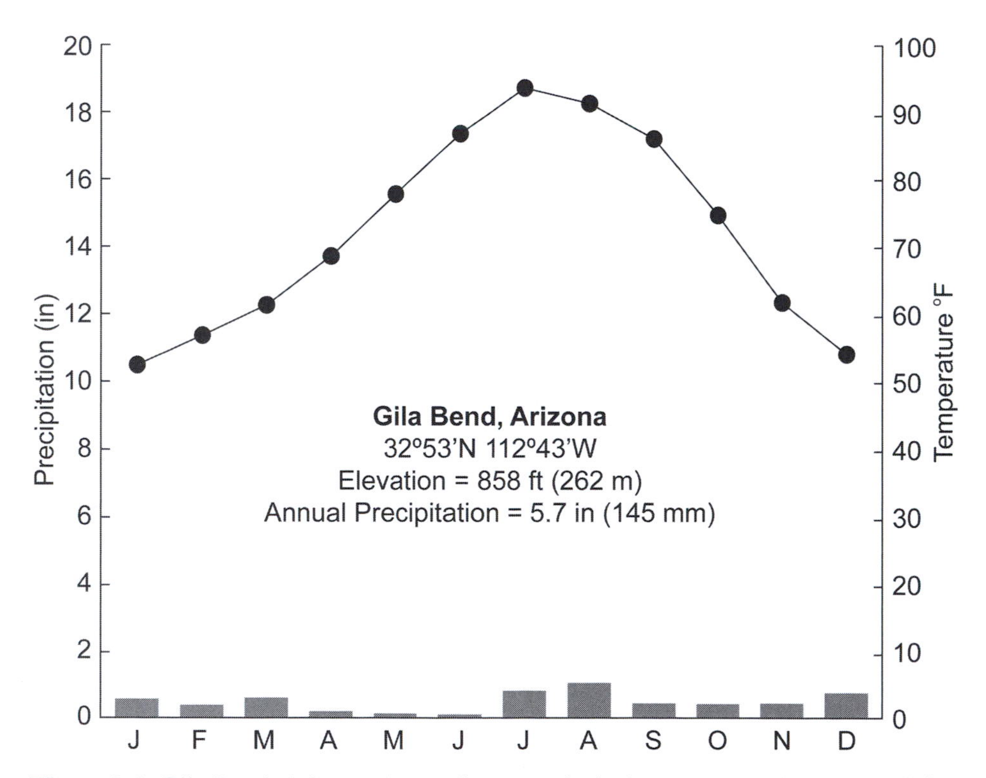

Figure 2.1 Gila Bend, Arizona, has a climate typical of many warm deserts. Precipitation is low. Although temperatures vary seasonally, they are mild in winter and warm to hot in summer. *(Illustration by Jeff Dixon.)*

a cooling process because water needs energy to change into gas (water vapor). Because deserts have little water to evaporate, little cooling can take place and air temperatures remain high. Warm deserts are located inland, away from the cooling effect of any ocean. Strips of desert along the coast have different climate conditions (see Chapter 4).

Temperature Extremes

The highest temperature in the world, 136° F (57.8° C), was recorded at El Azizia, Libya, in the Sahara Desert. The record high for North America is 134° F (56.7° C), reached in Death Valley, California. These measurements are the air temperature in the shade.

In the Northern Hemisphere, the northern boundaries of warm deserts are subject to occasional incursion of polar airmasses that bring unusually cold temperatures for short time periods. North American deserts and Southwest Asian deserts are especially susceptible because of the large continental areas to the north. The Sahara and Southern Hemisphere deserts escape these cold temperatures. Cold air is modified as it crosses the Mediterranean Sea. Similar cold airmasses do not exist in the Southern Hemisphere because of the lack of large landmasses (excluding Antarctica, which is too far away to affect deserts at these latitudes).

The average temperatures, however, give an incomplete description of conditions. Official temperatures around the world are measured in the shade, 5 ft (1.5 m) above the ground. The thermometer must be shaded so it measures only the air temperature, not radiant energy received from the sun. The air is not heated directly by the sun's rays but by energy radiated from the ground. Solar radiation, which is shortwave in length, passes through the atmosphere and is absorbed by the ground. The ground then reradiates that energy in longer wavelengths, also called infrared. (Night-vision goggles intercept infrared radiation, allowing the wearer to "see" an object or person in the absence of light.) The longwave energy cannot easily pass through the atmosphere and is absorbed, thus heating the air. Therefore, temperatures are highest at ground level, decreasing with height (see Figure 2.2). When the official thermometer reads 110° F at 5 ft (43° C at 1.5 m), the temperature at ground level may be 160° F (71° C).

Mirages

Have you ever looked at something through a glass of water? The image you see is distorted because the air and water have different densities, meaning how closely spaced the molecules are. When light goes through substances with different densities, the light rays are refracted, or bent, distorting the image. During the day, air near the ground becomes much hotter than the air above it. The air at the ground is less dense because the heat has caused it to expand, whereas the cooler air above is more dense. When the sun's rays pass through layers of air with different densities, the rays are refracted. The most common mirage is seemingly wet pavement in front of your car caused by the sky's reflection off the hot road.

A profile from below ground surface to several feet into the air shows a variety of temperatures. The most extreme temperature differences are within 6 ft (1 m) of the surface. On a bush only 3 ft (1 m) above the ground, the air temperatures would be 120° F (49° C), 40° F (22° C) cooler

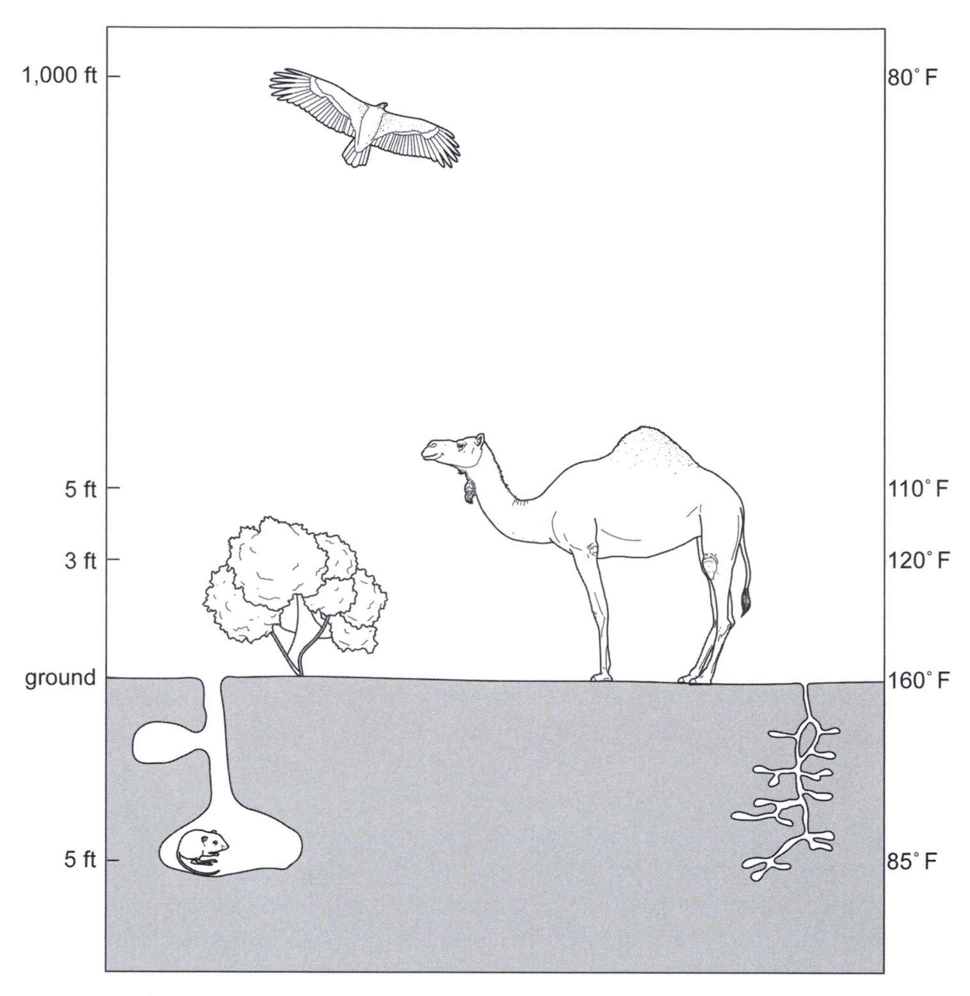

Figure 2.2 Temperatures vary according to height above the ground surface or depth into the soil, providing microhabitats for animals. It is hottest at the surface, but conditions are more moderate with height above the ground and with depth. *(Illustration by Jeff Dixon. Adapted from Page 1984.)*

than the surface. A bird flying at 1,000 ft (300 m) would experience air temperature of only 80° F (27° C). Because dry desert soil does not conduct heat efficiently, the energy absorbed at the surface does not penetrate deeply into the ground. At a depth of 5 ft (1.5 m), where many animals wait out the day in burrows, the temperature may be only 85° F (29° C), 75° F (42° C) cooler than at the surface. These localized temperature differences create important microhabitats.

Precipitation

Precipitation in warm deserts is usually 10 in (250 mm) or less a year, and all of it comes in the form of rain. Snow is a rare occurrence, usually only at higher elevations. Some deserts, (Chihuahuan, Monte, and Thar) have predominantly summer rainfall, while others (Mojave and Iranian) receive rainfall primarily in winter. The Sonoran Desert has a biseasonal rainfall distribution, both in summer and in winter. Other deserts (Sahara and Arabian) have no distinct season when rain is expected. Rainfall in Australia varies depending on location on the continent.

Uneven heating of the ground and air above the ground creates hot areas from which air rises. The rising air, called convection or a thermal, may extend to 20,000–30,000 ft (6,000–9,000 m), but in spite of the height, it rarely rains because the air is too dry to form clouds. Many desert birds, however, take advantage of thermals because the rising air keeps them aloft with little effort on their part. High temperatures and convection cause thunderstorms only when a moist airmass invades the desert. Every summer, convectional storms bring rain to some deserts like the Sonoran, but they may not occur for years in the central Sahara. Winter rains are generally more gentle and soaking because they are caused by cyclonic storms and are not violent downpours. Because precipitation in most deserts is unpredictable and unreliable—in season, location, and amount—plants and animals have to be prepared for long periods of drought.

Relative humidity in warm deserts can be as low as 2 percent but is usually 20–50 percent depending on the season. Because relative humidity in summer is quite low, a decrease in the nighttime temperature during summer rarely causes dew to form. In winter when the air is already cooler, nighttime temperatures may more readily drop below the dew point (the temperature at which condensation begins) and cause condensation. Dew in any season is an important source of moisture.

Several interrelated factors cause the aridity in these locations. Because of high pressure, air is sinking toward the Earth's surface. It compresses as it subsides, and because of the adiabatic process, it warms. The increasing temperature lowers the relative humidity and promotes evaporation from surface water or from plants and animals. Circulation of air around high-pressure cells is clockwise in the Northern Hemisphere and counterclockwise in the

Humidity

Relative humidity, expressed as a percent, is a measure of how much water vapor is in the air compared with how much water vapor the air is capable of holding. (Compare it to a partly filled glass of water relative to the size of the glass.) Warm air can evaporate and hold much more water vapor than cold air can. As the temperature changes, the relative humidity also changes. (A large glass can hold more than a small glass, and as glass size changes, how full the glass is also changes.) Assuming no change in the amount of water vapor in the air, as temperature decreases, relative humidity rises. If relative humidity exceeds 100 percent, the excess water vapor "spills" out of the air. (If you pour the water into successively smaller glasses, the glasses become fuller, until water spills over the edge.) In other words, condensation occurs, and the liquid water becomes clouds, fog, or dew. Conversely, as temperature rises, relative humidity drops and no condensation occurs. (Pour the same amount of water into a larger glass, and the glass is less full.) The low relative humidity also means that the hot, dry air will evaporate whatever water is available, contributing to desert conditions.

Southern Hemisphere. In both cases, prevailing winds blow from higher latitudes and are marginally cooler than if they were coming from warmer, lower latitudes. Cooler air is more stable than warmer air, meaning that it will sink instead of rise, warming adiabatically as it does so. Currents along the western sides of continents at this latitude bring cooler water from higher latitudes toward the Equator. When onshore winds from the subtropical high-pressure system, which are cooler and stable to begin with, blow over the cold current, they are cooled further. The air becomes even more stable, and subsidence and subsequent warming are enhanced. Most of the warm deserts are at low elevations. Higher elevations are cooler than sea level at approximately 3.5° F for every 1,000 ft (1° C per 100 m). Regions on the lee side of mountains or basins between mountains are dry due to additional adiabatic warming. As air crosses the mountains and descends, it becomes both warmer and drier.

General Adaptations

Although genera and species may vary throughout the world, many warm desert plants have similar growthforms and similar adaptations. Depending on rainfall, vegetation varies from very little to comparatively lush scrublands. Dominant growthforms are shrubs or scrubby trees concentrated along drainage channels or in rocky soils. While some adaptations such as stem succulents are predominantly found in warm deserts in the Americas, many different desert plants worldwide have similar adaptations of small leaves and deep root systems. Acacia and mesquite are represented by many species in almost all warm deserts, but other genera also have similar growthform characteristics. Plants growing in areas with poor drainage or high evaporation must have a tolerance to salt. Alkaline soils in salt flats and playas in all warm deserts support a community of halophytes composed of several genera and species depending on geographic location. Annual grasses and forbs may cover otherwise bare ground after a substantial rain.

Because of scarce resources, most warm desert animals tend to be small rather than large. While large animals and birds can travel long distances in search of food and water, small creatures must contend with a limited local environment. Small animals such as kangaroo rats in North America and jerboas in Eurasia do not need to drink free water, surviving with metabolic water produced from their food. Small animals must be more conservative of moisture because of their larger surface area compared with body mass. Unlike larger animals, they cannot survive a high loss of body weight in water. Many small animals spend the heat of the day in cool burrows, only emerging at night. Many lizards are adapted to burrowing into sand dunes. Long ears of kit fox, fennec fox, jackrabbit, and Patagonian hare are useful in radiating excess heat.

Regional Expressions of Warm Deserts

North America

The three warm deserts of North America are located in the southwestern part of the continent, roughly south of 35° N and west of 100° W, in southwest Texas, southern New Mexico and Arizona, southeastern California, and adjacent Mexico, including parts of Baja California (see Figure 2.3). Based on evidence regarding stability of continents and position of landmasses and climate systems, North American deserts have been in existence since the early Cenozoic and exhibit both similarities and differences in climate and biota. The three deserts, Sonoran, Mojave, and Chihuahuan, are differentiated by rainfall patterns and vegetation.

Each of the three warm North American deserts has distinct vegetation. The Sonoran is characterized by subtrees, several kinds of cacti including tall columnar types, many different perennial shrubs, and both winter and summer annuals. The

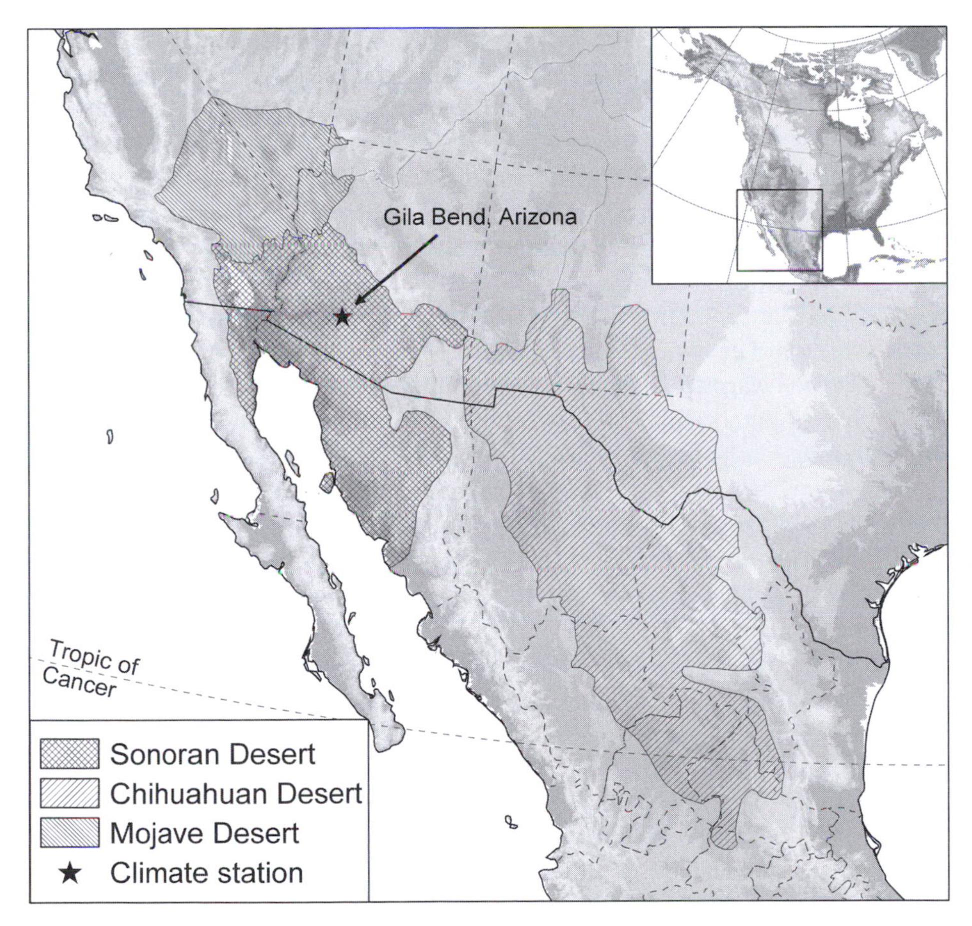

Figure 2.3 The three warm deserts in North America are concentrated on the western side of the continent. *(Map by Bernd Kuennecke.)*

term subtree is used to differentiate short, scrubby trees from large trees such as oak or spruce. The Mojave has widely spaced, shorter perennial shrubs, moderately tall yuccas, and winter annuals. It also has fewer cacti, both in numbers and in species. Vegetation in the Chihuahuan varies according to latitude, but generally is characterized by large leaf succulents like yuccas and agaves. Both small and large cacti are numerous and some areas have tall columnar species. Grasses are abundant, and annuals are summer growers. Many succulent plants are large in all three deserts, but especially in the Sonoran and Chihuahuan. Because precipitation is sporadic and unreliable, plants need to have a considerable amount of moisture stored to get them through periods of prolonged drought.

Vegetational differences are predominantly due to seasonality of rainfall. The Mojave Desert in southeastern California is affected by cyclonic storms coming from the Pacific Ocean during the winter. The Chihuahuan Desert in southern New Mexico, extreme western Texas, and south to San Luis Potosi, Mexico, receives summer thunderstorms from the Gulf of Mexico. Between the extremes, the Sonoran Desert in southern Arizona and adjacent Sonora and Baja California in Mexico has a biseasonal pattern, rain from both winter cyclonic systems and from summer thunderstorms. The rainfall season also determines how useful that total might be to plants. Winter rains are generally cyclonic, widespread, and may last a day or more. The more gentle rains soak into the soil. In contrast, summer rainfall is due to convection. Violent and localized thunderstorms that may last less than an hour release torrential downpours. Rather than soaking into the soil, water becomes runoff and flash floods.

Considerable difference in temperature exists in the three warm deserts in North America. The Sonoran at the lowest elevation, less than 1,850 ft (550 m), is subtropical and warmest. Both the Mojave and Chihuahuan are higher and cooler. Three-quarters of the Mojave is between 1,850 and 3,650 ft (550 and 1,100 m), and one-half of the Chihuahuan is higher than 4,000 ft (1,200 m). All three are categorized as warm deserts because most precipitation falls as rain rather than snow.

Plants common to North American warm deserts. Several plants and communities are common to more than one North American warm desert. Creosote bush, a low-branching shrub 3–4 ft (1–1.2 m) tall with widely spreading lateral roots and small, waxy leaves, is characteristic in lowland areas of all three deserts (see Figure 2.4). Its northern limit of distribution is considered the boundary between warm deserts and cold deserts. Regularly spaced 15–30 ft (4.5–9 m) apart with bare ground between, it is commonly associated with bursage. Creosote originated in South America and evolved into five different species. Only one species is found in North American deserts, but three genetic races based on the number of chromosome pairs occur, each corresponding to one of the warm deserts. The three types of creosote have a different appearance, bushiest in the Mojave and most open in the Chihuahuan. (Creosote bush is not the source of the substance creosote, which comes from wood tar. The plant is only named for its tarry smell after a rain.)

Figure 2.4 Creosote bush, shown here in Big Bend National Park, Texas, in the Chihuahuan Desert, is the most common plant in warm deserts of North America. *(Photo by author.)*

Of the three North American warm deserts, the Sonoran and the Chihuahuan share the most genera and species. The cooler Mojave Desert with a stricter winter precipitation regime has only a few species found in all three, notably ocotillo, saltbush, woolly plantain, the introduced salt cedar, and prickly pear, cholla, and barrel cacti. Mesquite is a significant plant in the Chihuahuan Desert, less common in the Sonoran, and absent from the Mojave. Paloverde is prominent in both the Sonoran and Chihuahuan but is also absent from the Mojave.

In favorable years, annuals blanket the ground with flowers for only a few weeks. They are often more numerous in terms of number of species than are perennials, but their appearance is sporadic. Rock Valley, Nevada, in the Mojave Desert has 10 common perennials compared with 41 annuals. Numbers for the Sonoran Desert near Tucson are comparable, 8 perennials to 48 annuals. Several genera of annuals are common to all three deserts.

Riparian habitats along large rivers often have dense forests, locally called bosques, of willows, mesquite, salt cedar, and large cottonwoods.

Animals common to North American warm deserts. Because the development of North American deserts is relatively recent, less than 10,000 years ago, many mammals, birds, and reptiles are found in all three warm deserts. Some have their centers of location in one or two deserts, while others have distinct species or subspecies more restricted in location.

Small mammals common to all North American warm deserts include kangaroo rats, pocket mice, field mice, woodrats, grasshopper mice, ground squirrels, antelope squirrels, cottontails, jackrabbits, skunks, and the California leaf-nosed bat. Less common are gophers and desert shrews. While genera may be the same in all three deserts, species are frequently different. Coyote, followed by mule deer, is the most common large mammal, widespread in both range and habitat. Although inconspicuous, badgers are found in all three warm deserts. Mountain lions and bobcats are native but rare. Whitetail deer and javelina are limited to the Sonoran and Chihuahuan deserts. Ring-tailed cats and coati (only in the Sonoran and Chihuahuan) are present but rare.

Two species of jackrabbits live in the American Southwest, black-tailed and antelope. These rabbits are actually hares. A major difference is that rabbits burrow to escape the heat, but hares do not. Jackrabbits rest during the day in shallow depressions on the shady side of a bush. Except for early morning and late evening in summer, the north side (in the Northern Hemisphere) never gets direct rays from the sun. The ground temperature in the slight depression in the shade is cooler than both the surrounding air and the ground surface in the sun. Heat from the soil surface and the jackrabbit's large ears radiates up toward the sky, not down into the depression. The animal takes advantage of this small microclimate to wait out the midday heat. Water sources are generally too far for small desert animals to travel to, and 80 percent of the jackrabbit's diet consists of green, succulent plants, especially after rains. They also eat mesquite and cactus in the dry part of the year.

Invasive Trees

Salt cedar, also called tamarisk, is a deciduous shrub or tree native to the Mediterranean region and southern Asia. Deliberately brought to the western United States as early as the 1700s for use as shade, windbreaks, and erosion control, its lacey foliage and attractive pink flowers also made it desirable as an ornamental. By the 1870s, it had escaped from cultivation, and by 1935, it had spread to many of the western states. An extremely invasive phreatophyte, it is a major problem in riparian zones where native willows, cottonwoods, and mesquite are displaced. Salt cedar is tolerant of adverse conditions—heat, cold, drought, flood, salt, fire—and grows quickly, as much as 13 ft (4 m) in a season. It produces copious flowers and seeds, but also reproduces vegetatively, a definite advantage because it can send up several sprouts after the aboveground parts have been decimated by fire. It transpires so much water that some springs and water courses have dried up since the tree arrived. Well adapted to salty soils, it can tolerate 36,000 ppm, whereas native willows and cottonwoods can tolerate only 1,500 ppm. Salt cedar excretes salt crystals through its leaves. The salt then accumulates at the base of the plant, increasing salinity and preventing native species from growing. It may also increase the risk of wildfires and floods because of its dense growth habit and tendency to block drainage channels. Eradication is a challenge. Repetitive burning and digging out roots combined with herbicides does work, but it is time-consuming and expensive.

The whitetail antelope squirrel, only active in morning and late afternoon, is an example of a rodent that is well adapted to the desert. Only 6 in (15 cm) long and weighing 4 oz (110 g), it may not need to drink for more than a month and can utilize water with a higher salt content than the ocean. It needs only 2 percent of its body weight in free water even with a diet of dry food. Like all rodents, it does not sweat and cannot benefit from cooling due to evaporation. Because it cannot survive an elevated body temperature for an extended time, it spends only a short time in the heat of the day and seeks shade or its burrow for respite. Its kidneys produce concentrated urine. Although present in all three warm North American deserts, it is restricted to the cooler areas (the Mojave, Baja, and the Chihuahuan) and is absent from the hottest part of the Sonoran.

The Roadrunner is a symbol of the desert in all three regions (see Figure 2.5b). Although they do fly for short distances, the bird's four splayed toes are better suited for the ground. At speeds up to 15 mph (24 kph), they are fast enough to catch and eat lizards. Roadrunners also feed on rattlesnakes, avoiding the snake's fangs and stabbing it with its beak. Gambel Quail are commonly seen running along the ground, only flying into cover when startled. Several less conspicuous birds are also common to all three deserts, notably Burrowing Owl, thrasher, Mourning Dove, and Phainopeple, which resembles a brown Cardinal. Several birds that are widespread in North America, such as Red-tailed Hawk and Turkey Vulture, are present in all three deserts.

Many reptiles are common to all three deserts, notably two rattlesnakes, Mojave and western diamondback, and the desert spiny lizard. Several reptiles are present in both the Sonoran and Mojave deserts but are absent in the Chihuahuan, particularly chuckwalla, Gila monster, and desert iguana. The banded gecko and desert tortoise in the Mojave and Sonoran both have equivalents in the Chihuahuan Desert, the Texas banded gecko and bolson tortoise. Several species of horned lizard occur, each limited to one or two deserts.

Some birds and rodents are oblivious to cactus spines. Mourning Dove, Costa's Hummingbird, and Cactus Wren nest in cholla, and the spines provide good

(a) (b)

Figure 2.5 Birds commonly seen in North American warm deserts are (a) Cactus Wren and (b) Roadrunner. *(Courtesy of Shutterstock. Copyright: Paul S. Wolf.)*

Spadefoot Toads

Couch's spadefoot toad, found in the Sonoran and Chihuahuan deserts, is an amphibian that needs water to survive. As its water hole dries, the adult toad uses its hind feet as shovels to dig 3 ft (1 m) into the still-moist ground. When it aestivates, its skin becomes largely impervious to water loss, but the toad can lose 50 percent of its body weight as it waits as long as two years for rain. When enough rain creates a water area for reproduction, the toads come back to the surface and complete their life cycle in as little as two to six weeks. No equivalent spadefoot lives in the Mojave.

protection (see Figure 2.5a). The white-throated woodrat, commonly called a packrat, is well adapted to life with cholla cactus. It not only safely climbs on the plants but also carries away segments to surround its nest, securing it from predators. Nests accumulated by generations of packrats can be more than 7 ft (2 m) wide, usually in the shade. Compared with a 167° F (75° C) temperature of the ground in the open desert, it may be only 115° F (46° C) at the entrance, and a cool 88° F (31° C) in the shallow nest. The animal has no need to drink water. All moisture needed comes from green vegetation, such as mesquite pods, grass, and cholla cactus. In spite of the poisonous oxalic acid content of the cactus, cholla accounts for nearly one-half of the packrat's diet, up to 90 percent in the driest time of the year. The packrat is not affected by the toxin and gets valuable moisture from the cactus segments. Like many desert animals, the packrat avoids heat by being active at dawn and dusk and at night. Several species of packrat share these characteristics, at least one each in the Sonoran, Mojave, and Chihuahuan deserts.

Desert Fish

Distinct species of small desert pupfish (Cyprinodons), only 1–2.5 in (2.5–6 cm) long, are found in isolated pools, streams, or marshes in the Sonoran and Mojave deserts. During the Pleistocene (Ice Age) when southwestern deserts were wetter, these pupfish had a continuous distribution in an integrated drainage system. As the climate changed, rivers and streams dried up, isolating the pupfish populations to evolve separately. One species is found at Devil's Hole at Ash Meadows, Nevada, part of Death Valley National Park. Another species is at Quitobaquito Springs in Organ Pipe Cactus National Monument in southern Arizona. Their desert pools are often saltier than the ocean as water evaporates and salt accumulates.

Sonoran Desert. The Sonoran Desert extends from 22° N in Mexico and the Baja peninsula to 35° N in central Arizona. The landscape features basin and range topography, with small eroded fault block mountains and extensive areas of alluvial fans, bajadas, and playas. About 80 percent of the landscape consists of basins filled with both coarse and fine alluvium. Many of the desert mountains rise above the desert climate and environment. Although interior drainage is normal between mountain ranges, some major rivers flow toward the Gulf of California. The Colorado River, separating California from Arizona, empties a small amount of water into the sea. The Salt and Gila Rivers, dammed upstream of Phoenix, rarely contain water. In Mexico, the Sonoita River and the Sonora River never reach the Gulf. Rio Yaqui did in the past, and Rio Magdalena rarely does.

Although mild except at higher elevations, winter temperatures vary with latitude and are slightly cooler in Arizona than in Mexico. Summer temperatures are similar regardless of latitude. Longer daylight hours and continentality ensure that summer temperatures are uniformly hot. Ninety consecutive days with maximum daily temperature above 100° F (38° C) are common. Winters are mild and rarely freeze except at higher elevations. Many Sonoran Desert plants are killed by 36 continuous hours of temperatures below freezing, which in places marks the boundary of desert vegetation.

The southern part of the Sonoran is influenced by the subsiding subtropical high-pressure system, and the desert region as a whole is in the rainshadow of the southern Rocky Mountains in the United States and the Sierra Madre Occidental in Mexico. These north-south trending mountain ranges block moisture-bearing winds originating in the Gulf of Mexico. Cyclonic storms carried by westerly winds exert more influence in the northern and western parts, and all regions experience thunderstorms in summer. The Sonoran Desert has a complex assemblage of plants because some plants are adapted to winter rains, while others need summer moisture (see Plate III). The biseasonal precipitation pattern promotes greater plant variety than found in the winter-rain Mojave or the summer-rain Chihuahuan.

Plant distributions closely follow the physiography of the region, particularly variation from fine and sometimes salty sediment in the valleys to coarse gravel and boulders at the top of alluvial fans. The distinct composition of plants according to position on the bajadas is related to the amount of moisture available in the soil. While finer soils may have an appreciable amount of moisture, capillary attraction to small soil particles makes it harder for plant roots to extract that water. On middle to upper slopes of bajadas where rocks are larger, more water is available to plants.

The plant most associated with the Sonoran Desert is saguaro cactus (see Figure 2.6a). A saguaro begins life as a seedling in the protective shade of a shrub

Figure 2.6 Signature plants of the warm deserts of North America: (a) Stem succulents, such as saguaro cactus in the Sonoran Desert. *(Photo courtesy of Dee Fuerst.)* (b) Joshua tree, a tall yucca, in the Mojave Desert. *(Photo by author.)* (c) Large leaf succulents, such as soaptree yucca in the Chihuahuan Desert. *(Photo by author.)*

called a nurse plant, such as a creosote bush or paloverde. Growth is slow. After 10 years it may be only 4 in (10 cm) tall, and after 25 years, it may reach 2 ft (0.6 m). It begins growing arms at 75 years, is mature at 100, and may live for 250. It is estimated that only one of 275,000 seeds survives to produce a mature plant. A mature plant is 50 ft (15 m) tall, usually branched, and weighs 10 or more tons. An equal plant mass exists below ground, in a taproot and shallow roots that radiate 35 ft (11 m) in all directions. The extensive root system serves two purposes—stability and a wide source of moisture. Creamy white flowers appear on the tops of the plants in May. The fruit and seeds are important food to many desert birds, animals, and Native Americans. Saguaro are absent from Baja California.

A variety of growthforms, including grasses, shrubs, subtrees, and many large and small cacti grow in the Sonoran Desert. It differs from other North American deserts in that is has big arboreal (tree-size) cactus, many subtrees, and succulent elements rather than low shrubs. Three subtrees—blue paloverde, foothill paloverde, and ironwood—are widespread indicator species of the Sonoran Desert, although blue paloverde is not found in Baja California. Other typical desert plants include several trees and shrubs of the pea family, including mesquite and acacia. A tall spiny shrub, ocotillo, is also common throughout the desert area (see Figure 2.7). A relative of the ocotillo, the cirio or boojum tree, has a more limited

Figure 2.7 Drought-deciduous plants in the Sonoran Desert include (a) ocotillo, which is related to (b) boojum or cirio found in Baja California. *(Photos by author.)*

distribution, mainly in Baja. Of many types of cacti, several species of cholla are dominant. Other cacti with local distribution are organ pipe along the Arizona-Mexico border, and cardon in Mexico. Conspicuous shrubs are creosote bush, bursage, brittlebush, and wolfberry. Riparian habitats where more water is available underground support a variety of phreatophytes, such as paloverde, mesquite, cottonwood, willow, and the introduced salt cedar.

Succulence, spines, deep or wide-spreading root systems, as well as being drought-deciduous, are major desert adaptations. Cacti may be up to 80 percent water. Large species like saguaro, cardon, and cholla have an interior woody framework that holds the fleshy tissues together. This wood is used for building materials by Native Americans and Mexicans. Ocotillo stems are also woody, but even when seemingly dead, they will grow if planted. Living fences in Arizona and Mexico are made by poking ocotillo wands into the ground. Drought-deciduous plants include ocotillo, creosote, and paloverde. Saltbush and salt cedar grow in soils too salty for most other plants. Plants often have more than one type of adaptation to aridity and high temperatures.

Large animals can move long distances to find food and water, while small animals must be either adapted to desert conditions or able to evade the heat and aridity. Pronghorn, mule deer, and coyotes are good examples of Sonoran Desert animals with large ranges. Desert bighorn sheep have an additional advantage; they can tolerate loss of a large percentage of body weight, which is rapidly replenished when they drink. Small mammals like antelope squirrels and kangaroo rats are primarily nocturnal and spend the hot day in burrows. Jackrabbits depend on shade and their long ears to survive the heat.

Javelinas, also called peccaries, are wild pigs that frequent ravines and washes at night. The animal's huge head, almost one-half its body, ends in a pig-like snout used to root for food. These mammals live in small groups of 5–10, and eat just about anything—spiny cactus, roots, tubers, lizards, and snakes. Because of their poor vision, they may seem aggressive. When they sense they are in danger, they fight ferociously with sharp hooves and sharp teeth.

Camels in North America

In the mid-nineteenth century, military men convinced Secretary of War Jefferson Davis that camels would be good pack animals in the southwestern deserts. Congress agreed, and at a cost of $30,000 approximately 60 animals were shipped to Texas in 1856. On a trek from Texas to California, they carried heavy loads (600–800 lbs each, 270–360 kg); ate cactus, mesquite, and greasewood (plants that horses and mules would not touch); walked 25–30 mi (40–50 km) a day; and maintained good health. Even though the camel's padded feet were more suited to deep sand than to rocky surfaces, the experiment should have been a success, but no one liked the animals or wanted to work with them. They were strange, stubborn, smelly, noisy, and vicious. Army mules were terrified. After only four years, the experiment was interrupted by the Civil War. After the war, railroads expanding westward replaced the need for long-distance desert pack animals. The remaining camels were released to freely wander, and occasionally a feral camel would be spotted as late as 1930. Hadj Ali, whose name was Americanized to Hi Jolly, came from Syria to train army wranglers in camel handling. He died in 1902 and is buried in Quartzsite, Arizona.

Resident birds include hawks and Turkey Vultures, all common elsewhere in North America. Birds specific to the Sonoran Desert include Gila Woodpeckers and Ladder-backed Woodpeckers. Gila Woodpeckers peck holes in saguaro cactus in search of insects. They also enlarge cavities for nesting spots, which are then used by other birds, such as Elf Owls, after the woodpeckers no longer need them. As a protective measure, saguaro sap coats the interior of the nest cavity, which prevents water loss from the plant. This hardened sap is so durable that the cactus "boot" outlining the nest hole can sometimes be found as a hard shell in the desert after the fleshy part of the cactus has rotted away. Gambel Quail, Roadruners, Phainopeplas, Cactus Wren, and Curved-bill Thrashers are frequently seen.

Lizards are plentiful, including western whiptail, horned lizards, desert spiny lizards, desert iguana, and chuckwalla. Poisonous species are common, especially five species of rattlesnake. The Arizona coral snake and Gila monster are also highly venomous. Growing up to 2 ft (0.6 m) long, the poisonous Gila monster is North America's largest lizard. Bird and lizard eggs, young birds, and small rodents are their normal diet. They hold their prey in their jaws, chewing the poison into the victim. They will do the same to a human but only after strong provocation. Arizona coral snakes are small, less than 20 in (50 cm), but deadly. In contrast, western diamondback rattlesnakes grow up to 6 ft (1.8 m) long. Sidewinders are 18–30 in (45–75 cm). Scorpions are small, 1–5 in (2.5–13 cm), and the smallest species has the worst venom. Arizona coral snake and Sonoran gopher snake are distinct to the Sonoran Desert. Not all snakes, however, have venom. Western shovelnose, desert rosy boa, gopher snakes, and others are not poisonous.

Many Sonoran Desert landscapes have been degraded because of overgrazing in the late 1800s. The many grasses that formerly grew between larger perennials have been replaced by an increase in cholla and prickly pear. The loss of nurse plants like paloverde is detrimental to future saguaro populations. Hiking, off-road vehicle use, grazing, and animal hooves all damage desert vegetation. Desert land converted to irrigated cropland often accumulates salts, rendering the soil unproductive.

Sonoran Desert subdivisions. Scientists divide the Sonoran Desert into seven regions based on climate, species composition, and plant growthform. Two subdivisions have more affinity with tropical thorn forests than with deserts and are not discussed here. The Vizcaino subdivision in central Baja is affected by fog (see Chapter 4).

Straddling the Colorado River and forming a horseshoe shape around the Gulf of California, the Lower Colorado River Valley subdivision is the hottest and driest part of the Sonoran Desert. What little rainfall it receives, primarily in winter, is unreliable. Much of the landscape is flat plains, sand dunes, or salt flats, which give it a simple species composition. The low bajadas and the few granite or volcanic hills and low mountains support slightly more complex communities. An extensive sand dune area, the only large one in North American deserts, is found around the Colorado River Delta near Yuma.

Only two communities dominate, both with much bare ground. Sandy alluvial flats are covered with white bursage and creosote bush, often in association with brittlebush. Mixed scrub along the washes is dominated by blue paloverde, honey mesquite, and wolfberry. The lack of subtrees to serve as nurse plants to seedlings may be the reason no saguaro grows in the Lower Colorado River area. Few perennials grow on desert pavement plains, which tend to be dry and salty. Even creosote and white bursage are confined to small drainage channels. After winter rains, ephemerals like woolly plantain, which is important forage for animals, may appear. Salt flats, originally dominated by saltbush and honey mesquite, have been converted to cultivation, particularly in the Coachella and Gila River valleys.

Coarser soils on the higher bajada slopes contain more moisture and support a more complex plant community in both growthform and species, particularly foothill paloverde, catclaw, and ocotillo. Cacti, especially chollas, are well represented on the bajadas. Phreatophytes like cottonwood, willows, and salt cedar are restricted to Colorado River floodplains. The sandy areas near Yuma support perennial grasses, such as big galleta, which stabilize the dunes

Stands of native desert fan palms are found in moist, shady canyons north of the Salton Trough and in adjacent Baja California west of the Colorado River. Commercial plantations of date palms, native to the Sahara, cover many acres in the Coachella and Imperial Valleys.

Because of sparse vegetation, few large animals live in the Lower Colorado River Valley. Desert bighorn may be found in the rugged mountains, and Sonoran pronghorn are occasionally found on sandy plains and desert pavement. Because they tolerate and benefit by human presence, coyotes are ubiquitous. Burrowing rodents, such as round-tailed ground squirrel, and their predator the kit fox are characteristic of sandy plains. Birds are also poorly represented, but several raptors prey on small mammals. Reptiles, however, are numerous and varied. Each distinct habitat—rocky outcrops, bajadas, talus, sandy flats, and washes—supports a different assemblage of reptiles. Many, such as fringe-toed lizard and flat-tailed horned lizard, are endemic to the Lower Colorado. Sidewinders are specifically adapted to sandy areas.

Salton Sea

The Salton Trough and the Imperial Valley are an extension of the Gulf of California but are separated from the sea by alluvial deposits of the Colorado River Delta. Much of the Salton Trough is below sea level, in places more than 250 ft (75 m), with no outlet to the Gulf. Shoreline deposits indicate that the Salton Trough was the site of a large freshwater lake as recently as 400–1,800 years ago, but no lake was recorded at the time of Spanish exploration. Although the Salton Sea (occupying the deepest part of the depression) has held water periodically, it is not an entirely natural feature. In 1904, floodwaters from the Colorado River followed the course of the Imperial Ditch, which under normal conditions carried only irrigation water to the Imperial Valley. By July of that year, 87 percent of the Colorado River's flow went to the Salton Sea instead of to the Gulf of California. By the time the normal direction of flow was restored in 1907, the Salton Sea was 67 ft (20 m) deep and covered 443 mi^2 (1,147 km^2). With no more influx of water, high evaporation in the desert climate dropped the lake level to 25 ft (7.6 m) only five years later. Because the Salton Sea is an enclosed lake with no natural outlet, salts concentrate as water evaporates, posing an environmental problem.

The Colorado River is a barrier to some plants and animals. The Elf Owl and Gilded Flicker are absent from California because the saguaros they require for nesting sites are rarely found west of the river. Different species of antelope squirrels and pocket mice live on each side, and no javelina are native to California. Gila monster and coral snake are also restricted to Arizona.

Predominantly in south-central Arizona between Gila Bend and Tucson, the Arizona Upland subdivision is both cooler and wetter than the Lower Colorado River Valley. It is higher in elevation, 500–3,000 ft (150–900 m), and has many coarse bajadas. Annual rainfall, generally 10 in (250 mm), is low in the west but increases eastward. The pattern is biseasonal with both summer and winter rain. Densely vegetated with complex communities, the Arizona Upland is the stereotype of the American desert, a landscape crowded with subtrees, shrubs, and both tall and small cacti. It has a great diversity of plants, but they may not all be present in one locality. Limestone surfaces, for example, are drier because water percolates through the rock. Therefore, limestone areas often support a sparse cover of creosote bush while adjacent gravelly bajadas have both a greater variety and density of plants. However, the most abundant plants thrive in many habitats. Although not as numerous as other species, saguaro is a conspicuous visual dominant.

Variation in species composition and complexity of community is determined by position on the bajada, predominantly due to differences in soil texture, which contribute to moisture content (see Figure 2.8). The valleys and lower, flatter parts of bajadas are similar to the Lower Colorado River Valley with expanses of cresote bush and white bursage, along with some acacias and chollas. A broad ecotone exists along the gentle slopes of bajadas from creosote-bursage communities on the flats to scrubby woodland in stonier locations. Mid- to upper-bajada slopes support diverse communities of tall columnar cacti, subtrees, shrubs, and small to medium cacti. This area is sometimes referred to as a paloverde-cactus desert because the most common plant association is dominated by foothill paloverde and saguaro, with many ironwood, mesquite, and ocotillo. Subtrees 10–20 ft (3–6 m) tall and saguaro up to 40 ft (12 m) tall stand above the general 1–2 ft (0.3–0.6 m) shrub layer. Saguaros become common higher on the slope, both because of more soil

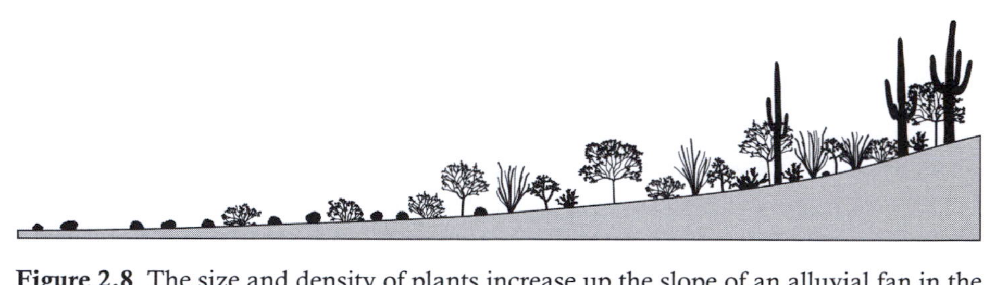

Figure 2.8 The size and density of plants increase up the slope of an alluvial fan in the Sonoran Desert. Different species occur at different levels, according to soil texture or rockiness. *(Illustration by Jeff Dixon.)*

moisture and the subtrees, which act as nurse plants for seedlings. Many trees, such as blue paloverde, mesquite, and catclaw acacia, are the same as those found along washes in the Lower Colorado River Valley, but because more water is available on the coarse bajadas, the plants are not restricted to water courses. Growing at higher elevations with more precipitation, jojoba is almost wholly confined to the Arizona Upland, where it provides important forage.

Cacti, particularly saguaro, barrel, and more than a dozen species of prickly pear and cholla, are a conspicuous part of the desert scene (see Plate IV). Several are best represented or confined to this subdivision. Two additional columnar cacti, senita and organ pipe (also called pitaya dulce because of its sweet fruit), are locally important in the southern part of this section. Because they are frost sensitive, these two cacti are more common to the south and in Mexico.

Perennial grasses such as grama, tobosa, and sacaton provide sparse groundcover between larger species, especially on deeper soils. Winter annuals dominate in the north, but summer annuals become more numerous in the south where more summer rain falls. Almost pure stands of saltbush occupy alkaline soils. Dry washes are lined with trees of catclaw, mesquite, and blue paloverde.

The density and variety of vegetation combined with biseasonal precipitation support a variety of animal life. Desert mule deer and javelina are common large animals. Small animals include bats, jackrabbits, cottontail rabbits, and several burrowing rodents, which are preyed on by gray fox and coyote. The Harris antelope squirrel is endemic to this subdivision. The presence of trees, biseasonal rainfall, and mild winter temperatures are conducive to a rich bird fauna, some resident, some migratory. Most of the reptile life is also common to other parts of the Sonoran Desert or even to other North American deserts. Some, however, have a more limited distribution in this subdivision, notably the Gila monster and Arizona coral snake.

The Central Gulf Coast subdivision is a narrow strip on both the eastern and western sides of the Gulf of California, including the two large islands in the Gulf—Tiburon and Angel de la Guardia. It is restricted to the coastal region by adjacent mountains and hills. In some localities steep mountains or hills drop directly into the sea, while in other areas bajada slopes extend to the coast. Soils are shallow, coarse, and rocky. Annual rainfall is meager, least in the north and increasing to the south. Neither the total precipitation nor season is reliable. The coastal location modifies the temperature, and both summers and winters are less extreme than in the rest of the Sonoran Desert.

The region is distinctive for its plant community of subtrees and tall cacti. Even though large stem succulents like cardon visually dominate, the region may be called a bursera-jatropha desert, also called a sarcocaulescent desert because of the short, swollen trunks or stems of dominant plants. The main floral elements are widely spaced shrubs of sangre de drago, lomboy, and ocotillo, among widely spaced subtrees of blue paloverde, ironwood, and elephant tree. Both sangre de drago and elephant trees generally are not found in other subdivisions, and their prevalence defines this subdivision. Although present, creosote bush is much less important here. Several species of cholla are common.

The predominant community on deep granite soils and coarse bajadas is composed of elephant trees (also called torchwood or torote) and 10–13 ft (3–4 m) high cardon cacti. Other small trees or large shrubs are paloverde and ocotillo. A sparse lower shrub layer, less than 6.5 ft (2 m) tall, may include bursage, brittle bush, and teddy bear cholla. The lack of a small shrub layer presents a more open landscape with more bare ground than in the Arizona Upland. The drier, flat areas on finer alluvium at the base of the bajadas are dominated by ocotillo, sangre de drago, and creosote bush, with scattered brittlebush, barrel cacti, and cholla. Larger cacti are confined to ephemeral water courses. Saltbush grows on fine-textured salty coastal flats, especially on the mainland.

Although the Baja California side of the Gulf has more diversity in plant life, an interesting and anomalous area occurs on the mainland south of Puerto Libertad in Mexico. Several species common to Baja are found only in a localized area in the Sierra Bacha. Cooler summer temperatures, north-facing granite slopes, and higher relative humidity may mimic conditions of the Vizcaino subdivision of the Sonoran Desert in Baja (see Chapter 4).

The fauna of the Central Gulf Coast subdivision is similar to the rest of the Sonoran Desert.

The Plains of Sonora subdivision on the Mexican mainland around Hermosillo is the least diversified. Wetter than most desert biomes (10–15 in, 250–380 mm), it is transitional to more humid thorn scrub farther south (see *Grassland Biomes* in this series). Summers are hot and wet, winters are warm and dry, and frost is infrequent. The landscape is primarily flat with fine clay soil. Widely spaced low-branching subtrees and shrubs distinguish this subdivision. More herbaceous cover may be an indication of a grassier landscape in relatively recent times. Trees, especially ironwood, paloverde, and mesquite (all in the pea family), which are 13–33 ft (4–10 m) tall, dominate. Creosote and white bursage are only locally important, and cacti are not abundant.

Because it is transitional to thorn forest, species composition changes with latitude, becoming more complex to the south. In the north, open forest mixes with desert species of creosote, ocotillo, organ pipe cactus, senita, and four species of cholla. In the middle region, creosote and brittlebush coexist with more trees and shrubs, particularly elephant trees and lignum vitae. MacDougal ocotillo replaces *F. splendens,* Sonora paloverde replaces foothill paloverde, and different species appear. As trees gain importance, cacti numbers diminish. At the southern limit, tree species and numbers increase, and creosote, brittlebush, and columnar cacti are absent.

The only distinction in the fauna is that birds dominate because of the trees.

Mojave Desert. Located in southeastern California, southern Nevada, and extreme northwestern Arizona, the Mojave Desert is the smallest of the four deserts in the United States. The Mojave is different from the other warm deserts for several reasons. It is only under the influence of the subtropical high-pressure cell in summer. In winter, aridity is caused by its location in the rainshadow of the Sierra Nevada and the Transverse Ranges. Because the majority of the Mojave is high desert, 2,000–5,000 ft (600–1,500 m), both summers and winters are cooler than in the Sonoran Desert. Winters in the high desert often have frost and occasional snow. January minimum temperatures average just below freezing, and July maxima average 97° F (36° C). Annual precipitation, falling primarily in winter and spring, averages 5 in (130 mm). The general landscape of the Mojave is similar to the Sonoran Desert, with rugged mountains, extensive bajadas, and many dry lakebeds that were part of an integrated drainage system during the Pleistocene.

The Mojave is considered by some scientists to be merely transitional between the warm Sonoran Desert and the cold Great Basin Desert. Although it shares many of its plant and animal species with those deserts, a Mojave core makes it distinct, and 25 percent of its plants are endemic. Biodiversity is limited, but yuccas may be locally common. Indicator species are spiny menodora, Joshua tree, bladder-sage, Mojave dalea, goldenhead, and scalebroom. Cacti are less abundant than in the Sonoran Desert, and none are large. Some cactus species are widespread in other deserts, while others like Mojave prickly pear, silver cholla, beavertail, and many-headed barrel cactus are centered in the Mojave.

Although Joshua tree, one of few Mojave endemics, is a signature plant, most of this desert is too hot and too dry for it (see Figure 2.6b). This tall, tree-like yucca grows at higher and cooler elevations above the creosote flats, primarily along the boundary with the Great Basin. Joshua trees grow up to 40 ft (12 m) tall with many branches. Tips of the branches have groups of creamy white lily-like blossoms in early spring.

The Mojave and Sonoran deserts overlap in a broad transition zone. Dominant plants include creosote bush, all-scale, brittlebush, desert holly, and Mojave yucca, all of which are also significant in parts of the Sonoran Desert. Several Sonoran indicator species are entirely absent from the Mojave. Teddy bear cholla, a common Sonoran Desert cactus, has only a local distribution in the Mojave.

Typical vegetation on the flats and lower bajadas is widely spaced perennial low shrubs (see Figure 2.9). The major community on the middle bajadas where soils are deep, loose, and sandy is dominated by creosote bush and white bursage. The association of these two plants covers 70 percent of the Mojave Desert. Creosote bush reproduces vegetatively, and clones may be thousands of years old. Yucca species, particularly Joshua trees, are visually dominant but other plants are more numerous. Other shrubs commonly found growing

Yuccas

Yuccas and moths have a symbiotic or codependent relationship, meaning that they require the other to survive. The Joshua tree depends on the yucca moth (*Tegeticula*) for pollination. The moth lays her eggs at the base of the flower, in the ovary, while pollinating the plant. When they hatch, the larvae have a ready supply of seeds for food. No other insect or bird pollinates the yucca, and the moth lays eggs nowhere else. Each of the four species of *Tegeticula* is adapted to a particular species of yuccca.

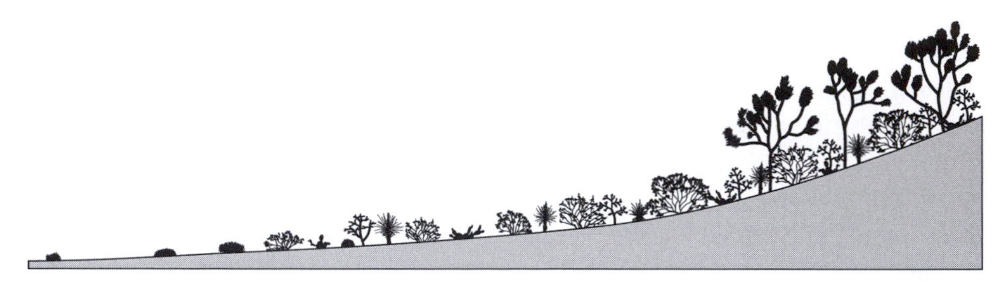

Figure 2.9 Community composition, along with size and density of plants, changes from salt bushes on the playas to creosote bushes and Joshua trees with increasing elevation on alluvial fans in the Mojave Desert. *(Illustration by Jeff Dixon.)*

alongside creosote are brittlebush, bladder sage, and shadscale. Where soils have a surface desert pavement or are underlain by caliche, both of which prevent deep root penetration and cause drier conditions, the major codominant is shadscale. Yuccas and beavertail cactus may be more common on desert pavement.

Several species of saltbush make up the plant community on dry or salty playas, and other halophytes may be present. Although allscale is most common, any of these salt-tolerant associations also occupy playas in the Great Basin and Sonoran deserts.

The northern boundary of the Mojave Desert is abrupt because of the higher elevation in the Great Basin. Shadscale and blackbrush are dominant in both deserts. Shadscale is tolerant of temperature and precipitation extremes and soil variation, all of which explain its location both on the northern edge of the Mojave and on caliche soils.

The Mojave is rich in annuals. Of the 250 species, at least 80 are endemic. The majority are winter annuals responding to September-December rainfall, but summer annuals also occur. The time of rain is critical in determining which species germinate.

Mammals of the Mojave are similar to those of the other North American warm deserts—desert bighorn sheep, mountain lion, coyote, kit fox, mule deer, and bobcat. Large mammals that range far and need more resources live only at the edges because of the sparse desert vegetation.

Death Valley

Famous for having the lowest point in North America, 282 ft (86 m) below sea level, Death Valley is an extreme environment in the Mojave Desert. Because of its low elevation and mountain-enclosed location, Death Valley has recorded the highest temperature in North America. Annual precipitation averages 4 in (50 mm). During the Pleistocene, glacial Lake Manley, 90 mi (145 km) long and 600 ft (180 m) deep, filled the valley. Salts crystallized as the lake evaporated, leaving an eroded salt crust called Devil's Golf Course. Some of the salt was economically valuable, and in the 1880s, mule teams began to haul borax from Death Valley to a railhead at Mojave, California, 165 mi (265 km) away. The trip took 10 days, and the animals also carried 1,200 gal (4,540 L) of water. Wagon loads weighed 36 t. Pupfish are found in isolated springs and desert streams, remnants of the glacial lake. Notable is the endemic *Cyprinodon diabolis* found in only one 200 ft^2 (18.5 m^2) location, Devil's Hole. The small fish, whose population varies from 200 to 800 depending on the season, lives in water four times as salty as the ocean and at temperatures up to 113° F (45° C).

Except for coyote and mule deer, large animals are rarely seen. Smaller animals with smaller ranges, such as kangaroo rat, Great Basin pocket mouse, and white-tailed antelope squirrel, are characteristic of Mojave creosote communities but are also found in similar creosote habitats in the Sonoran. The sparse resources of the Mojave Desert mean that each individual small rodent may need more than 15 ac (6 ha) on which to forage for seeds, leaves, invertebrates, and small vertebrates. Although plentiful in numbers, fewer species of kangaroo rats and pocket mice live in the Mojave than in the Sonoran or Chihuahuan deserts. Few rodent species are restricted to the Mojave, evidence that this desert is more recent and transitional in nature. The northern region has Great Basin species of kangaroo rats and pocket mice. Logically, the southern region has species more common farther south, such as western mastiff bat and round-tailed ground squirrel. While the whitetail antelope ground squirrel neither aestivates nor hibernates, the endemic Mojave ground squirrel has times of inactivity or dormancy—aestivation in hot dry periods and hibernation in the cooler winter.

No birds or reptiles are limited to the Mojave Desert. LeConte's Thrasher is centered here, but it is also common in parts of the Sonoran Desert. Even the desert night lizard, which lives among dead leaves of Joshua trees, is found in the Sonoran and Chihuahuan deserts. Most lizards and snakes in the Mojave are subspecies of more widespread species (see Figure 2.10). While not endemic, many lizard and snake species are distinctive in the Mojave, such as regal horned lizard,

Figure 2.10 The desert horned lizard is a reptile typical of the Mojave Desert. *(Photo by author.)*

Desert Shrimp

Fairy shrimp (*Brachinecta mackini*) survive drought as cysts, actually embryos encased in a shell, in dry playas. The area may be dry, with all life inactive, for decades. When cool temperatures coincide with sufficient rain (winter rain in this region is more dependable) and freshwater accumulates, it may take only three weeks to complete the fairy shrimp life cycle. Because of isolation, genetic variations exist in geographically separate pools.

Mojave patchnose snake, and Mojave rattlesnake. Chuckwallas, lizards up to 8 in (20 cm), are also characteristic. When disturbed, the animal threatens by opening its mouth, then escapes into a crevice where it inflates its body one-half again its normal size, making it impossible for a predator to pull it out. Kelso Dunes in Mojave National Preserve is a distinct community with seven endemic insects. The Mojave fringe-toed lizard is not endemic but is rare elsewhere.

Chihuahuan Desert. In the United States, the Chihuahuan Desert follows the Rio Grande in southern New Mexico and straddles the U.S.-Mexico border south through Big Bend National Park in southwest Texas. The center, however, is in the states of north-central Mexico, covering eastern Chihuahua, Coahuila, northeastern Durango, northeastern Zacatecas, and San Luis Potosi. Elevations are high compared with the Mojave and Sonoran deserts. One-half of the Chihuahuan Desert is more than 4,000 ft (1,200 m). The highest part, more than 6,000 ft (1,800 m), is in southern Coahuila.

The physical landscape is typical basin and range topography with many interior drainage basins (called bolsones in Mexico), gravel flats, low hills, and steep bajadas. About 80 percent of the substrate is limestone and gravel plains. Gypsum sand dunes and igneous rock areas are characteristic. Sand dunes support populations of endemic plants. Although most of the area is subject to interior drainage, exterior drainage reaches the Gulf of Mexico via the Rio Grande and its tributaries. The central highland region in the south, Zacatecas and San Luis Potosi, consists of eroded volcanic mountains.

Most of the Chihuahuan Desert in Mexico is located in a large basin between the Sierra Madre Occidental and Sierra Madre Oriental. Regions in the United States and Chihuahua are open to the Gulf of Mexico on the east but are bounded by uplands to the west. Little precipitation falls in winter because highlands block most cyclonic storms coming from the west. In summer, hot and humid winds from the Gulf of Mexico drop up to 70 percent of the annual total. Precipitation averages 9 in (230 mm), but is variable and can be 3–12 in (75–300 mm). More rain, 16 in (400 mm), falls at the boundaries where grassland has recently been replaced by desert vegetation. Although this amount of rainfall is more than that received by most other deserts in North America, not all is available for plant use. Because summer rain comes in the form of violent thunderstorms, runoff is high, and because of high summer temperatures, evaporation is also high. Thunderstorms are variable in both amount of moisture and geographic extent, and summer rainfall is inconsistent. For example, annual rainfall in San Luis Potosi Valley averages 14 in (360 mm), but has been as low as 4.7 in (120 mm) and as high as 27.6 in (700 mm). More reliable are occasional winter rains from cyclonic storms, especially in the north, but it is usually dry from January to May. Unlike winter-rainfall deserts, nothing flowers in winter. The occurrence of snow depends on latitude, being more common in the southern United States and decreasing southward.

The continental climate is characterized by hot summers, over 100° F (38° C), and cold winters. At higher elevations, however, summer temperatures during the day may be 10°–20° F (5.5°–11.0° C) lower than in the Sonoran Desert. Freezing is common, especially in the north and at higher elevations, but also in the lowest areas along the Rio Grande and farther south due to cold-air settling into valleys. On some winter days, temperatures may not rise above freezing.

Compared with the Sonoran, and especially to the Mojave, the Chihuahuan Desert is well watered and rich in plants and animals. The Chihuahuan Desert is the largest of the creosote-dominated deserts in North America. Plants from the pea and sunflower families are prominent. Indicator species of the Chihuahuan Desert are lechuguilla, ocotillo, and two shrubs, tarbush and mariola, all of which are found in most parts of the desert. Plants that are conspicuous because of their size or abundance are soaptree yucca and Engelman prickly pear (see Figure 2.6c). Prickly pear is found in more mesic desert, and soaptree yucca is often in moister grassland as well as in mesic desert.

The Chihuahuan is a shrub-dominated desert where leaf succulents are locally prominent and diverse (see Plate V). The few trees are confined to drainage channels and rocky slopes. Grasses are more abundant because of summer rains. Just as the Joshua tree is characteristic of the Mojave Desert and the saguaro of the Sonoran Desert, large leaf succulents are characteristic of the Chihuahuan Desert. More than a dozen species of agave and at least seven species of yucca grow here. The three most common are soaptree yucca, lechuguilla, and Parry's century plant. Spanish bayonet yuccas grow up to 25 ft (7.6 m) tall in Big Bend National Park. Beargrass and sotol, both with long, thinner leaves compared with agaves and yuccas, are conspicuous large plants. Other agave species and mescalito are also widespread and abundant.

Agave species are often called century plants because it is believed that they bloom only once in 100 years. That is an exaggeration, but it may be 20–50 years before an agave blooms. The plant must store enough energy to send up its flower stalk. When it does bloom, the stalk grows incredibly fast, often more than 1 ft (0.3 m) per day until it may be 15–20 ft (4.5–6 m) tall. After this tremendous expenditure of energy, the plant dies, but not before it sends out runners to make new plants. You may see a cluster of small agaves around a dry and dead central plant.

Although the Chihuahuan Desert is especially rich in cactus species, most are inconspicuous, small to medium size, either clumping or prostrate, and not the arborescent (tree-size) types found in the Sonoran Desert. Both cholla and prickly pear species are prominent. Engelman prickly pear and *Echinocactus horizonthalonius* can occur in dense stands. Two large species of barrel cactus are conspicuous

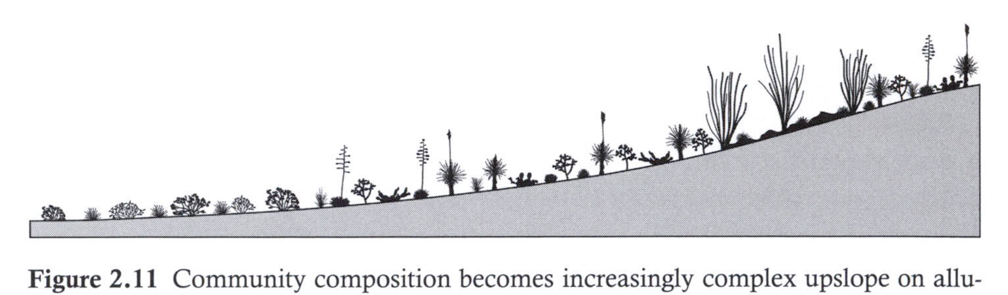

Figure 2.11 Community composition becomes increasingly complex upslope on alluvial fans in the Chihuahuan Desert. Leaf succulents and ocotillo occupy the highest and stoniest soils. *(Illustration by Jeff Dixon.)*

due to their size, but they are not dominant or abundant. Many endemic cactus species and subspecies occur.

The desert can be divided into three regions. Accounting for 40 percent of the total, the Trans-Pecos section in the north covers all of the Chihuahuan Desert in the United States and one half of Chihuahua in Mexico. The middle region is the Mapimian section, covering part of the Mexican states of Chihuahua, Coahuila, and Durango. Both of these regions are typical basin and range topography with many playas. In the southern states of Zacatecas and San Luis Potosi is the Saladan region, characterized by extreme elevation differences, ranging from 1,600 ft (500 m) valleys to 9,800 ft (3,000 m) peaks. Most comprehensive studies have been in the Trans-Pecos subdivision, and the flora becomes more complicated southward into Mexico.

The most common community on plains with low relief, especially in the north, consists of creosote bush. Tarbush and viscid acacia may coexist with creosote or form almost pure stands on their own. These three plants dominate both visually and floristically, covering 70 percent of the desert. Plant communities become more complex with increasing relief up the bajada into the hills (see Figure 2.11). Highest on the bajadas and rock outcrops, leaf succulents (yuccas, sotols, agaves, and beargrass) become numerous, and ocotillo and lechuguilla become more common. Lechuguilla is especially numerous on rocky outcrops and in some localities may be the dominant plant. Large woody shrubs such as coldenia, catclaw, lotebush, and allthorn also become more prominent. The higher elevation succulent scrub communities make a gradual transition to wetter grassland and may also have grama grass and an occasional juniper.

In the Mapimian area, creosote bush grows with many yucca and opuntia species. Codominants vary according to locale, but include lechuguilla, mesquite, ocotillo, yuccas, and several agave species and cactus species.

Wax

Candelilla, a shrub in the Chihuahuan Desert, is a source of a wax used for a variety of purposes, including an additive in cosmetics such as lip balm, and in chewing gum, lubricants, and polishes. The wax is extracted by boiling the thin, waxy stems with sulfuric acid. Because it has a high melting point, 154° F (68° C), candelilla wax is mixed with other waxes to increase their hardness. Overharvesting of plants from the wild has reduced their populations.

Other communities include shrubby mesquite, grassland, saltbush, and gypsum dunes. Nonsalty alluvial soils support dense stands of mesquite, with a few shrubs. Twenty percent of the Chihuahuan Desert is grassland with shrubs. Summer-growing grasses common on the grassland biome to the east extend their range into the desert because of abundant summer rains. Grass is also plentiful in this desert because of cooler temperatures and the prevalence of calcium carbonate in limestone substrate, which promotes grass growth. Grassland swales, dominated by grama grass, tobosa, muhly, and dropseed, occupy enclosed basins in the Chihuahuan Desert. These grasslands often surround a salty center with halophytes such as saltgrass and saltbush.

Sand dunes at the edges of playas are quartz in volcanic areas, but more often they are gypsum because of the abundance of limestone. Dune areas support communities with a type of sagebrush, mesquite, and soaptree yucca. Three well-known gypsum dune areas are White Sands National Monument in New Mexico, west of Cuatro Cienegas in Coahuilla, and near Samalayuca in Chihuahua. Although gypsum dunes have fewer species, less vegetation, and few annuals, many genera and species are confined to gypsum sands in Chihuahua, Mexico.

Distinct differences exist between soils derived from limestone and igneous rocks. Because they are drier, limestone slopes support desert scrub, while igneous slopes at the same elevation support grassland. Major plants on limestone are lechuguilla, yucca, candelilla, and ocotillo. Igneous substrate supports a cactus-mesquite type of vegetation with opuntia species, large columnar cacti, and mesquite. The best development of this arboreal cactus scrub is in the south. A soaptree yucca woodland, where yuccas up to 50 ft (15 m) tall and sotols tower over the desert scrub, is transitional to grassland in the Saladan region.

Although most of the Chihuahuan Desert is less studied than other North American deserts, and the southern part in Mexico even less so than that in New Mexico and Texas, it is one of the world's three most biologically rich and diverse deserts (along with the Great Sandy Tanmi of Australia and Namib-Karoo in southwestern Africa). Of the 3,500 plant species, as many as 1,000 are endemic, 29 percent of the total, including 16 endemic genera. The endemism is due to isolating basin and range topography and climate changes since the end of the Pleistocene 10,000 years ago. Endemics include cacti, butterflies, spiders, scorpions, ants, lizards, and snakes. Central Coahuila near Quatro Cienegas is an endemic center in desert scrub and gypsum dunes, containing many locally endemic cacti. The area was a climatic refuge during the Pleistocene. The Chihuahuan Desert is home to one-fifth of all the cactus species in the world, about 350 of 1,500. The genera *Coryphantha* and *Opuntia* are especially diverse.

Few mammals or birds are restricted to the Chihuahuan Desert. Most are general desert species, although some species of pocket mouse, woodrat, and other rodents are centered here. Although characteristic, the Scaled Quail and White-necked Raven are also found outside the desert's borders. Most birds are either adjacent desert grassland species or widely distributed desert species. Some amphibians and reptiles, however, are distinct to the Chihuahuan. Although not restricted to this desert, some species are centered here, notably two geckos (Texas banded and reticulated), little striped whiptail lizard, and Texas horned lizard. Several snakes, such as Trans-Pecos rat snake, Texas black-headed snake, and western coachwhip, are also representative of this area. The two most common rattlesnakes are the widespread Mojave rattlesnake and western diamondback. Some species currently found in the Chihuahuan Desert environment, such as the bolson tortoise and pronghorn, are relict grassland species "trapped" in deteriorating conditions. The bolson tortoise and the Coahuilan box turtle are both endemic. Two whiptail lizards (*Cnemidophorus neomexicanus* and *C. tesselatus*) are distinctive because populations are entirely female and reproduce asexually.

South America

Monte Desert. The Monte Desert extends from approximately the Tropic of Capricorn near the Bolivian border in the north to 45° S in Argentina (Figure 2.12). It is

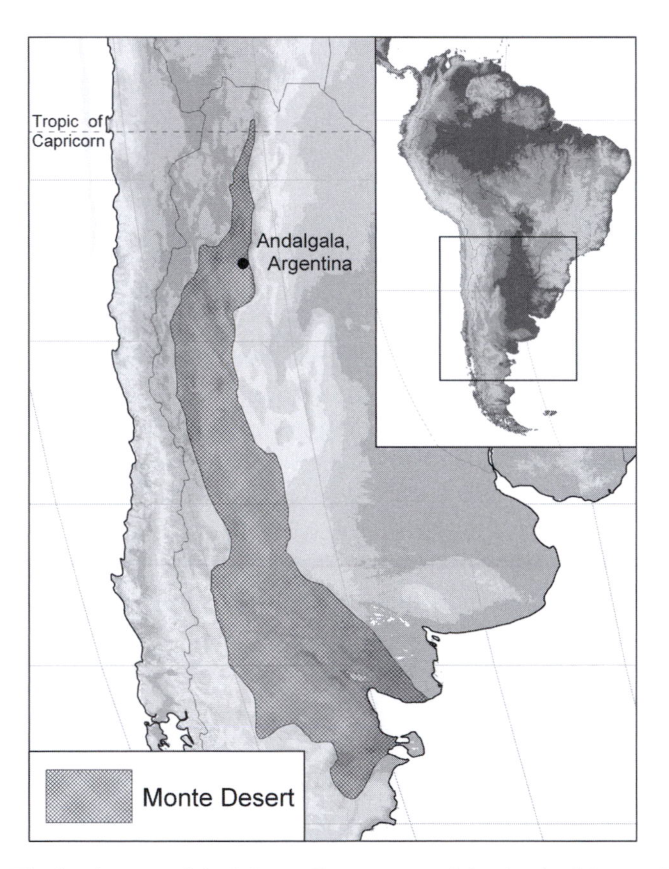

Figure 2.12 The landscape of the Monte Desert east of the Andes Mountains is characterized by a series of mountains and basins. *(Map by Bernd Kuennecke.)*

a relatively low valley, generally 3,000–4,000 ft (900–1,200 m), between high mountains. Elevations, however, range from sea level at its southern extent where it reaches the Atlantic coast (Rio Negro and Chubut Provinces) up to 9,000 ft (2,800 m) in the north (Salta Province). Bounded on the west by the Andes Mountains (20,000 ft, 6,000 m), on the north by the Bolivian Plateau (10,000–16,000 ft, 3,000–5,000 m), and on the east by a series of mountain chains (16,000 ft in the north tapering to 3,300 ft in the south, 5,000–1,000 m), its location makes it a rainshadow. Whatever direction the wind blows, the Monte is on the lee side of mountains.

Mountain ranges, actually foothills to the Andes, break up the topography of the large valley, and desert vegetation occupies basins between those mountains. Annual rainfall averages 8 in (200 mm), but can be 3–12 in (80–300 mm), generally wetter in the north and drier in the south. The very arid localities, with less than 4 in (100 mm) rainfall per year are in the centers of mountain-enclosed basins. The abrupt mountain and valley topography causes variation in precipitation and vegetation over short distances. Because the continuously high Andes block westerly winds and winter cyclonic storms, more than half of the annual precipitation falls in summer, and in some areas, 80–90 percent falls in summer. The southern parts of the Monte Desert, which are closer to cyclonic storm tracks, receive more winter rain. Winters are cool, 37°–70° F (3°–21° C), due to the high elevation, but frost is rare. Due to both higher elevation and the maritime influence on the smaller landmass, maximum temperatures in summer hover around 90° F (32° C) rather than the 100° F (36° C) more common in warm deserts.

The major plant community is dominated by waxy, evergreen shrubs of creosote bush (called jarilla in South America), retamo, and mancapotrillos, often found with mata sebo, monte negro, and mesquite. Diversity increases up the bajadas, with more arborescent cacti, small cacti, trees, and both tall and short shrubs. The middle and lower bajada slopes are dominated by shrub communities, changing to columnar cacti on the upper slopes. The more complex cactus scrub communities of *Trichocereus, Cereus,* and terrestrial bromeliads are more abundant in the north, while the cooler south is more dominated by low shrubs (see Plate VI). Mesquite, chilca, and pajaro bobo are riparian plants, found along washes. Clay soils support saltbush, and salty locations have a community of seepweed and pickleweed. Because of the lack of winter precipitation, no winter or spring ephemerals or winter-growing shrubs occur, and the total number of annual species is small.

Cacti are common and varied, with species and genera not found elsewhere. Genera endemic to South America include *Echinopsis, Gymnocalycium,* and *Parodia*, as well as many others. Common endemic species include *Trichocereus terscheckii, Cereus aethiops,* and several *Opuntia*.

Separated by 6,000 mi (9,600 km) and in different hemispheres, the Monte Desert in South America and the Sonoran Desert in North America share many characteristics of climate, landforms, and growthforms. One reason for the similar appearance is that several genera of plants—creosote bush, acacia, mesquite, paloverde, prickly pear cactus, and more—are found in both deserts. The two deserts share 50 of the same or closely related species. In a comparison of two sites (Bolson de Pipanaco near Andalgala in Argentina and Avra Valley near Tucson, Arizona) with about 250 species in each, many similarities were noted. Although only 14 species were found to be the same in both deserts, 51 genera and 29 families were shared, representing approximately 50 percent of the flora in each. Creosote bush, a dominant plant in both deserts, is represented by only one species in North America, but by five in the Monte Desert. *L. cuneifolia* in the Monte is the ecological equivalent of *L. tridentata* in hot, dry areas of North America, while *L. divaricata* is found only in riparian locations and *L. nitida* is found in colder areas. Velvet mesquite in Arizona is closely related to several mesquite species in the Monte. Foothill paloverde in the Sonoran is replaced by *C. praecox* in the Monte.

Most species, genera, and even families, however, are different. Convergent evolution applies to unrelated organisms evolving similar morphology and physiology in response to similar environmental conditions. Plant adaptations to drought, heat, and salt are similar, although the plants may be in totally different genera or families. Many of the plants and animals in the Monte have environmental equivalents in the Sonoran. *Trichocereus* species, a tall columnar cactus, takes the place of the Sonoran Desert saguaro. Like paloverde in the Sonoran Desert, trees in the *Bulnesia* genus have only a few small leaves. Gray-green stems do most of the photosynthesis.

Some prominent species in the two deserts have no equivalent in the other. No bursage, ocotillo, agaves, yuccas, ironwood, brittlebush, or cholla grow in the Monte, and no other plants have taken their places. Plants in the Monte Desert with no equivalent in North America include an acacia and a senna. An obvious difference from the Sonoran Desert is the terrestrial bromeliads common in the Monte. Bromeliads are members of the pineapple family (Bromeliaceae), here represented by *Dyckia, Deuterochonia,* and *Tillandsia* (see Figure 2.13). They are leaf succulents that superficially resemble yuccas or small agaves with a rosette of leathery leaves. The leaves are usually lined with sharp, back-turned spines or spikes. Bromeliads can cover the ground in a dense mat between cacti, rocks, and shrubs. They have no equivalent in the Sonoran Desert, although *Hechtias,* a small spiny leaf succulent, grow in the Chihuahuan Desert.

Animals, both vertebrates and invertebrates, in the Monte are distinct. The desert supports few large mammals. Guanacos, a relative of llamas, used to be common in the northern Monte but populations have been destroyed by hunting.

Most characteristic are edentate mammals, members of the anteater and armadillo family that have small or no teeth. The screaming armadillo is one of the most common animals and is adapted to withstand heat and aridity. They do not use either respiration or perspiration for evaporative cooling, can withstand large daily changes in body temperature, and escape the heat by burrowing. They need little free water. An opportunistic feeder with food habits similar to skunks, the screaming armadillo gets moisture from insects, plants, and carrion. They are active during the day in winter but during the night in summer.

Figure 2.13 Bromeliads such as *Dyckia* are common plants growing among the cactus scrub in the Monte Desert of South America. *(Photo courtesy of Mark Muradian.)*

Rodents and other small mammals are rare in the Monte and not well adapted to desert environments. Most cannot exist on metabolic water alone and cannot survive more than a few days without drinking water.

The two major groups of rodents (caviomorphs and sigmodontines) have different origins and morphologies. The difference is based on variations in jaw muscles that facilitate gnawing. The most well-known caviomorph, from the family Caviidae, is the South American guinea pig. Sigmodontines are common in North America and are much more diverse than caviomorphs. They include rodents from several different families, such as ground squirrels, kangaroo rats, pocket mice, and woodrats. South America separated from Africa before the Cretaceous. Thus, the caviomorph animals originally shared with Africa had 45 million years of isolated evolution in South America. Sigmodontines migrated south from North America after the two Americas became connected via Central America only 2 million years ago. Porcupines are caviomorphs that migrated north through Central America to North America. The two different types of rodents are found in distinct habitats in the Monte. Caviomorphs occupy desert locations, while sigmodontines are rare and found in moist riparian habitats.

Some Monte rodents share adaptations with North American species and are examples of convergent evolution, while others do not. The desert cavy looks like a ground squirrel, but it has no tail and is an herbivorous guinea pig. Tuco-tucos are burrowing rodents that look and act like gophers. The fact that they eat creosote bush, which contains many toxic compounds, indicates that the two species have had a long evolutionary history together. The tuco-tuco has a symbiotic relationship with Mendoza heliotrope. The tuco-tuco eats the tubers of this perennial herb and as the rodent cleans its burrow, it deposits some tubers in mounds at the burrow openings. The loose soil of the mound, enriched with droppings, is good habitat for the heliotrope, ensuring that both the tuco-tuco and herb will survive. The Patagonian hare, also called mara, is not related to rabbits or true hares; it is a caviomorph (see Figure 1.6b). At 30 pounds (14 kg), it is a large mammal for the Monte. Like the jackrabbit, which it resembles, it is a runner, and at 30 mph (48 kph), it is the fastest rodent in the world. The mara is also the only Monte mammal that is crepuscular.

Two unrelated animals evolved similar mechanisms in adaptation to the desert environment. The plains vizcacha rat lives in burrows under saltbushes in sparsely vegetated Monte Desert habitat. Like the Great Basin chisel-tooth rat (see Chapter 3), it is able to scrape off and discard the outer salt crust on the saltbush leaves. It does not use teeth but stiff, hairy bristles in its mouth to do so. The gerbil mouse, also found in salt flat areas, can get water from cactus and can drink water with a salt content four times the concentration of seawater.

The Monte has few carnivore species, reflective of few prey species. Although an occasional puma may visit the upper slopes or the ecotone with thorn scrub, most predators are small, such as foxes (Argentine gray fox) and weasels. The lesser grison and Patagonian weasel are both nocturnal and eat birds, small mammals, lizards, and snakes. The small predator, the mouse opossum, weighing less than 1 oz (28 g), lives in riparian habitats. It uses its prehensile tail to climb trees where it eats bird eggs, insects, and fruit.

Notable absences occur in the fauna. Few seed-eaters live in the Monte Desert because few annuals grow to produce seed. In contrast to other warm deserts where convergent evolution has produced different species of rodents that hop, no bipedal mammals like the kangaroo rat have evolved.

Only 10 of fewer than 100 bird species are common to both North American and South American deserts. Equivalent species, however, fill similar niches in terms of foraging. For example, the Lesser Wagtail-tyrant gleans insects from shrubby foliage, just as the Black-tailed Gnatcatcher does in the Sonoran. Both the Elegant Crested Tinamou in the Monte and Gambel's Quail in the Sonoran eat seeds and fruit on the ground. Two species of Monte Caracara feed on carrion like ravens do in North America. Most other birds have no equivalent. The number of birds increases with the complexity of the plant community because of more nesting sites and food. The Andean Condor is found in the mountains of northern Argentina and the adjacent desert. Two flightless birds are both rheas. *Rhea americana*, 5 ft (1.5 m) tall and 50 lb (22.5 kg), is an ostrich-like bird found near Andalgala. The other rhea (*Pterocnemia pennata*) prefers the scrub desert of the southern Monte and Patagonia.

No reptile species are common to both the Sonoran and Monte deserts, and only 1 of 19 lizard genera and 2 of 28 snake genera are the same. However, several equivalent pairs occur. *Uma* species in the Sonoran and *Liolaemus* species in the Monte both have fringed toes and nasal valves, making them well adapted to burrowing into sand. *Coleonyx variegatus* (gecko) in the Sonoran and two species of *Homonota* in the Monte occupy rocky habitats and are nocturnal. *Uta stansburiana* in the Sonoran and *Liolaemus darwini* have similar morphology, behavior, and reproductive characteristics. Two poisonous snakes, a rattlesnake and a viper, take the place of North American rattlesnakes.

Africa

Sahara Desert. The Sahara, which means desert in Arabic, roughly 15° to 30° N, is actually several deserts combined (see Figure 2.14). Depending on what boundaries are recognized, it covers an expanse of 3,000 mi (4,800 km) from the Atlantic Ocean to the Red Sea and 1,000 mi (1,600 km) north to south—about the size of the United States including Alaska. It covers 3.5 million mi^2 (9 million km^2) with fewer than 800 mi^2 (2,000 km^2) of oases (not including the Nile River valley). The landscape is almost universally barren and includes rock, sand, desert pavement, salt flats, washes (wadis), and even a few deeply dissected mountains.

Four major types of Saharan landforms are recognized—hills or mountains, regs, ergs, and hammadas. Ahaggar, the major mountain mass in southern Algeria, is also associated with surrounding, smaller mountains. The Tibesti Mountains are in Northern Chad. On simplified maps, this entire mountainous area is referred to as the Tibesti Massif. Much of the Sahara is at a low elevation, sea level to 2,000 ft (600 m), but mountains in the Tibesti Massif rise to 9,000–11,000 ft (2,700–3,300 m).

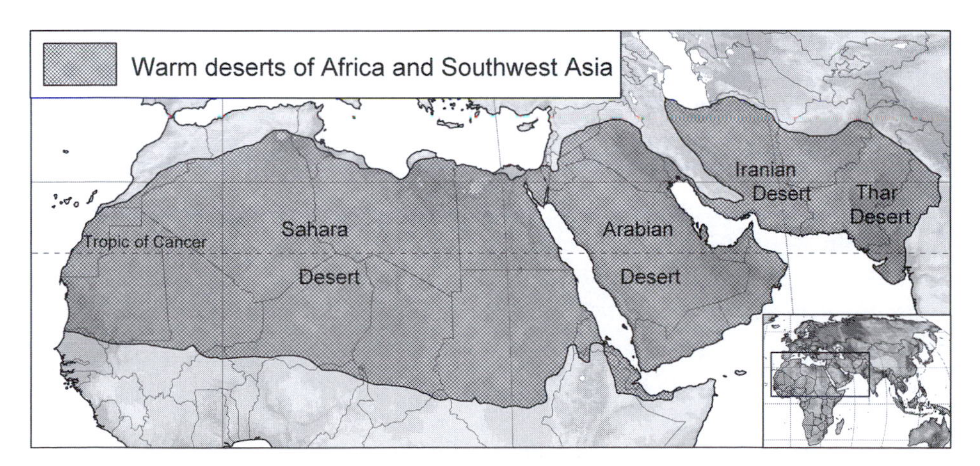

Figure 2.14 Warm deserts in Africa and Asia stretch from the Atlantic Ocean east to the Indus River Valley in Pakistan. *(Map by Bernd Kuennecke.)*

The deepest part of the Qattara Depression in northeastern Libya is 436 ft (133 m) below sea level.

In a simple way, the Central Sahara west of the Nile River can be viewed as a single large mountain remnant, actually two major mountain masses, surrounded by vast slopes of alluvial fans. The foundation rock of the Sahara, ancient granite and schist, was pushed up in central Sahara to form the Ahaggar and Tibesti Mountains. Intermixed with the crystalline rocks are basaltic rocks, forming plateaus and volcanic monoliths. Except where it is exposed in the mountains, the crystalline rock is overlain by layers of sandstone, limestone, gravel, or sand. The Tassili n'Ajjer Mountains on the northeast edge of Ahaggar are sandstone layers carved into plateaus, canyons, and spires similar to canyonlands in southwestern United States. Salt pans, an accumulation of calcium carbonate eroded from the limestone, are common beneath steep cliffs. In central Mauritania, cliffs of tilted sandstone called dhars extend for hundreds of miles.

Even in ancient times, drainage in northern Africa was to the interior. Rivers either dried up or evaporated before reaching the sea. Rivers radiating out from the Tibesti and Ahaggar Massifs created gigantic alluvial fans and bajadas, resulting in the gravel plains or regs of today. The sediment is successively finer with greater distance from the mountains. Winnowed from the gravel by wind, sand was then deposited in lower elevations as sand dunes.

Surrounding all the mountains and covering more than one-half of the Sahara are gravel plains of desert pavement called regs (or serirs). They are the most sterile and lifeless parts of the desert, with few oases. West of Ahaggar, the Tanezrouft reg in southwestern Algeria and northern Mali covers 200,000 mi^2 (500,000 km^2). The Libyan reg in eastern Libya, western Egypt, and northwestern Sudan is even larger, covering 340,000 mi^2 (880,000 km^2). The Tenere reg to the south is in northern Niger. Dune areas called ergs occupy 25 percent of the Sahara and surround the regs farther from the mountains and at lower elevations. In northern Algeria, the Great Eastern and Great Western ergs border the Atlas Mountains. To the west is Erg Chech in northeastern Mauritania and western Algeria. Also in the west between Tanezrouft and the Atlantic is the Saharan Empty Quarter, known as the Majabat al-Koubra, primarily in Mauritania. (A different area also called the Empty Quarter is on the Arabian Peninsula.) Other major sand areas are the Bilma and North Chad ergs in eastern Niger and northern Chad, and the Ubari and Murzuq ergs in western Libya. A hammada is a solid, smooth rock surface with no loose debris like a reg. North of the mountains in Libya and Algeria are extensive limestone plateaus. In places, the limestone hammadas have been scoured smooth by wind-blown sand, resulting in a landscape of yardangs (see Plate I). Many are small, but some are 600 ft (180 m) high and 0.5 mi (0.8 km) long.

Climate of the Sahara. The vast expanse of deserts in North Africa and Southwest Asia is completely influenced by the subtropical high-pressure cell. Many areas receive less than 1 in (25 mm) of rainfall yearly, and 3–4 in (75–100 mm) is considered good. Areas at the margins of the deserts with 4–16 in (100–400 mm) of rain are semidesert. Low rainfall compared with potential evapotranspiration of 10–15 ft (3–4.5 m) per year emphasizes the aridity of North Africa. Precipitation is unreliable and localized. When it does rain, it comes in a torrential downpour. It may be years between rains, and two extremely dry regions (Tanezrouft reg and the southern Libyan Desert) have no water or plants. In contrast, the Tibesti Mountains cause some orographic precipitation that occasionally produces streams that run into the adjacent desert.

The southeastern Sahara gets water from the Nile River. Rivers that empty into Lake Chad also supply some surface and groundwater. In the north, some water comes from the Atlas Mountains and other highlands as ephemeral streams or groundwater in wadis. The Eastern Desert, from the Nile to the Red Sea in both Egypt and Sudan, is extremely arid and has few plants. However, petrified trees and many wadis provide evidence that it was fertile in wetter times. Sandstone beneath Saharan sands absorbs water from the equatorial area or from the mountains, and some groundwater may be a relic from wetter Pleistocene times.

The Sahara is one of the hottest places on Earth. Depending on elevation, temperatures range from 130° F (55° C) down to possibility of frost. Summer maxima average 95°–113° F (35°–45° C), and 122° F (50° C) or more is common. Because of continentality, summers are hotter in the interior and cooler near the coast. In winter, coastal and low-elevation desert locations average 50°–55° F (10°–13° C), while the interior massifs may be as low as 28° F (−2° C). Frost is common in the mountains because of elevation and also in the northern ergs because of higher latitude. Snow may even fall occasionally in the high Ahaggar Mountains. Daily temperature ranges can be extreme. Although unusual, the record is a daytime high of 100° F (37.5° C) down to nighttime low of 31° F (−0.5° C).

Because of unequal heating of the desert surface, strong and unpredictable winds often develop. Known by several names—khamsin, sirocco, shalali, simoom—they often blow for days and reduce visibility to zero. They may occur 20–90 days a year, and decrease the relative humidity to only 5–15 percent. Blown sand is too heavy to be lifted more than 5 ft (1.5 m) off the surface, but smaller dust particles can be blown higher than 10,000 ft (3,000 m).

The Sahara was not always the arid landscape it is today. On a human timescale, evidence exists that the climate has become increasingly drier. Ancient civilizations left relics and drawings of a wetter period. As little as 8,000 years ago, the region was a savanna. Native rock paintings illustrate a landscape with giraffes, oryx, and elephants, followed in time by cattle herds and

Salt

People who work or exercise in hot climates are frequently advised to take salt tablets, because when you sweat your body loses salt. Is this good advice? A human body does need about 8 oz (225 g) of salt for biochemical processes, and without enough salt, problems such as muscle cramps occur. Except under extreme circumstances, however, the amount of salt a person normally ingests with food is adequate. Taking extra salt is actually poor advice because your blood already becomes saltier as your body loses moisture due to perspiration.

Mediterranean vegetation as the climate dried. By 4,700 years ago, Mediterranean plants were found only in the mountains and were replaced by thorn trees in the Sahara. Camels became common only 400 years ago. Only a few old Mediterranean plants—oleanders, duprez cypress, and olive trees—remain in the mountains, some 1,000 mi (1,600 km) across inhospitable desert from their origin. By their size, the olive trees are estimated to be 3,000–4,000 years old. As the climate became more arid over the last 8,000 years, interior lakes dried into extensive salt flats, locally called chotts. The salt, which may be several feet thick, is mined, loaded on camels, and taken long distances to market. The northern Sahara, on the edge of Mediterranean climate, has winter rainfall and biota related to Europe. The southern Sahara has a slight summer rainfall maximum and affinity with Old World Tropics. The dry and barren central Sahara, with no distinct seasonality of precipitation, prevented much north-south migration of plants or animals.

Plants of the Sahara. Most of the Sahara has little perennial vegetation. It is estimated to have only 500 species of plants, with slightly more diversity in the west where slightly more precipitation falls. The dry eastern part is very sparse. Most plants are xerophytes, ephemerals, or halophytes. The regs, which cover most of the area of the Sahara, are the most devoid of life. Only six wells exist in the Tanezrouft, an area four times the size of England. After a rain, however, 20 percent of a seemingly lifeless reg may be briefly covered with ephemerals. A few acacias, tamarisk, giant milkweed, hackenkopf, joint pine (not a pine tree), and wild jujube may be found along wadis close to the mountains, tapping deep moisture. Hammadas where cracks afford good access to groundwater may also support a few plants.

Saharan ergs support more life than regs because sand allows moisture to soak in, and lack of capillary action allows moisture to remain at depth. Most life is in dry lakebeds or in the hollows between dune crests where water accumulates during a rare rain. Ephemerals such as *Cleome droserifolia,* prickly clover, and ciliate plantain, may germinate within three days after a rain and ripen seed in 10–15 days—a short life cycle. The two most common plants (common meaning widely dispersed) are "had" and "afozo," both food for camels. Had is a compact, blue-green shrub. In spite of the small yellow thorns on its branches, it is a mainstay of camels in the desert. Afozo is a millet grass that is not nourishing, but will do when nothing else is available. Both plants extend roots as much as 50 ft (15 m) into the sand.

Even though mountain areas are still very much desert with barren rock, they support more life than either regs or ergs. Depressions in the rock house permanent pools called gueltas that support fish, frogs, toads, shrimp, molluscs, and small crustaceans. The water attracts animals and supports scattered plants.

Semidesert margins of the Sahara that receive more rainfall support more vegetation. Steppes with perennial grasses are found in Morocco, northern Algeria, Tunisia, and Libya. Shrub steppes are dominated by *Anthyllis henoniana* and field sagewort. Saline depressions support halophytic species such as herbaceous glasswort and shrubby saltwort, saltbush, and bean-caper. Similar steppe communities are also found in more moist depressions where precipitation is 2–4 in (50–100 mm).

The west coast of the Sahara, approximately 8° to 17° N in the countries of Mauritania, Western Sahara, and southern Morocco, is distinct from the rest of the desert. The Atlantic Ocean moderates both summer and winter temperatures. Winter rains, high humidity, and slight fog ameliorate the aridity. Vegetation can be quite dense and is characterized by cactus-like stem succulents, particularly several euphorbias. Other common succulents are a kalanchoe and a senecio. Most of these species of succulent shrubs are more common north of this latitude where it is wetter. The coast of Mauritania has more typical Saharan species.

What Causes an Oasis?

Where rock layers are interrupted by folds and faults (big cracks), the water in the rock seeps toward the surface and becomes available to palm trees and agriculture. Oases are more common in regions where sandstone occurs because the spaces between the grains of sand hold water. If the water moves too quickly through the rock, the water will be salty rather than fresh.

Even life around an oasis is sparse. Plants growing only at oases or along exotic rivers include acacia, date palms, white bean-caper, cane, wild sugarcane, and Japanese blood grass.

Animals of the Sahara. In spite of the lack of vegetation, the Sahara supports about 70 species of mammals. Originally the desert was home to 20 large animals (such as addax, hartebeest, gazelle, oryx), forming small herds that migrated long distances to find food. A combination of hunting and increasingly drier conditions has limited them to the most remote areas. Most are probably extinct, but some gazelles may still be present in small numbers. Thin bodies, thin necks, and long legs of gazelles radiate energy and help prevent overheating. Most animals are small and inconspicuous, either blending in with the color of the sand or seeking rare shade during the day. Many burrow to escape surface heat. Most Sahara mammals get sufficient water from food and never or rarely need to drink. Some animals may expel concentrated body waste with little water loss and lose 30–60 percent of their body weight without damage.

Because the regs are almost barren of plants, they cannot support animals. More life is found in the sand dunes. Many insects, rodents, lizards, and snakes live in communities where bushes trap sand. Rodents are common. Gerbils, and their larger relatives the jirds, live in burrows beneath bushes. By foraging close to home, they escape danger by retreating along the shortest path to their burrow entrances. The fat sand rat is abundant but restricted to dry wadis and the edge of brackish water. Halophytes in those areas have a high water content but also a high salt content. Excess salt is expelled from the sand rat's body in urine at a concentration four times that of seawater. These small mammals are able to tolerate the oxalic acid in the halophytes. The strong hind legs of jerboas enable them to leap and run fast to escape danger, a trait that enables them to forage over larger territories than either gerbils or jirds. Jerboas also live in burrows and seal their tunnels against desert air to maintain a high relative humidity and keep the temperature low. The Egyptian spiny mouse frequents rocky areas but can also survive in both barren regions and more vegetated habitats. As its name implies, its back consists of spiny hairs, a possible deterrent to predators. Mole rats, which have completely adapted to life underground, and porcupines are also common.

Common carnivores are jackal, fennec fox, pale fox, and Ruppell's fox. Large carnivores such as cheetah and leopard are probably extinct. Fennec fox (not a fox but superficially resembling foxes) is the only carnivore living in open desert, not near water sources or in oases. It seems to be independent of free water, not needing to drink. It weighs less than 2.2 lbs (1 kg) and has a mixed diet—lizards, insects, rodents, and plants. Desert adaptations include being nocturnal, spending the day in a deep burrow, panting, and producing concentrated urine.

Of 90 species of resident birds, only one is endemic, a chat. Some birds, such as Sandgrouse, Rock Pigeon, and Trumpeter Bullfinch, require access to water because they need to drink regularly. Some birds rarely need to drink and derive sufficient moisture from food. Bea-eaters eat insects, and Barbary Partridge depend on green leaves. Other birds that rarely need to drink include Brown-necked Raven, Night-hawk, and Courser. Many birds that stop at oases or mountain rock pools are occasional migratory species making the trip from Europe to central or southern Africa. Ostrich used to be common in the Sahara, but are now absent due to hunting and increasing aridity. Their size is both an advantage and a disadvantage. Although they can run long distances to find water, they cannot use microclimates to escape the heat.

High-elevation environments, such as the Tassili Plateau at 2,000 ft (600 m), support more animals than the lower desert. Although rare, Barbary sheep may occasionally be spotted. This is also the environment of the cape hare, the Sahara equivalent of the North American jackrabbit. Mountain gazelle replaces the goitered gazelle found in dune areas. Birds that require daily water are found here. Rock dassies (also called hyrax), distant relatives of elephants, live in rocky colonies in the massifs.

The Sahara is home to about 100 species of reptiles. Land tortoise, gecko, chameleon, and monitor lizard are common. Skinks occur in sand dunes and use their paddle feet to push themselves into cooler layers of sand. The horned viper, one of the most poisonous creatures in the Sahara, conceals itself in sand and waits for a lizard, mammal, or bird. Other venomous snakes are the Egyptian cobra, also called asp, and blunt-nosed viper.

Insects, such as ants, beetles, and scorpions, are plentiful, obtaining water from food, either vegetation or other insects. Their skin is impermeable to water loss, and they can easily find shelter because of their small size. Some desert beetles

Water from Feathers

The Sandgrouse needs to drink and is always found within 30 mi (50 km) of a water source (see Plate VII). When drinking, the male ruffles his breast feathers and soaks them in the water. In this way, he takes water back to the young who then suck the water from the feathers.

disturb sand on the steep side of a dune and allow the small avalanche to cover them up.

The Nile River is a physical barrier to movement between the eastern and western deserts. The desert region east of the Nile has closer affinity to the Arabian Peninsula and Southwest Asia.

Camels. Camels are the stereotype of a desert animal (see Figure 2.15). A common belief is that water is stored in the hump. Although it serves as a source of energy like fat does in any animal, the hump is not a water source. Survival time without water depends on a variety of factors—green or dry vegetation, temperature, wind, sun, weight carried, and distance walked. Camels can survive conditions that would be brutal to humans for several reasons.

Unlike humans who must maintain a constant body temperature regardless of environment, the camel's body can change temperature. In a process called vasodilation, its body stores heat during the day and dissipates it at night when air is cooler. In summer, the camel's core body temperature varies 11° F (6° C), lower in the morning and higher in the afternoon. About 6:00 A.M., the core temperature drops because dilated blood vessels bring cool blood (cooled by night air) from the skin surface to the body core. With loss of cool blood, the skin then becomes hotter. As the day heats up, the camel's core temperature increases until mid-afternoon,

Figure 2.15 Dromedary camels graze the sparse Sahara Desert in Morocco. *(Photos by author.)*

Donkeys

Common beasts of burden in desert areas, donkeys' tolerance to heat and water loss is similar to that of camels. Donkeys are able to keep cool in the heat and conserve water, but they can also tolerate water loss. After only four days without water, a donkey in the Sahara can drink 2.5 gal (10 L) of water, up to 20 percent of its body weight, in less than two minutes. The amount of water consumed over a two-hour period to replenish water loss may be more than 6.5 gal (25 L). Donkeys are not as efficient as camels, however, because of their smaller size, thinner fur, and less efficient digestion system.

the time coinciding with the highest air temperatures. In late afternoon, blood flow takes heat from the core back to the skin surface, where it is conducted into cool night air. For a camel to maintain a constant body temperature like a human does, it would need the evaporative cooling of 1.3 gal (5 L) of water every day, an amount not available in the desert. In humans, a rise in body temperature indicates failure of the body's cooling system and potential death. In camels, a rise in body temperature is an adaptation to regulating water conservation. Additionally, the hotter body during the day means less difference between the environment and the camel, so the camel absorbs less heat from the air.

Camels do sweat, but it is usually not visible because perspiration evaporates quickly, leaving the animal dry. You might see sweat where evaporation is impeded, like under a saddle. A well-hydrated camel will sweat because it has no need to conserve water. The camel's fur also helps keep the animal cool. Because the fur creates an insulating layer, evaporation of sweat takes place from and cools the skin instead of the fur above it. Dry air in the fur inhibits conduction of heat from the air into the animal. In short fur (or tight clothes on humans), evaporation takes place away from the skin, cooling the wrong place, with no insulating layer of air.

Camels have behavioral traits that help avoid heat. When resting, it stretches out, exposing more surface area to the sun. A dehydrated camel, however, sits with its legs beneath, facing the sun to present the smallest surface area to solar rays. If allowed, the camel will lie down in the cool morning. It will not move from the spot except to reorient itself to the sun as the day progresses. Moving to another location completely would mean that it would absorb heat from the ground, something to avoid. During the hottest time of the day, you might see camels clumped together in a seemingly uncomfortable mass, but by maintaining this side-to-side proximity, they expose minimal combined surface to the hot air.

Camels use and lose water, but it is kept to a minimum. Camels sweat, but they do not pant. Like many other desert animals, their kidneys are efficient. A camel's bladder is small, indicating a small volume of urine. Water-deprived camels in summer may expel less than 18 oz (510 g) per day, the same minimum volume for a much smaller human. Little water is lost in feces. Even fresh camel dung is so dry and full of plant fibers that it is used for fuel.

It would be logical to assume that the urea (nitrogen) content of urine would increase with dehydration of the camel, but it is exactly the opposite. A camel deprived of water is usually deprived also of feed and protein. The camel uses its own urea in a recycling process. As protein is digested in the alimentary tract, it releases nitrogen (urea), which is then recycled back into the rumen to be used again to synthesize protein.

A camel's body is tolerant to dehydration and can withstand water loss up to 40 percent of its body weight, twice that which would trigger lethal body temperatures in most other animals. When humans become dehydrated, water is lost from blood plasma, interfering with circulation and the ability of the blood to take heat to the surface to be dissipated. Therefore, the body overheats and death may occur. In camels, little water is lost from plasma, blood volume remains normal, and normal circulation is maintained. Water is lost, instead, from intracellular spaces. When humans are dehydrated, it will take hours for water to be assimilated into the body. Camels can drink 25–30 percent of their body weight, up to 30 gal (115 L) in minutes. This would be comparable to a 180 lb (81.5 kg) human losing 50 lb (23 kg), and then drinking 6 gal (23 L) of water. The camel drinks to *restore* lost water, not to *store* it for future use. When it is satiated, it will drink no more. In winter the animal has no need to drink because plants provide enough moisture.

Asia

Arabian Desert. The Arabian Desert, which has not been well studied, covers most of the Arabian Peninsula including parts of Iraq, Jordan, Syria, and the Sinai Peninsula in the north (see Figure 2.14). Landforms include mountains, escarpments, regs, and ergs. Rub'al-Khali (the Empty Quarter), covering 250,000 mi^2 (650,000 km^2) in the southeastern part of the peninsula, is a desolate area that contains the largest body of sand in the world. A sandy corridor (ad-Dahna Desert) connects it to another sandy region in the north (an-Nafud Desert). The quartz sand in the Rub'al-Khali, red because of iron oxide, is as much as 800 ft (250 m) deep, and dunes are 500–820 ft (150–250 m) high. A smaller, isolated sandy area (Wahiba sands) occurs on the coast of Oman. Mountains up to 9,800 ft (3,000 m) occupy the southwest, with escarpments facing the Arabian Sea in southern Yemen and the Red Sea in Saudi Arabia. The rock surface gently slopes inland to the northeast under the Rub'al-Khali. Flat coastal plains of marine sediments line the Persian Gulf on the eastern side of the Arabian Peninsula where shallow depressions are intermittently flooded with tidal saltwater. Slightly inland from the Persian Gulf, well-watered oases develop around artesian springs and wells. The Sinai Peninsula is primarily a barren, inhospitable reg, relieved by only a few oases (see Plate VIII). The north is flat and sandy, while the south is mountainous. Jebel Katherina (Saint Catherine) at 8,625 ft (2,629 m) is closely followed by Mount Sinai at 7,496 ft (2,285 m).

The climate is dry, averaging less than 1.4 in (35 mm) per year. Rain falls in winter but is unreliable, and rain may not fall for a year or more. Slightly more rain, almost 3 in (75 mm), occurs

Singing Sand

Vibrations of sand flowing down the steep face of a sand dune are sometimes audible. Although rare, the "singing" may be loud enough to affect conversation.

Star Dunes

Different types of sand dunes develop according to differing amounts of sand and strength of wind. Abundant sand and variable wind direction will create star dunes, a sand hill with dunes radiating from the center. The center peak of a star dune may be 300 ft (90 m) above the base at the ends of the radiating dunes. Star dunes remain in place, not because vegetation stabilizes the sand, but because wind direction changes. Many star dunes in the Sahara and Arabia are used as landmarks because the sand accumulation is stationary, even though individual grains are mobile.

closer to the Persian Gulf. It is also extremely hot. Maximum summer temperatures average 117° F (47° C) and can be as high as 124° F (51° C). Minimum winter temperatures average 54° F (12° C) but may drop below freezing in some places. Temperatures are more moderate along the Persian Gulf, averaging 94° F (35° C) in summer and 73° F (23° C) in winter. Although cooler in summer than inland locations, location close to the Gulf increases the humidity up to 90 percent.

Vegetation is sparse, including only scattered shrubs and an occasional tree. Because of slightly higher soil moisture, the wadis support most of the vegetation. Scrubby acacia and desert date trees are common, along with shrubs of Christ thorn jujube, capers, and joint pine (not a pine tree). The Rub'al-Khali supports only 37 species, almost half restricted to the outer margins of the dune area. Typical plants are shrubs such as hackenkopf, saltbush, and sand wormwood, as well as sedges. Hackenkopf and wormwood species are especially dominant where sand is deep. The only trees, acacia and ghaf (a type of mesquite), are sparsely located in drainage channels at the outer margins.

The rugged terrain of the southern Sinai is a local center of plant diversity, and the Saint Catherine Mountain region has 28 endemic species. Limestone bedrock supports bushy bean-caper along with *Reaumuria* species and *Gymnocarpus decander.* Although it is salt tolerant, the succulent berry-bearing glasswort also grows on nonsalty regs.

Northern Iraq is a steppe or semidesert where wild jujube, white broom, and Syrian sumac shrubs dominate. More arid areas have white-leaf wormwood with bulbous bluegrass. Saline soils have asphaltic sea-blite and *Chenolea arabica.* The coastal plain near the Persian Gulf supports small salt-tolerant plants and grass tussocks, primarily shrubs of *Rhanterium epapposum,* saxaul, hackenkopf, and scarlet bean-caper. Afozo and twisted-awn speargrass grow with sedge.

The oases near the Persian Gulf support communities of reeds and reed-mace. A unique community of a single tree species, ghaf, is found in long, wide woodlands in the Wahiba sands.

Most large animals are now rare, extinct, or in protected reserves. Sand gazelle, mountain gazelle, and white oryx have been successfully reintroduced after having been hunted almost to extinction (see Plate IX). Although oryx do not need to drink water, they maximize intake from plants by feeding early in the day when dew is heaviest (see Figure 2.16). The rare Nubian ibex, which can also survive without free water, is also protected. Mountain gazelle is often associated with acacia trees on gravel plains and mountain foothills, while sand gazelle frequents even drier areas. Arabian tahr, a remote relative of a wild goat, has a limited distribution in

Figure 2.16 White oryx is an endangered species in the Arabian Desert. *(Photo courtesy of Björn Jordan, Breeding Centre for Endangered Arabian Wildlife, Sharjah.)*

mountains in Arabia. The tahrs' need for almost daily water has contributed to their decline because they are easily hunted at water holes. They are highly endangered. Both the tahr and ibex have rubbery hooves that provide traction on steep rocks.

The desert supports a wide variety of rodents, including three species of jerboa that look and act like kangaroo rats in North America and have no need for water (see Figure 2.17). Small, mouse-like gerbils and the larger jirds are plentiful; several species in three genera occupy different habitats. Baluchistan gerbil occupies saline flats, Wagner's gerbil lives in rocky areas, and Cheeseman's gerbil is found in sand. King jird is endemic to the Yemen highlands, and both Arabian jird and Sunderval's jird live in sandy burrows. Fat-tailed gerbils store fat in their tail, which serves the same purpose as a camel's hump. The Indian crested porcupine, which weighs up to 29 lb (13 kg), is the largest rodent in Arabia. Nocturnal, it spends the day in dens hidden in vegetation. The small rock hyrax, or dassy, occupies rocky outcrops. Cape hare, Egyptian spiny mouse, and Ethiopian hedgehog are also found.

Predators or carrion-eaters include foxes, jackals, and cats. Arabian red fox is found in a variety of habitats, including arid, rocky, and coastal environments. It has even adapted to urban areas. The Arabian wolf is endangered and rare. Golden jackals, known only in the northern part of the peninsula, are opportunist feeders and will eat anything, including rodents, birds, eggs, and carrion. Leopards are rare but still roam the rugged mountains, feeding on gazelle, tahr, and hyrax. The small, white sand fox is nocturnal and not adapted to digging, so it must use natural rock

Figure 2.17 Rodents are common small animals in many deserts. (a) The lesser Egyptian jerboa has strong hind legs for jumping. (b) The fat-tailed gerbil stores fat and energy in the tail. (c) Baluchistan gerbil forages close to its burrow. (d) Jirds, such as the Libyan jird, are similar to gerbils but larger. *(Photo courtesy of Björn Jordan, Breeding Centre for Endangered Arabian Wildlife, Sharjah.)*

crevices and caves for shelter. Striped hyenas scavenge in open, rocky country and along tidal flats. The sand cat, which primarily hunts rodents, has paws covered with a dense mat of fine black hairs that give the animal support in soft sand and also protect the feet from hot surfaces The Near-East wildcat, restricted to the northern part of the desert, is replaced by Gordon's wildcat in most of the Arabian peninsula. The caracal is now restricted to mountain areas.

Arabian bird life is similar to that found in the Sahara. Houbara Bustard, Sandgrouse, Quail, Rock Pigeons, and Bee-eaters are occasionally seen. The coastal plain near the Persian Gulf has no distinct fauna except that the well-watered oases are habitat for marsh wildlife, such as frogs and Caspian pond turtles. Both the oases and salt marshes attract 250 species of migrating birds, and the tidal flats are important breeding grounds for waders and other water birds.

House Cats

According to DNA evidence, all the domestic cats in the world appear to be descended from the Near-East wildcat. Approximately 10,000 years ago, female wildcats took refuge from predators in granaries of emerging agricultural societies. The situation was mutually beneficial because the cats preyed on mice and rats that threatened human's grain supplies.

Up to 3.3 ft (1 m) long, the desert monitor is one of the largest lizards in Arabia. Strictly carnivorous, it eats primarily insects, rodents, and other reptiles, even snakes. Except at midday when monitors take shelter from the heat in burrows, they are active and hunt during daylight. Widespread and fairly common, they can defend themselves by either striking with their tail or by biting. Spiny-tailed lizards, also called dhab, live in barren gravel plains, and dig spiraling burrows as deep as 7.2 ft (2.2 m) deep. Strictly vegetarian, they have a low metabolism that allows them to survive on a calorie-poor diet. They never need to drink water, but may utilize dew. Reptiles also include three species of agama lizards, nine species of gecko in six families, three species of chameleons, and a fringe-toed lizard. Sand snakes are common. Several poisonous snakes, such as cobra, saw-scaled viper, carpet viper, and puff addder, hunt rodents.

Iranian Desert. Although centered on the large plateau in central Iran, the Iranian desert also includes parts of Afghanistan and Pakistan, a total of about 224,300 mi^2 (580,900 km^2) (see Figure 2.14). It is one of the least-known desert areas. Enclosed by mountain ranges, the plateau has a complex physical geography with a variety of landforms, including plains, saline rivers, alluvial fans, limestone outcrops, salt desert, salt marsh, and extensive dunes. Elevations are 2,000–5,000 ft (600–1,500 m). Deep alluvial fill has accumulated in the interior drainage basin of the plateau. Alluvial fans at the base of mountains are least salty and have the coarsest soil. Desert pavement is common. The lower parts of the plateau are saline, either dry salt flats or extensive salt marshes. Dasht-e-Kavir is a salty desert expanse southeast of the Caspian Sea, while Dasht-e-Lut is a hot sand and gravel desert in eastern Iran.

The region has a continental climate, with temperature extremes on the plateau. Summer maxima reach 108° F (42° C), and extreme winter minima drop to −4° F (−20° C). Annual precipitation is less than 8 in (200 mm), and most areas receive less than 4 in (100 mm). Rainfall from winter cyclonic storms is variable, and eastern and central parts of the plateau are driest. High summer temperatures coincide with little rain, intensifying the aridity.

Although the western part of the desert has Mediterranean affinities, little is known about the vegetation there. The central plateau typifies the region. Higher and colder elevations are dominated by a low shrubland of white-leaf wormwood and goat's thorn, perhaps a transition to cold mid-latitude deserts found farther north. Endemic shrubs and perennials include *Astragalus kavirensis* and *Heliotropum rudbaricum.* In the south where summers are hot, little plant life exists. In Afghanistan, the semidesert communities are dominated by hackenkopf and saxaul shrubs and other chenopods, along with sixweeks three-awn grass. Areas with more than 4 in (100 mm) of rain have bean-caper shrubs. Sandy regions support joint pine (not a pine tree), hackenkopf, heliotrope, and others. Psammophytes (sand-adapted plants) may account for one-third to one-half the total number of species in the sand deserts. Many salt cedar species are found, especially on the margins of sandy or gravelly areas of the Dasht-e-Lut.

Halophytes dominate in poorly drained areas on the margins of salt pans such as Dasht-e-Kavir. Characteristic plants are chenopod shrubs, such as *Halocnemum strobilaceum,* and species of *Aellenia*, saxaul, and saltwort. The salty soils support a number of endemics. Little to no vegetation can survive in the middle of the salt flats.

A surprising number of mammal and bird species survive this desert's harsh environment, although most of the larger ones are endangered. Striped hyena, caracal, wild sheep, mountain gazelle, goitered gazelle, Cape hare, leopard, wolf, golden jackal, red fox, and two cat species are all rare and found only in protected areas. Ruppell's fox lives in the driest and hottest desert regions, with habits similar to the kit fox in North America and fennec fox in the Sahara. Because of their small size, rodents such as hamsters and jirds are abundant. Hamsters are short-tailed mouse-like animals that are nocturnal, spending the day cool and secure in burrows. They transport food back to their burrows in cheek pouches and can carry more than either gerbils or jirds.

The region harbors more than 150 species of birds, including Houbara Bustard and Coronated Sandgrouse. Four-toed or steppe tortoise is found in the wormwood semidesert steppes. Geckos in two genera are endemic to basins between higher plateaus. Poisonous snakes include vipers and cobras. Both snakes are common in sandy areas, but cobras are also found in rocky areas and riparian habitats. The saw-scaled viper is active during the day, traveling over the sand like a sidewinder.

Thar (Great Indian Desert). On the eastern edge of the dry belt of North Africa and southwest Asia, the Thar Desert covers 170,000 mi^2 (440,000 km^2), from the Indus River valley on the west to the Aravalli Range on the east in western India and adjacent Pakistan (see Figure 2.14). Two major subdivisions make up this inhospitable region. The Marusthali (literally translated as "region of death") with shifting sand dunes is the driest. The northern part is called the Jaisalmer Desert; the southern part is the Mallani Desert. Farther east and at the base of the Aravalli Range, the Bagar is a hilly region that is both less arid and less sandy. Several landscapes—including gravel plains, sand dunes, sandy plains, rocky plateaus, floodplains along exotic rivers, salt playas, and saline marshland at deltas—exist on a smaller scale within these two subdivisions.

Although annual rainfall averages 12 in (300 mm), it can be 4–20 in (100–500 mm) depending on location, with higher amounts near the Aravalli Range and least in the Marusthali. Precipitation is unreliable. Monsoon winds from the southwest in late summer bring about 90 percent of the total rainfall, and most falls during a few intense storms with much runoff. Temperatures can be extreme. The hottest period occurs just before the monsoon season, with May and June mean maxima reaching more than 112° F (45° C). Extreme highs are more than 122° F (50° C). Winters, however, can be close to freezing, and frost is possible in January. Diurnal temperature changes are also high, and difference between day and night can be 27°–31° F (15°–18° C).

With increasing distance from the Sahara and more association with Asia, the biota becomes more distinct from that in Africa and Saudi Arabia, with more Indian elements. Vegetation is sparse, either xeric grasses or desert thorn scrub of low trees and shrubs, varying according to length of the dry season. With only seven months of drought, both shrubs and subshrubs are able to grow, but where the dry season increases to 9–10 months, only subshrubs can exist. A dry season lasting 11–12 months supports only a sparse population of annuals.

Vegetation also varies with water-holding capacity of the soil or rock, and different environments support different assemblages of plants. Joints and crevices or weathered areas in rocks allow infiltration of water. In rocky areas without cracks, runoff is high because no water penetrates, causing those rocky slopes to be barren. Granite foothills and the base of the slopes high on the alluvial fans support scrubby acacia trees and caper shrubs with cactus-like euphorbias in crevices. Sand-filled rock fissures have *Sarcostemma* species (a succulent milkweed) and wolfberry shrubs. On rhyolite hills, gum acacia, *Anogeissus pendula*, and *Salvadora oleoides* trees grow with caper and *Maytensis emarginata* shrubs. Rocky sandstone plateaus are dry because the rocks are porous. They are sparsely populated with many of the same species common on rhyolite, but also support *Euphorbia caducifolia* and *Mimosa hamata* shrubs. Three-awn and resurrection grasses grow on the lower slopes of sandy foothills where rainfall or runoff infiltrates.

Shifting dunes may have more soil moisture, but movement prevents plants from gaining a foothold. Dune vegetation includes hackenkopf and rattlebox shrubs with clumps of panic grass and herbaceous species of *Aerva*. Stabilized dunes support trees such as gum acacia and ghaf. Plant cover on playas depends on salt content. The center is usually barren salt crust, surrounded by a ring of plants with various tolerances to salt. Riverine alluvial plains have a scrubby vegetation of ghaf trees, along with caper and wild jujube shrubs and scattered babul acacia trees. Acacia, salt cedar, and *Salvadora oleoides* form dense thickets closer to river channels.

None of the species of mammals, birds, or reptiles are endemic. Small animals that have a limited range include Indian hare, and rodents such as northern palm squirrel, Indian gerbil, and Indian desert jird. Mice and shrews are common. Large mammals, which can move long distances to water and feed, are mountain gazelle, onager, and two antelope (blackbuck and nilgai). Blackbuck is a fast runner, capable of evading most predators (see Figure 2.18). The largest antelope in Asia, mature males take on a bluish tinge and are often called blue bulls. Both antelope feed primarily on grasses and frequently can be seen together on the flat plains. Large mammals are more likely to be found in the Indus River Valley than in the more-settled part of the desert. Common birds are Rose-colored Starling, Rose-ringed Parakeet, babblers, Indian Bustard, and Red-vented Bulbul. The region is also crossed by a flyway for cranes and flamingos. Carnivores include striped hyena, caracal, wolves, Bengal fox, and sand cat. The reptile fauna is similar to that of other Asian deserts, but with species more associated with the Indian subcontinent.

Figure 2.18 Blackbuck is a large ungulate found in the Thar Desert. *(Courtesy of Shutterstock. Copyright: Shelley Shay.)*

Australia

Australia's five deserts make up about 20 percent of the continent, about 580,000 mi^2 (1.5 million km^2) (see Figure 2.19). Inclusion of semiarid areas surrounding the desert increases the total to about 50 percent of the landmass. Although five deserts are often named, their boundaries are indistinct and they merge into a single arid region. The three largest deserts, Great Sandy, Great Victoria, and Simpson (Arunta), are covered by longitudinal sand dunes more than 100 m (160 km) long. The Gibson Desert in the west and the Sturt in the southeast are stony.

Like all warm deserts centered under a subtropical high-pressure cell, the equatorward edge of the Australian Desert experiences summer thunderstorms from monsoons and the poleward edge receives winter rain from mid-latitude cyclonic storms. The south may also get occasional summer rain from cyclonic storms. A broad transitional zone in the center receives little benefit from either storm system and is consequently drier. Much of the Australian desert is not only under the influence of the subtropical high-pressure cell, but is also in a rainshadow. The Great Dividing Range in eastern Australia blocks the southeast Trade Winds, keeping moisture on the east coast. Australian deserts are quite wet compared with other world regions, averaging 10–15 in (250–380 mm), with the higher values in the subtropical north. Mean values of desert precipitation, however, are always misleading because rainfall is sporadic and unreliable. Although morning dew may occasionally follow a rain, temperatures rarely drop low enough. Fog and dew are both rare.

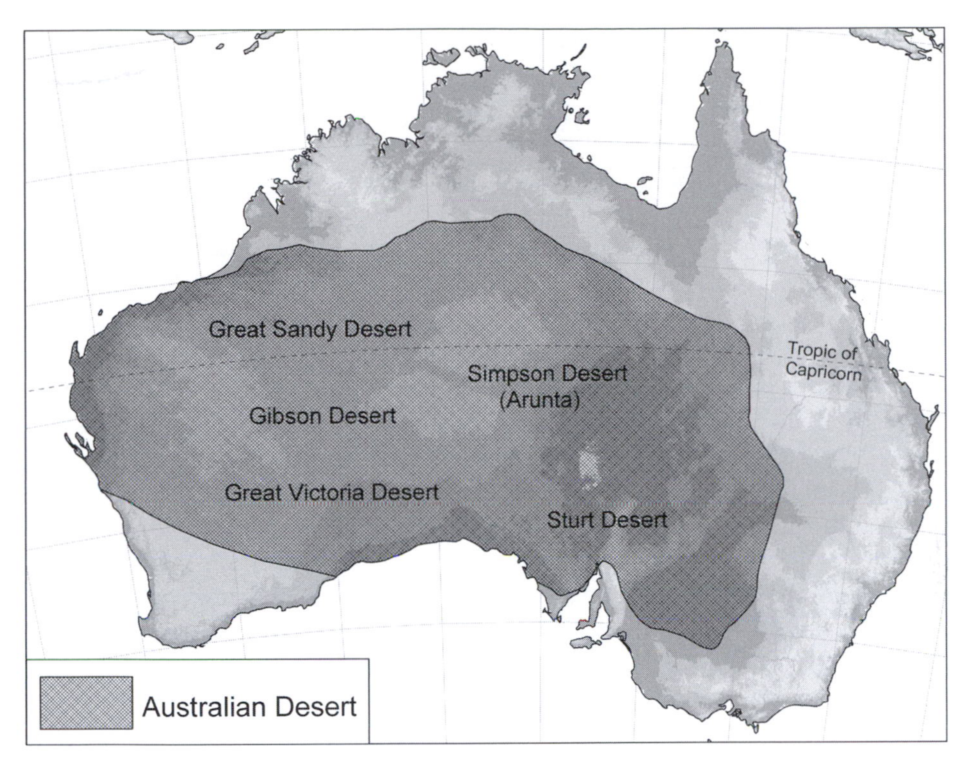

Figure 2.19 The five deserts in Australia cover a major part of the continent. *(Map by Bernd Kuennecke.)*

All Australian deserts have hot summers. Temperatures follow a continental pattern, with more variation in the interior of the continent. Winters are colder farther south because of latitude. Mean daily temperatures in summer (January) are 80°–90° F (27°–32° C), but maximum temperature for the day can rise to 120° F (49° C). Temperatures exceed 100° F (38° C) 100 to 145 days a year. Mean temperatures for winter (July) are 50°–65° F (10°–18° C). Overnight temperatures may drop slightly below freezing a few days every year, but the average frost-free period is usually more than 270 days.

Six different types of geological landscapes occur in Australian deserts. Low mountains and associated plateaus up to 5,000 ft (1,500 m), with local elevation change of only 1,000–2,600 ft (300–800 m), are found in the northwest, on the northern fringes, and in the center of the continent and southern desert fringes, not coincidental with any particular desert subdivision. The mountains are not high enough for snow but may enhance orographic precipitation in the immediate area. Water-cut gorges through mountain ranges create local oases with pools of water that support remnants from a wetter climate period (palms, fish, and aquatic insects), similar to the mountain pools in the Sahara. Highlands are usually surrounded by an apron of alluvial fans. Exposed continental shield is found in the

Great Victorian Desert in the southwestern part of Western Australia. The level surface of the shield is an ancient, eroded layer rich in iron. Some alluvium, dry salt lakes, and disconnected drainage also occur.

Stony deserts, primarily at the base of the Great Dividing Range to the east and in the northern half of South Australia in the Sturt Desert, are tablelands where wind erosion has developed a desert pavement, locally called gibber plains. The ephemeral (normally dry) drainage system of the Sturt Desert is integrated and flows to the interior of the continent, not to the ocean. Water channels flow into large salt lake basins such as Lake Eyre and Lake Torrens. Like Great Salt Lake and many playas in North American deserts, the Lake Eyre basin was occupied by a large lake, Lake Dieri, during wetter periods of the Pleistocene. Presently, rain barely dampens the surfaces, but during extreme rainfall events, the system still merges. Lake Eyre holds water roughly twice every 100 years. Riverine and clay plains are found in an arc at the foot of the Great Dividing Range. These are either clay derived from limestone or fine soils from alluvial deposits. Both the stony and clay plains are sedimentary deposits that are part of the Great Artesian Basin. Because the sand deserts in the Great Sandy, Gibson, Victorian, and Simpson deserts have no rivers and almost no water, they are uninhabited.

Plant communities are associated more with different types of landform, soil, or rock than with individual named deserts. Therefore, not all desert subdivisions are discussed here.

Plants. Unlike most other arid regions, Australian deserts have no succulents and few spiny plants. The lack of spiny plants may be related to the lack of large herbivores. Most herbivores in Australia are grazers, not browsers. The only major browse plant, particularly for euros (a type of kangaroo), is spinifex, which has evolved spiny leaves. However, the flora must still contend with both heat and aridity. Cork hopbush is a shrub with corky bark in the extreme climate of the Gibson Desert. To protect against surface temperatures that reach 158° F (70° C), some eucalyptus and mulga trees shed leaves or bark that accumulates as an insulating mulch layer at the base of the plant. Many plants, such as the shrub lamb's tail and forbs woolly foxglove and felty bellflower, have a hairy or woolly surface that provides protection from extreme heat and dry winds. Prevalence of hairs, white powder coatings, and waxy or resinous surfaces impede water loss during respiration. Some plants like mulgas have no true leaves, just modified flattened stems with few stomata. Plants are widely spaced and many have deep roots to tap groundwater. The

Sand Dunes

Individual sand dunes extend for 50–100 mi (80–320 km) and rise 33–100 ft (10–30 m) high. They lie several hundred feet or meters apart, about six to eight dunes within 1 mi (four to five dunes to 1 km). The sand is red due to an iron coating on the quartz grains. On a large scale, the dunes exhibit a gigantic counterclockwise swirl. The dune directions follow the prevailing winds of the subtropical high-pressure cell situated over the continent.

roots of spinifex grasses reach a depth of 33 ft (10 m). Trees such as river red gum and desert oaks (not related to *Quercus* oaks) may indicate underground water sources.

Scattered trees, shrubs, and perennial grasslands make up four basic vegetation types—acacia shrublands, arid hummock grasslands, arid tussock grasslands, and low chenopod shrublands. Acacia shrublands and hummock grasslands are most common, with saltbushes and other chenopods on saline soils. Major families represented are sunflower, Caesalpiniaceae, pea, mimosa (acacia), goosefoot (chenopod), and grass.

Acacia shrublands, with open-canopy acacia shrubs 10–20 ft (3–6 m) tall resemble savanna rather than desert. Dominated by 1 of 11 acacia species, these shrublands cover extensive areas of Australian deserts on rocky or stony substrate. Few acacia species, however, are restricted to Australian deserts. The understory can be any of several communities of grasses and forbs, and composition varies with soil type. A grassy ground layer includes lovegrass, three-awn, windmill, and crabgrass as well as several others. Perennial and annual forbs can include species of mulla mulla, sidas, Australian daisy, and yellow billy.

The hummock grasslands are the most extensive plant community in Australian deserts, especially in sand dune areas. Dominated by two genera of spinifex, they are locally called spinifex grasslands, with an occasional tree or shrub that may be senna or emu bush. Different species of *Triodia* are prominent according to geographic locality and rainfall pattern. Spinifex grasslands also include small patches of other grasses such as three-awn, feather pappusgrass, and lovegrass. Grass hummocks can be 5 ft (1.5 m) high and 20 ft (6 m) in diameter. Ground between the hummocks is bare except for annuals after a rain.

Tussock grasslands of Mitchell grass are found primarily on the eastern and northeastern edge of the arid region on riverine and clay plains. Tussocks are variable: 0.3–5 ft (0.1–1.5 m) diameter and spaced 1.5–6.5 ft (0.5–2 m) apart. Higher precipitation can support a more dense pattern of grasses. One species dominates in the central and north, while another is restricted to the south. Many other grasses also occur in this community.

Chenopod shrub-steppe, on the southern desert edge (southeastern Great Victoria) and in the lower elevations of the Lake Eyre Basin (Sturt Desert) is dominated by halophytes in the goosefoot family—saltbush, bluebush, and bindieyes. Representative shrubs can be 1–3 ft (0.3–1 m) both in diameter and height. Normally bare ground may be covered with annuals after a rare rainfall.

Animals. Australia's current animal population is derived from both the fauna on the continent at the time it separated from Gondwanaland (the combined continents) in the geologic past and later immigrants from southeastern Asia. Gondwanaland components include frogs and marsupials, while the Asian components include reptiles, rodents, and bats. Each vegetation group has its own restricted community of animals.

Australian animals, whether placental or marsupial, face the same problems of heat, drought, and salinity as those in other deserts and have evolved similar adaptations to deal with conditions. Most small animals cannot tolerate high temperatures and escape heat by nocturnal activity and daytime burrowing. Most need no free water, producing sufficient metabolic water from food, and pass concentrated urine and dry feces. The spinifex hopping mouse is typical of small desert rodents. Nocturnal, it spends days in burrows 3.3 ft (1 m) deep where conditions are cool and slightly moist. The mouse plugs the entrance with moist sand. It maintains its normal 65 percent body weight in water by eating only dry spinifex and grass seeds. It has dry feces, concentrated urine, and no sweat glands. The fawn hopping mouse needs occasional water but can drink water twice as salty as the ocean and probably survives on halophytes. The mulgara, a small crest-tailed marsupial mouse, lives in the driest central deserts. Like the grasshopper mouse of the southwestern United States, it is carnivorous, eating insects, small reptiles, and even small rodents. The water content of its food is enough to sustain it, and it reduces water loss by concentrating a lot of urea in a small volume of urine. The blind marsupial mole lives in loose, sandy soil either in dune areas or along stream beds, and rarely comes to the surface. In both appearance and habits, it resembles golden moles of arid southwest Africa. The fat-tailed dunnart, a mouse-like marsupial, stores fat in its tail. Although introduced wild rabbits do well in the desert, they need green vegetation and cannot live on dry food alone. They can, however, tolerate a water loss of 50 percent of their body weight, allowing them to survive drought conditions until it rains and fresh plants grow.

Most marsupials use the same mechanisms for evaporative cooling as do mammals, by panting and sweating. Kangaroos can regulate their body temperatures by opening their mouths, not quite panting but similar. Red kangaroos need more water for temperature regulation than euros (also called hill kangaroos). They find shelter from heat under trees and shrubs, exposing the least amount of body surface to the hot air. Euros take cover in caves or under rock ledges. Thick fur also provides insulation.

One-third of Australian desert mammals are wallabies, small insectivorous marsupials, and seed-eating or herbivorous rodents. Compared with many warm deserts, Australia has few small seed-eating mammals. The seed-eating niche may have been taken by birds and ants in Australia.

Introduced foxes and cats have decimated the native small fauna. Some already may be extinct and known only from museum collections. The only carnivorous mammal, the dingo, introduced by Aborigines thousands of years ago, is considered part of the native fauna. Recent extinctions of small native animals in Australia can be linked with low populations of dingoes. These wild dogs are significant in reducing numbers of introduced predators that prey on native fauna. Where dingoes are scarce, natives animals have little protection against alien predators. Several bats are present, but none are restricted to the desert; their distribution is more dependent on water than on type of vegetation.

Marsupials are the largest group of mammals in Australian deserts, with an amazing variety in size, diet, and habitat. The tiny insect-eating marsupial mouse in tussock grasslands weighs less than 0.35 oz (10 g), while large male red kangaroos can weigh up to 185 lb (85 kg). Populations of red kangaroos and euros increased after human settlement and provision of water sources. Groups of red kangaroos live in acacia woodland where they find shade and herbaceous food. They are not normally found in grassland, but stock grazing destroys shrubs and encourages new growth of lovegrass, which attracts red kangaroos. Euros ordinarily live solitary lives in rocky hills, feeding on low-nutrient spinifex grasses, but they also expanded their range when grazing influenced the spread of spinifex. Euros are the most desert-adapted kangaroo, living on poor quality food and going up to 90 days without free water. Even in the hottest weather, they only drink once every 14 days. Hare-wallabies are found in hummock grasslands, while rock-wallabies prefer rocky hills. Spiny anteater (echidna), a monotreme, is widespread in all Australia habitats, but is also important in the deserts where it feeds on abundant ants and termites (see Figure 2.20a).

Dog Fence

Beginning in the 1880s, Australians built a fence, 3,300 mi (5,320 km) long across the country, to keep dingoes away from the fertile sheep-grazing grounds of southeastern Australia. Perhaps because of the lack of dingo predation, kangaroo populations south of the fence increased, resulting in increased grazing competition for sheep. Predators found north of the dog fence are the dingo, perentie, and sand goanna.

Birds can fly long distances to find free water, and also have an advantage in desert heat because their normal body temperature of 104° F (40° C) is higher than that of most mammals. If caught by heat or drought, however, they will die. Although more than 200 species of birds have been recorded, most are migrants or water birds arriving after heavy rains. The majority are small passerines, but parrots and pigeons are also common. Colorful species are most conspicuous, and in good water years, flocks may number in the thousands. Several of these birds, including Zebra Finch, many types of parrots, and parakeets such as Galah, Little Corella, and Budgerigar, are common in the pet trade. Most desert birds need access to water, and although in general they have no major adaptations to saltwater, exceptions occur. The Zebra Finch, native to arid central Australia, can drink water slightly saltier than seawater.

Only 40 birds are desert dwellers, especially the Chestnut-breasted Quail-thrush, a ground bird found in stony scrubland and hills. Red-capped Robins are the most common of small dry-country birds. The Rufous-crowned Emu-wren, which prefers to run on the ground hiding behind spinifex clumps, is one of the smallest. An insect-eater, it needs no water. The Painted Firetail is also found in spinifex near mountains and gorges. The Inland Dotterel lives on gibber plains and claypans where it is nocturnal. It also needs no free water, getting enough from insects and plants. Orange Chats occupy saltbush margins of playas. Bustards used to be common in most of Australia, but they now are found only in remote parts of the interior.

In dry years, some Australian birds do not nest or reproduce. The sex organs of both males and females atrophy. Pairs do not even try to mate, and no nest is built. If rain comes, the birds can begin the breeding process within one week, and they often flock to rainy areas to do so.

The Australian deserts have more reptiles than any other desert, 40 species of snakes in three families (Typhlopidae, Boidae, and Elapidae). Small snake species eat both insects and small lizards. Blind snakes live underground and eat termites and ants. Large pythons (Boidae) and some members of Elapidae are carnivorous. Several highly venomous snakes, such as the mulga snake, fierce snake, and death adder, all large Elapids, live in the desert.

The lizard fauna is the richest in any desert in the world, with more than 190 species of lizards in five families (Gekkonidae, Pygopodidae, Agamidae, Varanidae, and Scincidae) (see Figures 2.20b and 2.20c). Many are widespread, while others have restricted habitats. They are especially diverse and abundant in spinifex grasslands. Geckos and skinks are common. Unlike other desert regions where lizards are active during the day, almost half are nocturnal, avoiding the heat of the day by retreating to humid burrows. Common and conspicuous, several species of dragon lizards are diurnal. They regulate their body temperature by orienting a

Figure 2.20 Australian deserts have unique animal life. (a) Spiny anteater, or echidna, eats insects. (b) Bearded lizards, such as this central netted dragon lizard, are common. (c) The thorny devil lizard has a unique way of accessing moisture. *(Courtesy of Shutterstock. Copyright: (a) Clearviewstock; (b) Litwin Photography; (c) Steve Lovegrove.)*

broad surface area of their bodies to the sun when the air is cool and the least surface area to the sun when it is hot. Like many other diurnal lizards, it may minimize surface contact by raising its body and tail away from the hot ground. They may also climb shrubs or take shelter in burrows to avoid the hottest part of the day. Some species change body color according to temperature, dark to absorb more radiation and light to reflect it. The thorny devil lizard soaks up water from dew or the ground in wrinkles in its skin. Capillary action moves the water through the tiny creases toward the mouth. In contrast to the majority of lizards that eat insects, two large monitor lizards—perentie and sand goanna—are carnivores that often eat carrion. The perentie is the largest lizard in Australia, growing to more than 8 ft (2.5 m). Its habitat is primarily rocky outcrops where it feeds on insects, birds, and small mammals. The sand goanna uses powerful legs to dig lizards and reptile eggs out of the sand.

Amphibians are generally not physiologically adapted to desert conditions. However, some have developed behavioral adaptations to survive. Douglas' toad and others are associated with permanent water areas such as springs or pools in streambeds. They take refuge in moist places under rocks or roots if the water dries up. Desert-adapted frogs burrow into the soil and aestivate most of their lives, avoiding hot and dry conditions. Some absorb water, while others use dead skin as a protective covering. The water-holding frog fills a large bladder, one-half the size of the rest of the body, with dilute urine before it aestivates. It burrows into moist mud that dries to a hard waterproof shell where the frog can survive for up to three years. Others, such as the Australian spadefoot, can tolerate extreme dehydration, losing up to 40 percent of body weight, and can rehydrate quickly after rain. When enough rain falls, the aestivating frogs emerge to complete their life cycle in two to six weeks before the pool of water dries out, enduring water temperatures of up to 102° F (39° C).

Like fairy shrimp in North America, invertebrates in Australian deserts wait for favorable conditions and then quickly live their entire life cycle in temporary pools. The most common example is the tadpole shrimp which can grow to 3 in (75 mm). Its offspring survive drought in tough-shelled eggs. As the adults die in masses when the ephemeral water evaporates, they provide a feast for herons, egrets, and other water birds.

Insects are plentiful—ants, termites, grasshoppers, beetles, and moths. Insects that cannot move long distances are well adapted to arid conditions, while flying insects such as grasshoppers and locusts can move to more favorable areas as necessary. Most desert arthropods have hard exoskeletons that lose little moisture. Silverfish, termites, and ants are examples of insects with thick cuticles or behavioral traits that limit water loss. Although silverfish have a waterproof skin, they only forage during cool nights when humidity is higher. Termites and ants spend most of their time in elaborate sealed nest systems. Hundreds of species of ants occur, many more than in any other desert, including honey ants that have a replete caste that stores nectar in their abdomens for the entire colony. Several species of trap-door spiders enclose the entrance to their vertical tunnel with a circular, hinged disk of soil held together by spider silk. The trap door fits flush with the ground and is almost undetectable. When the spider senses the vibration of an insect passing nearby, it quickly emerges to capture its prey.

Australian desert subdivisions. The Simpson (Arunta) and Sturt deserts, 225,000 mi^2 (583,000 km^2) covering one-sixth of Australia, together make one of the world's largest interior drainage basins. The region is predominantly level, from below sea level to 1,000 ft (300 m), with occasional low mountains and mesas. Extensive floodplains and braided channels dominate in the northeast, locally called Channel Country. The rivers originate in adjacent areas but flow to the interior, draining into swamps or lakes such as Eyre. Flooding in the floodplains occurs every two to three years, but enough water to fill the interior lake basins is rare. When flooded, the normally dry and barren lakes support large bird populations and even fish in the larger lakes. The Coongie Lakes are exceptionally rich in species. Animal populations vary according to variations in climate, increasing during wet times and declining during dry periods. Stony flats with desert pavement outline the floodplains. In the south and west, small sand dunes alternate with claypans or saline lakes in the interdune areas.

Vegetation varies according to the landform and substrate. Floodplains and gibber plains support ephemeral grasses and herbs and chenopod shrubs. Woodlands with short trees outline drainages. Senna and shrubby acacia sparsely cover low mountain slopes. Dune vegetation is complex depending on the part of the dune—crest, slopes, interdune, shifting, or stabilized—but spinifex dominates. Claypans and saline lakes are mostly bare when dry, but ephemeral herbs may sprout after rare floods. Lake edges may be lined with saltbush. Because the Simpson Desert has a sparse human population, its native vegetation is relatively pristine except for grazing pressure from domestic stock and introduced rabbits, pigs, and goats. Because of the availability of water, the Simpson Desert supports a rich fauna. Floodplains along water courses provide habitat for a diverse population of birds, bats, and frogs. Spinifex grasslands are diverse in reptiles.

The Great Victoria Desert in western and southern Australia is isolated and relatively untouched not only because of extreme temperatures and low rainfall, but also because it is a nuclear test site. Much of the region is covered by sand dunes. Common plant communities consist of three different types of open woodland or scrubland containing eucalyptus species, mulga, and chenopod shrubs. The Giles Corridor is a narrow strip of acacia shrubs that is continuous across the entire desert, through the Lake

Mound Springs

The Great Artesian Basin system underlies most of the Simpson Desert. Mound springs, which cover small areas, develop where artesian water naturally flows to the surface, providing water in an area of sparse rainfall. These permanently wet oases in a dry environment are isolated islands of available moisture surrounded by desert and are home to endemic plants, snails, and fish.

Carnegie Region of the Great Victorian Desert and southern part of the Gibson Desert. Gibber plains are barren with little vegetation except annuals after rains.

Few endemic species occur here, especially birds and mammals, because these animals travel long distances to find favorable conditions and are not isolated. Diversity in reptiles, however, is high, especially in the gecko, agamid, skink, and elapid families. Late Pleistocene climate change resulted in isolated populations and pockets of vegetation where subspecies evolved. Habitat diversity also contributes to species diversity. Several endangered mammals are still found here. No plant extinctions are known, but several animals have become extinct within the last 200 years. Introduced rabbits threaten native plants by overgrazing, and house mice threaten native animals through competition for scarce resources.

Further Readings

Books

Mares, Michael A. 2002. *A Desert Calling: Life in a Forbidding Landscape.* Cambridge, MA: Harvard University Press.

McGinnies, Willam G. 1981. *Discovering the Desert: Legacy of the Carnegie Desert Botanical Laboratory.* Tuscon: University of Arizona Press.

Internet Sources

Arizona-Sonora Desert Museum. n.d. "Center for Sonoran Desert Studies." http://www.desertmuseum.org/center.

Bradtke, Birgit, for Outback Australia. n.d. "Australian Desert Animals." http://www.outback-australia-travel-secrets.com/australian-desert-animals.html.

Breeding Centre for Endangered Arabian Wildlife. n.d. "Breeding Centre for Endangered Arabian Wildlife." http://www.breedingcentresharjah.com.

Jerusalem University. n.d. "Jerusalem Botanical Gardens." http://www.botanic.co.il/english/index.htm.

Appendix

Biota of the Warm Desert Biome (arranged geographically)

North American Warm Deserts

Some Characteristic Plants of the Sonoran Desert

Trees	
Whitethorn acacia	*Acacia constricta*
Catclaw acacia	*Acacia greggii*
Elephant tree or Torchwood or Torote	*Bursera microphylla and B. hindsiana*
Blue paloverde	*Cercidium floridum*
Foothill paloverde	*Cercidium microphyllum*
Sonora paloverde	*Cercidium sonorae*
Lignum vitae	*Guaiacum coulteri*
Ironwood	*Olneya tesota*
Cottonwood	*Populus fremontii*
Western honey mesquite	*Prosopis glandulosa*
Velvet mesquite	*Prosopis velutina*
Willow	*Salix* spp.
Salt cedar or Tamarisk	*Tamarix ramosissima*
Desert sand palm	*Washingtonia filifera*
Shrubs	
White bursage	*Ambrosia dumosa*
Four-wing saltbush	*Atriplex canescens*
Brittlebush	*Encelia farinosa*
MacDougal's ocotillo	*Fouqueria macdougalii*
Ocotillo	*Fouqueria splendens*
Sangre de drago	*Jatropha cuneata*
Lomboy	*Jatropha cinerea*
Creosote bush	*Larrea tridentata*
Wolfberry	*Lycium andersonii*
Jojoba	*Simmondsia chinensis*

Cactus	
Saguaro	*Carnegiea gigantea*
Barrel cactus	*Ferocactus acanthodes*
Organpipe or Pitaya dulce	*Lamaireocereus thurberi*
Senita	*Lophocereus schottii*
Teddy bear cholla	*Opuntia bigelovii*
Engelman prickly pear	*Opuntia phaeacantha*
Staghorn cholla	*Opuntia versicolor*
Cardon	*Pachycereus pringlei*
Grasses and forbs	
Grama grass	*Bouteloua* spp.
Tobosa grass	*Hilaria mutica*
Big galleta grass	*Hilaria rigida*
Woolly plantain	*Plantago insularis*
Sacaton or Dropseed grass	*Sporobolus* spp.

Some Characteristic Animals of the Sonoran Desert

Herbivores	
Harris antelope squirrel	*Ammospermophilus harrisii*
White-tailed antelope squirrel	*Ammospermophilus leucuris*
Desert kangaroo rat	*Dipodomys deserti*
Black-tailed jackrabbit	*Lepus californicus*
White-throated woodrat or Packrat	*Neotoma albigula*
Mule deer	*Odocoileus hemionus*
Desert bighorn sheep	*Ovis canadensis*
Javelina or Peccary	*Pecari angulatus*
Round-tailed ground squirrel	*Spermophilus tereticaudus*
Badger	*Taxidea taxus*
Kit fox	*Vulpes macrotis*
Carnivores	
Coyote	*Canis latrans*
Western mastiff bat	*Euops perotis*
Mountain lion	*Felix concolor*
Bobcat	*Lynx rufus*
Gray fox	*Urocyon cinereoargenteus*
Birds	
Burrowing Owl	*Athene cunicularis*
Red-tailed Hawk	*Buteo jamaicensis*
Gambel Quail	*Callipepla gambelii*
Costa's Hummingbird	*Calypte costae*
Cactus Wren	*Campylorhynchus brunneicapillus*

(*Continued*)

Turkey Vulture	*Cathartes aura*
Roadrunner	*Geococcyx californianus*
Gila Woodpecker	*Melanerpes uropygialis*
Elf Owl	*Micrathene whitneyi*
Phainopepla	*Phainopepla nitens*
Ladder-backed Woodpecker	*Picoides scalaris*
Curve-billed Thrasher	*Toxostoma curvirostre*
Mourning Dove	*Zenaida macroura*
Reptiles and amphibians	
Glossy snake	*Arizona elegans*
Western shovelnose snake	*Chionactis occipitalis*
Western whiptail lizard	*Cnemidophorus tigris*
Banded gecko	*Coleonyx variegatus*
Western diamondback rattlesnake	*Crotalus atrox*
Sidewinder	*Crotalus cerastes*
Mojave rattlesnake	*Crotalus scutulatus*
Desert iguana	*Dipsosaurus dorsalis*
Desert tortoise	*Gopherus agassizii*
Gila monster	*Heloderma suspectum*
Desert rosy boa	*Lichanura trivirgata*
Arizona coral snake	*Micruroides euryxanthus*
Flat-tailed horned lizard	*Phrynosoma m'calli*
Desert horned lizard	*Phrynosoma platyrhinos*
Sonoran gopher snake	*Pituophis melanoleucus affinis*
Chuckwalla	*Sauromalus obesus*
Couch's spadefoot toad	*Scaphiopus couchi*
Desert spiny lizard	*Sceloporus magister*
Fringe-toed lizard	*Uma notata*

Some Characteristic Plants of the Mojave Desert

Trees	
Cottonwood	*Populus fremontii*
Willow	*Salix* spp.
Salt cedar or Tamarisk	*Tamarix* spp.
Shrubs	
White bursage	*Ambrosia dumosa*
Shadscale	*Atriplex confertifolia*
Desert holly	*Atriplex hymenelytra*
Allscale	*Atriplex polycarpa*
Blackbrush	*Coleogyne ramosissima*
Brittlebush	*Encelia farinosa*
Ocotillo	*Fouqueria splendens*
Creosote bush	*Larrea tridentata*

Scalebroom	*Lepidospartum latisquamum*
Spiny menodora	*Menodora spinescens*
Mojave dalea	*Psorothamnus arborescens*
Bladder-sage	*Salazaria mexicana*
Large leaf succulents	
Joshua tree	*Yucca brevifolia*
Mojave yucca	*Yucca schidigera*
Cactus	
Many-headed barrel	*Echinocactus polycephalus*
Beavertail	*Opuntia basilaris*
Teddy bear cholla	*Opuntia bigelovii*
Silver cholla	*Opuntia echinocarpa*
Mojave prickly pear	*Opuntia erinacea*
Grasses and forbs	
Goldenhead	*Acamptopappus shockleyi*
Woolly plantain	*Plantago insularis*

Some Characteristic Animals of the Mojave Desert

Herbivores	
White-tailed antelope ground squirrel	*Ammospermophilus leucuris*
Desert kangaroo rat	*Dipodomys deserti*
Great Basin kangaroo rat	*Dipodomys microps*
Black-tailed jackrabbit	*Lepus californicus*
Mule deer	*Odocoileus hemionus*
Desert bighorn sheep	*Ovis canadensis*
Great Basin pocket mouse	*Perognathus parvus*
Mojave ground squirrel	*Spermophilus mohaviensis*
Round-tailed ground squirrel	*Spermophilus tereticaudus*
Carnivores	
Coyote	*Canis latrans*
Western mastiff bat	*Euops perotis*
Mountain lion	*Felix concolor*
Bobcat	*Lynx rufus*
Badger	*Taxidea taxus*
Kit fox	*Vulpes macrotis*
Birds	
Burrowing Owl	*Athene cunicularis*
Red-tailed Hawk	*Buteo jamaicensis*
Gambel Quail	*Callipepla gambelii*
Costa's Hummingbird	*Calypte costae*

(*Continued*)

Cactus Wren	*Campylorhynchus brunneicapillus*
Turkey Vulture	*Cathartes aura*
Roadrunner	*Geococcyx californianus*
Phainopepla	*Phainopepla nitens*
Poorwill	*Phalaenoptilus nuttallii*
Le Conte's Thrasher	*Toxostoma leconteri*
Mourning Dove	*Zenaida macroura*
Reptiles and amphibians	
Banded gecko	*Coleonyx variegatus*
Western diamondback rattlesnake	*Crotalus atrox*
Mojave rattlesnake	*Crotalus scutulatus*
Desert iguana	*Dipsosaurus dorsalis*
Desert tortoise	*Gopherus agassizii*
Gila monster	*Heloderma suspectum*
Regal horned lizard	*Phrynosoma solare*
Mojave patchnose snake	*Salvadora hexalepis mojavensis*
Chuckwalla	*Sauromalus obesus*
Desert spiny lizard	*Sceloporus magister*
Mojave fringe-toed lizard	*Uma scoparia*
Desert night lizard	*Xantusia vigilis*

Some Characteristic Plants of the Chihuahuan Desert

Trees	
Catclaw acacia	*Acacia greggii*
Viscid acacia	*Acacia neovernicosa*
Cottonwood	*Populus fremontii*
Western honey mesquite	*Prosopis glandulosa*
Willow	*Salix* spp.
Salt cedar or Tamarisk	*Tamarix* spp.
Shrubs	
Sage	*Artemisia filifera*
Saltbush	*Atriplex acanthocarpa*
Coldenia	*Coldenia* spp.
Lotebush	*Condalia lycioides*
Candelilla	*Euphorbia antisyphilitica*
Tarbush	*Flourensia cernua*
Ocotillo	*Fouqueria splendens*
Allthorn	*Koeberlinia spinosa*
Creosote bush	*Larrea tridentata*
Mariola	*Parthenium incanum*
Large leaf succulents	
Lechuguilla	*Agave lechuguilla*
Parry's century plant	*Agave parryi*
Sotol	*Dasylirion* spp.

Mescalito	*Hechtia montana*
Beargrass	*Nolina* spp.
Soaptree yucca	*Yucca elata*
Spanish bayonet	*Yucca whipplei*
Cactus	
Coryphantha	*Coryphantha* spp.
Echinocactus	*Echinocactus horizonthalonius*
Rainbow cactus	*Echinocereus pectinatus*
Barrel cactus	*Ferocactus hamatacanthus*
Mexican fire barrel cactus	*Ferocactus pringlei*
Myrtillocactus	*Myrtillocactus geometricans*
Prickly pear	*Opuntia macrocentra*
Engelman prickly pear	*Opuntia phaeacantha*
Grasses and forbs	
Grama grass	*Bouteloua* spp.
Salt grass	*Distichlis spicata*
Tobosa grass	*Hilaria mutica*
Muhly grass	*Muhlenbergia* spp.
Dropseed grass	*Sporobolus* spp.

Some Characteristic Animals of the Chihuahuan Desert

Herbivores	
Texas antelope squirrel	*Ammospermophilus inerpres*
White-tailed antelope ground squirrel	*Ammospermophilus leucuris*
Pronghorn	*Antilocapra americana*
Black-tailed jackrabbit	*Lepus californicus*
Mexican woodrat or Packrat	*Neotoma mexicana*
Mule deer	*Odocoileus hemionus*
Javelina or Peccary	*Pecari angulatus*
Collared peccary	*Pecari tajacu*
Nelson's pocket mouse	*Perognathus nelsoni*
Mexican ground squirrel	*Spermophilus mexicanus*
Carnivores	
Coyote	*Canis latrans*
Western mastiff bat	*Euops perotis*
Mountain lion	*Felix concolor*
Bobcat	*Lynx rufus*
Badger	*Taxidea taxus*
Kit fox	*Vulpes macrotis*
Birds	
Burrowing Owl	*Athene cunicularis*
Red-tailed Hawk	*Buteo jamaicensis*

(*Continued*)

Gambel Quail	*Callipepla gambelii*
Scaled Quail	*Callipepla squamata*
Cactus Wren	*Campylorhynchus brunneicapillus*
Turkey Vulture	*Cathartes aura*
White-necked Raven	*Corvus cryptoleucus*
Roadrunner	*Geococcyx californianus*
Phainopepla	*Phainopepla nitens*
Mourning Dove	*Zenaida macroura*
Reptiles and amphibians	
Little striped whiptail lizard	*Cnemidophorus inoratus*
Texas banded gecko	*Coleonyx brevis*
Reticulated gecko	*Coleonyx reticulatus*
Western diamondback rattlesnake	*Crotalus atrox*
Mojave rattlesnake	*Crotalus scutulatus*
Trans-Pecos rat snake	*Elaphe subocularis*
Bolson tortoise	*Gopherus flavomarginatus*
Western coachwhip snake	*Masticophis flagellum lineatus*
Texas horned lizard	*Phrynosoma cornatum*
Couch's spadefoot toad	*Scaphiopus couchi*
Desert spiny lizard	*Sceloporus magister*
Texas black-headed snake	*Tantilla atriceps*
Coahuilan box turtle	*Terrapene coahuila*

South American Warm Deserts

Some Characteristic Plants of the Monte Desert

Trees	
Acacia	*Acacia furcatispina*
Retamo	*Bulnesia retama*
Paloverde	*Cercidium praecox*
Chilean mesquite	*Prosopis chilensis*
Mesquite	*Prosopis flexuosa*
Black mesquite	*Prosopis nigra*
Shrubs	
Pickleweed	*Allenrolfea vaginata*
Saltbush	*Atriplex lampa*
Chilca	*Baccharis salicifolia*
Monte negro	*Bougainvillea spinosa*
Senna	*Cassia aphylla*
Creosote bush or Jarilla	*Larrea cuneifolia*
Creosote bush or Jarilla	*Larrea divaricata*
Creosote bush or Jarilla	*Larrea nitida*
Mata sebo or Parrot wing	*Montea aphyla*

Mancapotrillos	*Plectocarpa* spp.
Seepweed	*Suaeda divaricata*
Pajaro bobo	*Tessaria dodonaefolia*
Large leaf succulents	
In the Bromeliad family	*Deuterochonia schreiteri*
Dyckia	*Dyckia velazcana*
In the Bromeliad family	*Tillandsia* spp.
Cactus	
Cereus	*Cereus aethiops*
Easter-lily cactus	*Echinopsis* spp.
Gymnocalycium	*Gymnocalycium* spp.
Pine cone cactus	*Opuntia glomerata*
Prickly pear	*Opuntia strobiliformis*
Prickly pear	*Opuntia sulphurea*
Parodia	*Parodia* spp.
Cardon	*Trichocereus pasacana*
Cardon	*Trichocereus terscheckii*
Grasses and forbs	
Mendoza heliotrope	*Heliotropium mendocina*

Some Characteristic Animals of the Monte Desert

Herbivores	
Tuco-tuco	*Ctenomys fulvus*
Patagonian hare or Mara	*Dolichotis australis*
Gerbil mouse	*Eligmodontia typus*
Guanaco	*Lama guanicoe*
Desert cavy	*Microcavia australis*
Plains vizcacha rat	*Typanoctomys varrerae*
Carnivores	
Screaming armadillo	*Chaetophractus vellerosus*
Hog-nosed skunk	*Conepatus castaneus*
Mountain lion	*Felix concolor*
Lesser grison or Weasel	*Galictis cuja*
Patagonian weasel	*Lyncodon patagonicus*
Mouse opossum	*Marmosa pusilla*
Argentine gray fox or Zorro gris chico	*Pseudolopex griseus*
Birds	
Elegant Crested Tinamou	*Eudromia elegans*
Chimango Caracara	*Milvago chimango*
Crested Caracara	*Polyborus plancus*

(*Continued*)

Darwin's Rhea	*Pterocnemia pennata*
Rhea	*Rhea americana*
Lesser Wagtail-tyrant	*Stigmatura budytoides*
Andean Condor	*Vultur gyrphus*
Reptiles and amphibians	
Viper	*Bothrups neuwiedi*
Rattlesnake	*Crotalus durissus*
Lizard	*Homonota horrida*
Lizard	*Homonota underwoodii*
Lizard	*Liolaemus darwini*

African Warm Deserts

Some Characteristic Plants of the Sahara Desert

Trees	
Acacia	*Acacia albida*
Acacia	*Acacia ehrenbergiana*
Acacia	*Acacia raddiana*
Desert date	*Balanites aegyptiaca*
Date palm	*Phoenix dactylifera*
Salt cedar or Tamarisk	*Tamarix aphylla*
Shrubs	
In the Pea family	*Anthyllis henoniana*
Field sagewort or Tall wormwood	*Artemisia campestris*
Saltbush	*Atriplex* spp.
Hackenkopf	*Calligonum comosum*
Giant milkweed	*Calotropis procera*
Had	*Cornulaca monocantha*
Joint pine	*Ephedra alata*
Euphorbia	*Euphorbia balsamifera*
Euphorbia	*Euphorbia regis-jubae*
Kalanchoe	*Kalanchoe faustii*
Saltwort	*Salsola longifolia*
Senecio	*Senecio* spp.
Wild jujube	*Ziziphus lotus*
White bean-caper	*Zygophyllum album*
Grasses and forbs	
Cram cram melon	*Cenchrus biflorus*
Cleome	*Cleome droserifolia*
Prickly clover	*Fagonia arabica*
Japanese blood grass	*Imperata cylindrica*
Afozo or Panic grass or Turgid millet	*Panicum turgidum*
Reed or Cane	*Phragmites communis*
Ciliate plantain	*Plantago ciliata*

Wild sugar cane	*Saccharum ravennae*
Alfa	*Stipa tenacissima*

Some Characteristic Animals of the Sahara Desert	
Herbivores	
Egyptian spiny mouse	*Acomys cahirinuss*
Four-toed jerboa	*Allactaga tetradactylis*
Barbary sheep	*Ammotragus lervia*
Dromedary camel	*Camelus dromedarius*
Mountain gazelle	*Gazella gazella*
Goitered gazelle or Sand gazelle	*Gazella subgutturosa*
North African gerbil	*Gerbillus campestris*
Lesser Egyptian gerbil	*Gerbillus gerbillus*
Baluchistan gerbil	*Gerbillus nanus*
Greater Egyptian gerbil	*Gerbillus pyramidum*
Porcupine	*Hystrix cristata*
Lesser jerboa	*Jaculus jaculus*
Greater jerboa	*Jaculus orientalis*
Cape hare	*Lepus capensis*
Libyan jird	*Meriones libycus*
Fat-tailed gerbil	*Pachyuromys duprasi*
Hyrax or Rock dassy	*Procavia capensis*
Fat sand rat	*Psammomys obesus*
Mole rat	*Spalax ehrenbergi*
Carnivores	
Golden jackal	*Canis aureus*
Fennec fox	*Fennecus zerda*
Pale fox	*Vulpes pallida*
Ruppel's fox or Sand fox	*Vulpes ruppellii*
Birds	
Barbary Partridge	*Alectoris barbara*
Trumpeter Bullfinch	*Bucanetes githagineus*
Night-hawk	*Caprimulgus aegyptius*
Rock Pigeon	*Columba livia*
Brown-necked Raven	*Corvus ruficollis*
Courser	*Cursorius cursor*
Bee Eater	*Merops apiaster*
Chat	*Oenathe monacha*
Lichtenstein's Sandgrouse	*Pterocles lichtensteinii*
Sandgrouse	*Pterocles senegaelus*
Reptiles and amphibians	
Sand viper	*Cerastes cerastes*
Chameleon	*Chamaeleon chamaeleon*

(*Continued*)

Egyptian cobra or Asp	*Naja haje*
Skink	*Scincus scincus*
Land tortoise	*Testudo kleinmanni*
Gecko	*Tropidocalotes tripolitanus*
Monitor lizard	*Varanus griseus*
Blunt-nosed viper	*Vipera lebetina*

Eurasian Warm Deserts

Some Characteristic Plants of the Arabian Desert

Trees	
Acacia	*Acacia ehrenbergiana*
Acacia	*Acacia raddiana*
Desert date	*Balanites aegyptiaca*
Ghaf	*Prosopis cineraria*
Salt cedar or Tamarisk	*Tamarix aphylla*
Shrubs	
Berry-bearing glasswort	*Anabasis articulata*
White-leaf wormwood	*Artemisia herba-alba*
Sand wormwood	*Artemisia monosperma*
Hackenkopf	*Calligonum comosum*
Hackenkopf	*Calligonum crinitum*
Caper	*Capparis cartilaginea*
Caper	*Capparis decidua*
In the Goosefoot family	*Chenolea arabica*
Salt bush	*Cornulaca arabica*
Joint pine	*Ephedra alata*
In the Pink family	*Gymnocarpus decander*
Saxaul	*Haloxylon salicornicum*
In the Tamarisk family	*Reaumuria* spp.
White broom	*Retama raetam*
In the Sunflower family	*Rhanterium epapposum*
Syrian sumac	*Rhus tripartita*
Asphaltic sea-blite	*Suaeda asphaltica*
Wild jujube	*Ziziphus lotus*
Christ thorn jujube	*Ziziphus spina-christa*
Scarlet bean-caper	*Zygophyllum coccineum*
Bushy bean-caper	*Zygophyllum mandavillei*
Grasses and forbs	
Sedge	*Cyperus conglomeratus*
Afozo or Panic grass or Turgid millet	*Panicum turgidum*
Reed or Cane	*Phragmites communis*
Bulbous bluegrass	*Poa bulbosa*

Twisted-awn speargrass	*Stipa capensis*
Reedmace	*Typha* spp.

Some Characteristic Animals of the Arabian Desert

Herbivores	
Dromedary camel	*Camelus dromedarius*
Nubian ibex	*Capra ibex nubiana*
Mountain gazelle	*Gazella gazella*
Sand gazelle or Goitered gazelle	*Gazella subgutturosa*
Cheeseman's gerbil	*Gerbillus cheesmani*
Wagner's gerbil	*Gerbillus dasyurus*
Baluchistan gerbil	*Gerbillus nanus*
Arabian tahr	*Hemitragus jayakari*
Indian crested porcupine	*Hystrix indica*
Lesser jerboa	*Jaculus jaculus*
Greater jerboa	*Jaculus orientalis*
Cape hare	*Lepus capensis*
Arabian jird	*Meriones arimalius*
Sundervall's jird	*Meriones crassus*
Libyan jird	*Meriones libycus*
King jird	*Meriones rex*
White oryx	*Oryx leucoryx*
Fat-tailed gerbil	*Pachyuromys duprasi*
Hyrax or Rock dassy	*Procavia capensis*
Carnivores	
Golden jackal	*Canis aureus*
Arabian wolf	*Canis lupis arabs*
Caracal	*Caracal caracal*
Gordon's wildcat	*Felis silvestris gordoni*
Near-East wildcat	*Felis silvestris libycus*
Sand cat	*Felis margarita*
Fennec fox	*Fennecus zerda*
Striped hyena	*Hyaena hyaena*
Arabian leopard	*Pantherus pardus nimr*
Ethiopian hedgehog	*Paraechinus aethiopicus*
Ruppel's fox or Sand fox	*Vulpes ruppellii*
Red fox	*Vulpes vulpes*
Birds	
Houbara Bustard	*Chlamydotis undulata*
Rock Pigeon	*Columba livia*
Quail	*Coturnix coturnix*
Bee Eater	*Merops apiaster*

(*Continued*)

Chestnut-bellied Sandgrouse	*Pterocles exustus*
Lichtenstein's Sandgrouse	*Pterocles lichtensteinii*
Reptiles and amphibians	
Sand viper	*Cerastes cerastes*
Chameleon	*Chamaeleon* spp.
Caspian pond turtle	*Clemmys caspica*
Saw-scaled viper	*Echis carinatus*
Carpet viper	*Echis coloratus*
Gecko	*Hemidactylus* spp.
Arabian cobra	*Naja haje arabica*
Gecko	*Pristuris* spp.
Sand snake	*Psammophis schokari*
Frog	*Rana ridibunda*
Gecko	*Stenodactylus* spp.
Spiny-tailed lizard	*Uromastyx thomasi*
Desert monitor lizard	*Varanus griseus*
Blunt-nosed viper	*Vipera lebetina*

Some Characteristic Plants of the Iranian Desert

Trees	
Salt cedar or Tamarisk	*Tamarix aphylla*
Shrubs	
In the Goosefoot family	*Aellenia* spp.
White-leaf wormwood	*Artemisia herba-alba*
Milk vetch or Goat's thorn	*Astragalus gossypius*
Milk vetch or Goat's thorn	*Astragalus kavirensis*
Hackenkopf	*Calligonum* spp.
Joint pine	*Ephedra foliata*
In the Amaranth family	*Halocnemum strobilaceum*
Saxaul	*Haloxylon salicornicum*
Bean-caper	*Zygophyllum* spp.
Grasses and forbs	
Sixweeks three-awn	*Aristida adscensionis*
Heliotrope	*Heliotropium rudbaricum*

Some Characteristic Animals of the Iranian Desert

Herbivores	
Hamster	*Calomyscus bailwardii*
Dromedary camel	*Camelus dromedarius*
Mountain gazelle	*Gazella gazella*
Sand gazelle or Goitered gazelle	*Gazella subgutturosa*

Cape hare	*Lepus capensis*
Iranian jird	*Meriones persicus*
Wild sheep	*Ovis ammon*
Carnivores	
Golden jackal	*Canis aureus*
Wolf	*Canis lupis*
Caracal	*Caracal caracal*
Pallas' cat	*Felis manul*
Sand cat	*Felis margarita*
Striped hyena	*Hyaena hyaena*
Leopard	*Pantherus pardus*
Ruppell's fox or Sand fox	*Vulpes ruppellii*
Red fox	*Vulpes vulpes*
Birds	
Houbara Bustard	*Chlamydotis undulata*
Coronated Sandgrouse	*Pterocles coronatus*
Reptiles and amphibians	
Desert horned viper	*Cerastes cerastes*
Spiny gecko	*Crytopodion* spp.
Saw-scaled viper	*Echis carinatus*
Arabian cobra	*Naja haje arabica*
Gecko	*Rhinogecko missonei*
Four-toed tortoise	*Testudo horsefeldii*

Some Characteristic Plants of the Thar Desert

Trees	
Whitebark acacia	*Acacia leucophloea*
Babul acacia or Egyptian thorn	*Acacia nilotica*
Gum Arabic acacia	*Acacia senegal*
In the Combretum family	*Anogeissus pendula*
Ghaf	*Prosopis cineraria*
In the Salvadora family	*Salvadora oleoides*
Salt cedar or Tamarisk	*Tamarix aphylla*
Shrubs	
Hackenkopf	*Calligonum polygonoides*
Caper	*Capparis decidua*
Rattlebox	*Crotalaria burbia*
Euphorbia	*Euphorbia caducifolia*
In the Bittersweet family	*Maytensus emarginata*
Mimosa	*Mimosa hamata*

(*Continued*)

Milkweed	*Sarcostemma* spp.
Wild jujube	*Ziziphus nummularia*
Grasses and forbs	
In the Amaranth family	*Aerva* spp.
Sixweeks three-awn	*Aristida adscensionis*
Resurrection grass	*Oropetium thomaeum*
Afozo or Panic grass or Turgid millet	*Panicum turgidum*

Some Characteristic Animals of the Thar Desert

Herbivores	
Blackbuck	*Antilope cervicapra*
Nilgai	*Bosolephs tragocamelus*
Northern palm squirrel	*Funambulus pennantii*
Mountain gazelle	*Gazella gazella*
Indian hare	*Lepus nigricollis*
Indian desert jird	*Meriones hurrianae*
Asian house shrew	*Suncus murinus*
Indian gerbil	*Tatara indica*
Carnivores	
Wolf	*Canis lupis*
Caracal	*Caracal caracal*
Sand cat	*Felis margarita*
Striped hyena	*Hyaena hyaena*
Bengal fox	*Vulpes bengalensis*
Birds	
Indian Bustard	*Chirotis nigricaps*
Rose-ringed Parakeet	*Psittacula krameri*
Chestnut-bellied Sandgrouse	*Pterocles exustus*
Red-vented Bulbul	*Pycnotus cafer*
Rose-colored Starling	*Sturnus roseus*
Common Babbler	*Turdoides caudatus*
Jungle Babbler	*Turdoides striatus*
Reptiles and amphibians	
Fringe-toed lizard	*Acanthodactylus cantoris*
Chameleon	*Chameleo* spp.
Saw-scaled viper	*Echis carinatus*
Northern saw-scaled viper	*Echis schureki*
Gecko	*Hemidactylus* spp.
Indian cobra	*Naja naja naja*
Spiny-tailed lizard	*Uromastyx hardwickii*
Desert monitor lizard	*Varanus griseus*

Australian Warm Deserts

Some Characteristic Plants of Australian Deserts

Trees	
Mulga	*Acacia aneura*
Desert oak	*Casuarina decaiseana*
River red gum	*Eucalyptus camaldulensis*
Shrubs	
Saltbush	*Atriplex* spp.
Felty bellflower	*Bonamia rosea*
Senna or Cassia	*Cassia* spp.
Emu bush	*Eremophila* spp.
Cork hopbush	*Kallstroemia platyptera*
Shrub lamb's tail	*Lachnostachys cliftonii*
Bluebush	*Maireana* spp.
Woolly foxglove	*Pityrodia axillaris*
Bindieyes	*Sclerolaena* spp.
Grasses and forbs	
Three-awn grass	*Aristida* spp.
Mitchell grass	*Astrebla* spp.
Australian daisy	*Calotis* spp.
Windmill grass	*Chloris* spp.
Crabgrass	*Digitaria* spp.
Feather pappusgrass	*Enneapogon* spp.
Lovegrass	*Eragrostis eriopoda*
Yellow billy	*Helipterum oraspedioides*
Spinifex grass	*Plectrachne* spp.
Mulla mulla	*Ptilotus* spp.
In the Mallow family	*Sida* spp.
Spinifex grass	*Triodia* spp.

Some Characteristic Animals of Australian Deserts

Herbivores	
Hare-wallaby	*Lagorchestes* spp.
Euro or Hill kangaroo	*Macropus robustus*
Red kangaroo	*Macropus rufus*
Spinifex hopping mouse	*Notomys alexis*
Fawn hopping mouse	*Notomys cervinus*
Blind marsupial mole	*Notorcyctes typhlops*
Rock wallaby	*Petrogale* spp.
Fat-tailed dunnart	*Sminthopsis crassicaudata*
Carnivores	
Dingo	*Canis familiaris*

(*Continued*)

Mulgara	*Dasycereus cristacauda*
Marsupial mouse	*Planigale ingrami*
Echidna or Spiny anteater	*Tachyglossus aculeatus*
Birds	
Rufous-crowned Emu-wren	*Amytornis woodwardi*
Australian Bustard	*Ardeotis australis*
Little Corella	*Cacatua pastinator*
Galah	*Cacatua roseicapilla*
Chestnut-breasted Quail-thrush	*Cinclosoma castanotum*
Painted Firetail	*Emblema picta*
Orange Chat	*Epithanura aurifrons*
Budgerigar	*Melopsittacus undulatus*
Inland Dotteral	*Peltohyas australis*
Red-capped Robin	*Petroica goodenovii*
Zebra Finch	*Poephila guttata*
Reptiles and amphibians	
Death adder	*Acanthophis antarcticus*
Dragon lizard	*Amphibolurus* spp.
Central netted dragon lizard	*Ctenophorus nuchalis*
Water-holding frog	*Cyclorana platycephala*
Spencer's burrowing frog	*Limnodynastes spenceri*
Thorny devil lizard	*Moloch horridus*
Australian spadefoot	*Notoden nichollsi*
Fierce snake	*Oxyuranus microlepidotus*
Mulga snake	*Pseudchis australis*
Douglas' toad	*Pseudophryne douglasi*
Perentie	*Varanus giganteus*
Sand goanna	*Varanus gouldii*

3

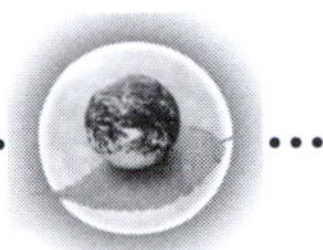

Cold Deserts

Cold deserts, also called mid-latitude as opposed to tropical or subtropical deserts, are distinguished from warm deserts not because they are perpetually cold like the Polar or Arctic regions (see *Arctic and Alpine Biomes* in this series), but because they are cold in winter and much precipitation falls as snow rather than rain. Cold deserts are located almost exclusively in the interior of continents in the Northern Hemisphere mid-latitudes, roughly 35° to 45° N. South America is the only exception. Because of long distances from the oceans, storms have lost most of their moisture by the time they reach continental interiors. Mid-latitude deserts are also in the rainshadow of mountain ranges or plateaus. The Great Basin in the United States lies in the westerly wind belt on the lee side of the Sierra Nevada and Cascade mountain ranges. Deserts such as the Gobi and Takla-Makan in Asia are situated in topographic basins surrounded by high mountain ranges, making them rainshadow environments regardless of wind direction. The Patagonian Desert in South America is in the rainshadow of the Andes but extends east to the Atlantic coast. A third reason for aridity is that colder winter air has a lower water-holding capacity than warm air does, so precipitation is limited.

Landforms are predominantly plains and plateaus, with much bare rock and soil. Fault-block mountains, alluvial fans, bajadas, playas, and mesas are all common. All cold deserts have interior drainage with enclosed saline depressions. Sand dunes occur where inland seas or lakes have evaporated, particularly at former deltas and beach shorelines. Dunes cover relatively small areas in North America and Patagonia but are extensive in Asia. Extensively eroded badlands occur on shale. Because pore spaces in shale or clay are tiny, water does not soak in. Badlands are

Figure 3.1 Cold desert vegetation is a shrub community with grasses and forbs. Salt flats at the lowest elevations only support halophytes. *(Illustration by Jeff Dixon.)*

usually barren with many small, dry drainage channels from runoff. Soils are rocky, azonal, or aridisols. Fine-textured clay or saline accumulations occur in enclosed depressions, but aridisols develop where better drainage allows salts to be leached out.

Scattered shrubs are the predominant vegetation, with an understory of forbs and grasses (see Figure 3.1). Density of undergrowth increases with more precipitation. Where plant cover is 50 percent or more, these regions are also referred to as semidesert or shrub-steppe.

Significant similarities exist in both growthform and genera among the cold deserts of the Northern Hemisphere, a factor related to the geologically recent separation of continents. Eastern Asia and western North America were often connected during the Cenozoic, and during the Pleistocene, a land bridge in Alaska provided migration routes. Many of the same genera, especially low bunch grasses and shrubs, are found in several Northern Hemisphere cold deserts. Common widely spaced low shrubs include sage, saltbush, and winterfat. Bunch grasses include wheatgrass and needlegrass. Differences, however, also exist. Blackbrush shrubs and galleta grasses only occur in North America, while saxsaul and Persian peach trees and *Calligonum, Reaumuria,* and *Anabasis* shrubs only grow in Asia. Patagonia's flora, where sunflower, verbena, and madder families dominate, is more distinct because North and South America have been separated for a longer geologic time period. Cushion plants shaped by strong winds and tall tussock grasses are prominent. Closed saline depressions in all cold deserts are dominated by communities of halophytes with low species diversity.

Climate

Because cold deserts are located in the mid-latitudes, they have a distinct winter and summer based on temperature variations (see Figure 3.2). The annual variation in temperature for cold deserts in the Northern Hemisphere is the most extreme because of their locations in the centers of large continents. Cold deserts are often at higher elevations than warm deserts, up to 6,500 ft (2,000 m). Precipitation may fall in both winter and summer. Plant growth, especially annuals, is abundant in the spring due to snowmelt and water stored in the soil.

Because of the high sun angle and longer days during summers in the mid-latitudes, daytime temperatures can reach 80°–90° F (27°–32° C). In basins that are

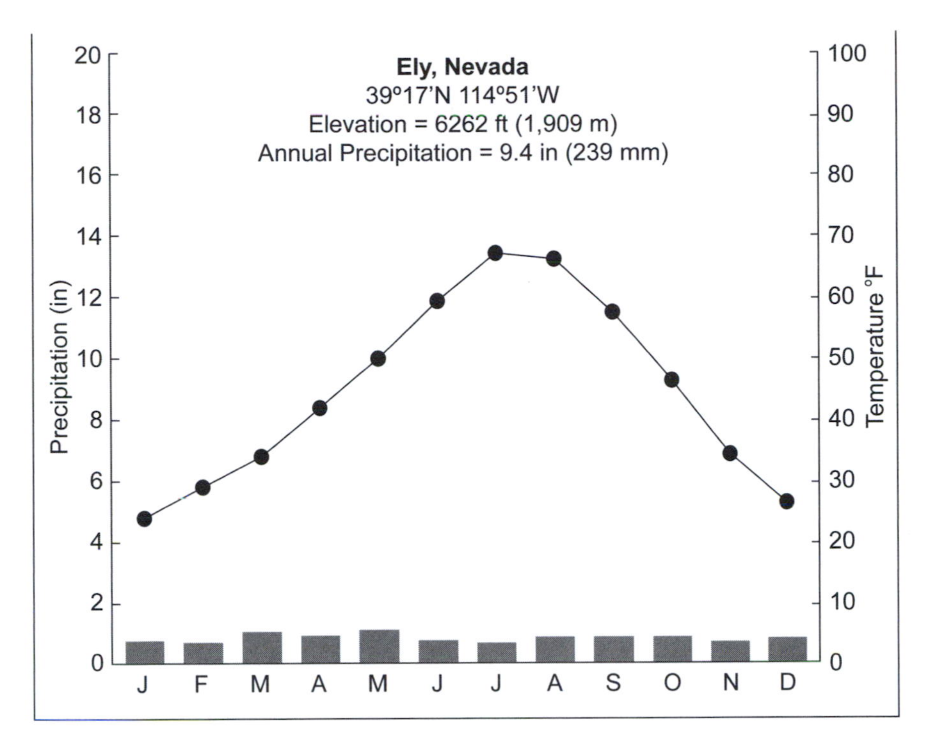

Figure 3.2 Temperature and precipitation for Ely, Nevada, in the Great Basin of North America are typical of cold deserts. Low precipitation and the extreme temperature change from summer to winter indicate continentality. *(Illustration by Jeff Dixon.)*

surrounded by mountains, the additional factor of adiabatic compression and warming in descending air increases the possibility of high temperatures. Extreme daytime highs can exceed 100° F (38° C). Summer nights can be cool, both because of elevation and cold air that drains into basins; temperatures may drop to 45°–65° F (7°–18° C).

While summer temperatures may be almost as high as in warm deserts, winter temperatures make cold deserts distinct. Low sun angle and short days in winter allow little absorption of solar radiation, leading to cooler temperatures. Temperature during the day may rise to only 25°–50° F (–4°–10° C), and temperatures in the highest latitude deserts are even lower. Even though the air temperature is low, however, a plant, animal, or surface exposed to the sun will absorb solar radiation and be warmer than the air. Night temperatures drop below freezing and may be below 0° F (–18° C). Depending on latitude and continentality, extreme cold temperatures can reach –40° F (–40° C). Cold deserts lie in the path of cyclonic storms, and both day and night temperatures are partly dependent on the type of airmass present.

Precipitation in cold deserts is generally less than 10 in (250 mm) a year. In many regions, the majority falls as snow in winter during cyclonic storms. Because of interior locations and rainshadows, the airmasses involved in cyclonic storms contain little moisture. Hot summer days generate convectional storms, but because of the low humidity, the air must rise very high before clouds form, and rain may evaporate before reaching the ground. Because snow falls in winter when both temperature and evaporation are low, snowmelt percolates slowly into the soil to replenish soil moisture. Summer rains in the form of violent thunderstorms cause more runoff than infiltration. Rainfall is unreliable in either time or place, and averages may not reflect reality in any given year.

Common Adaptations

Plants

In addition to being adapted to heat, aridity, and salinity, plants in cold deserts must contend with low temperatures and freezing. Soil moisture in winter is frozen and not available to plants, creating a physiological drought that forces them to go dormant. Shrubs dominate, but perennial forbs and grasses also grow. Rhizomes of perennial grasses store nutrients, allowing the aboveground parts to die back during cold weather or severe drought. Bulbs are common because they also avoid the adverse season and store nutrients. Several common garden bulbs, such as some species of crocus, tulip, lily, and iris, are cold desert plants. Many bulbs native to cold deserts do not fare well in warm climate gardens because they require cold temperatures in winter. Succulents are not abundant because freezing damages plant tissue. Cacti, mostly prickly pear, grow in the Great Basin of North America, but halophytes are more common. Cushion plants occur in cold, windy areas, particularly in the Patagonian Desert. The low, compact form limits moisture loss where wind contributes to high evaporation rates.

Many plants are evergreen and able to take advantage of sunny winter days to carry out photosynthesis. Several shrubs have a combination of both deep and shallow roots, tapping both deeper soil moisture from snowmelt and surface moisture from summer rains. Depending on their method of photosynthesis, plants grow at different times of the year. C_3 plants, which close their stomata and cease photosynthesis during hot weather, grow in spring and remain relatively inactive during summer. Using a different method of photosynthesis, C_4 plants can survive higher temperatures and continue to grow throughout the summer.

Animals

Animals must be adapted to either endure or escape both extreme heat and extreme cold. Adaptations to summer heat are similar to those exhibited by animals in warm deserts. While endotherms (warm-blooded mammals and birds) must maintain a constant body temperature in summer by eliminating excess heat, the opposite is true in winter. They must not lose too much heat to the cold air. Residents of cold deserts have different morphological, physiological, and behavioral methods of coping with winter cold. Because of differences in size-to-mass ratios, coping mechanisms for large and small animals often differ.

Many mammals and birds undergo physiological changes at the onset of decreasing temperatures in fall. Cold-acclimated small animals, including rodents such as voles and mice, along with black-tailed jackrabbit and hares, have an increased resting metabolic rate in winter that generates more heat to the body. In contrast, large mid-latitude ungulates such as deer or elk have a lower resting metabolic rate in winter than in summer, which is probably a function of better summer nutrition, not temperature. Shivering, meaning involuntary muscle contractions, also generates heat but only for a short time. Some mammals have a seasonal increased ability to produce heat internally without shivering. The increased amount of heat comes from metabolization of fat. As temperatures drop, the body is capable of generating more heat from the same amount of fat. Such changes have been observed in white-footed mice, hares, hamsters, and ground squirrels. Other factors besides temperature, such as a low-protein diet accompanying the onset of winter, may stimulate those physiological changes. In Asia, decreasing photoperiod (hours of daylight) in the fall triggers fat deposition in Syrian and Dzungerian hamsters, white-footed mice, and ground squirrels.

Vasodilation in hot climates moves more blood to an animal's skin where excess heat can be radiated or conducted into the air. During cold winters, vasoconstriction does the opposite. It restricts blood flow to the extremities, which are often able to endure temperatures much colder than the body core with no ill effects. A domestic dog outdoors in winter may not suffer even though its nose, ears, tail, and feet are colder than its body. Cold extremities also decrease the difference in temperature between the air and body, which reduces or slows heat loss.

A seasonal change occurs in the pelt of many mammals, both large and small. The thin, sparse summer coat is replaced by a thicker and denser one for winter, decreasing the amount of heat conducted to the air. Shrews, mice, voles, black-tailed jackrabbit, mule deer, and elk all grow more protective fur in winter, shedding it in spring. A pet cat or dog may undergo similar changes in fur.

Several small rodents occupy communal nests and by huddling together may reduce the amount of heat each loses by one-third. Many animals go into a state of torpor, or hibernation, to avoid cold conditions. These include hedgehogs, marmots, ground squirrels, and bats. The body's temperature drops, heart rate and respiration rates decrease, and metabolization decreases to a minimum, all to conserve energy.

Birds are primarily diurnal, feeding and gaining energy during limited winter daylight hours, then fasting during the long, cold night. Because of their small size, birds tend to lose heat quickly, but shivering and a resting metabolic rate four to six times higher than in summer are the major means of keeping warm. Birds usually have little fat to rely on for metabolic heat. Feathers and a down underlayer provide insulation, helping birds to retain heat. Some species undergo seasonal changes as they molt and grow new feathers, increasing heat retention in winter. Birds will use specific behavior to increase the insulation properties of their plumage by contracting muscles that fluff it up. They may also sit facing into the wind to keep the feathers parallel to the body and not ruffled. Nights are spent in nests or roosts in foliage, rocks, or tree cavities where the microclimate is more favorable. Some birds go into a torpid state overnight, lowering body temperature and metabolism until morning, another way to conserve heat and energy.

Most ectotherms (cold-blooded reptiles) scurry from sunny to shady microclimates as their body temperatures dictate. This behavior, however, is not enough for them to survive in cold weather, and most spend winter in a dormant state underground or in protected rocky areas. The desert tortoise in the Kyzylkum of Asia is active only in spring when the vegetation is green and tasty, becoming torpid both during the cold winter and the hot, dry summer. Most insects spend the winter as larvae or pupae.

Regional Expressions of Cold Deserts

North America

Great Basin. The Great Basin Desert, primarily north of 36° N, includes most of the intermontane basin between the Sierra Nevada and the Cascade Mountains on the west and the Rocky Mountains on the east (see Figure 3.3). Although commonly referred to as simply the Great Basin, centered in Nevada, this type of desert also extends north into eastern Oregon and Washington, east onto the Colorado Plateau, and northeast into Central Wyoming. Vegetation is semidesert scrub or shrub-steppe at elevations of 4,000–7,200 ft (1,200–2,200 m).

The region has a variety of landforms. In Nevada it is characterized by fault block mountains, alluvial fans, bajadas, and playas. Except for small sections in the southeast and northwest, the area has interior drainage. The elevation of the alluvial-filled enclosed valleys is high, 2,000–6,000 ft (600–1,800 m) and some of the mountains rise to 10,000–12,000 ft (3,000–3,600 m) or more. Wheeler Peak in Great Basin National Park in eastern Nevada is 13,063 ft (3,982 m). Landforms in eastern Washington and Oregon are basaltic lava plateaus, sometimes dissected by deep canyons, and sandy plains of volcanic ash. The Colorado Plateau consists of generally horizontal layers of sedimentary rock and deep canyons, but even the dry rivers carry water seasonally or during thunderstorms. The Wyoming Basin is a region of deep alluvial fill eroded from the adjacent Rocky Mountains, resulting in a fairly flat landscape.

Few large rivers exist in Nevada and Utah, and most drain to the interior. The Humboldt River begins in mountains of northeastern Nevada, but decreases in size as it flows westward toward Humboldt Sink, never reaching the ocean. The water evaporates or percolates into the soil. The Truckee River coming from the Sierra Nevada empties into Pyramid Lake, another interior basin. Sevier River begins in

Plate I. Wind-blown sand has sculpted soft limestone of the White Desert near Farafra Oasis in Egypt into landforms called yardangs. *(Photo by author.)*

Plate II. Poisonous creatures of the desert include (clockwise from top left) Gila monster, tarantula, scorpion, Cape cobra, diamondback rattlesnake, and death adder. *(Courtesy of Shutterstock. Copyright: Rusty Dodson; Lee & Marleigh Freyenhagen; EcoPrint; EcoPrint; Casey K. Bishop; Aliciahh.)*

Plate III. The Sonoran Desert near Tucson, Arizona, can appear crowded with a variety of cacti and subtrees. Summer thunderstorms darken the sky. *(Photo by author.)*

Plate IV. With sufficient moisture, cacti produce short-lived flowers in a variety of colors and shapes. Depending on the rainfall season, flowers appear in spring to late summer. *(Photos by author.)*

Plate V. El Capitan in Guadalupe Mountains National Park, Texas, forms the backdrop for leaf succulents of the Chihuahuan Desert. *(Photo by author.)*

Plate VI. In northwestern Argentina, a sparse forest of tall *Trichocereus pasacana* cacti fills a valley in the Monte Desert. *(Photo courtesy of Mark Muradian.)*

Plate VII. Common birds throughout the warm deserts of Africa and Asia, Sandgrouse (*Pteracles senegaelus* here), are well camouflaged against desert soils. *(Photo courtesy of Björn Jordan, Breeding Centre for Endangered Arabian Wildlife, Sharjah.)*

Plate VIII. The rugged Sinai Peninsula, shown here in the southern part near St. Catherine's, is part of the Arabian Desert. Tracks lead to a green oasis in the distance. *(Photo by author.)*

Plate IX. Mountain gazelle is a common ungulate in the Sahara, Arabian, Iranian, and Thar deserts. *(Photo courtesy of Björn Jordan, Breeding Centre for Endangered Arabian Wildlife, Sharjah.)*

Plate X. Thickets of *Verbena tridens* in southwestern Argentina are sculpted by wind in the Patagonian Desert. *(Photo courtesy of Keith Sauer.)*

Plate XI. A bactrian camel in the Gobi Desert, shaggy with winter fur, has depleted the fat stored in his humps. With water and feed during the summer, the humps will be restored. *(Photo courtesy of Paul Waddell.)*

Plate XII. The most typical plants of the foggy Atacama Desert in South America are the globular cactus, *Copiapoa longistaminea,* and the columnar cactus, *Eulychnia saint-pieana. (Photo courtesy of Mark Muradian.)*

Plate XIII. The author illustrates the size of an old welwitschia plant in Namibia. The young plant begins with the only two leaves it will ever grow. The red male cones are typical of this gymnosperm. *(Photos by author.)*

Plate XIV. Mesembryanthemaceae (shortened to mesemb) is one of the most varied succulent plant families in the Namib-Karoo Desert of southwestern Africa. Many plants are tiny and may resemble stones. *(Photos by author.)*

Plate XV. Quiver tree, called kokerboom in Afrikaans, is a tree-size leaf succulent, an aloe, growing in rocky regions of the Namib-Karoo in southwestern Africa. *(Photo by author.)*

Plate XVI. The large succulent caudiciform *Adenium socotranum* is found only on the island of Socotra. Given enough moisture from fog or rainfall, pink flowers appear on the tops of the stubby branches. *(Photos courtesy of Mark Muradian.)*

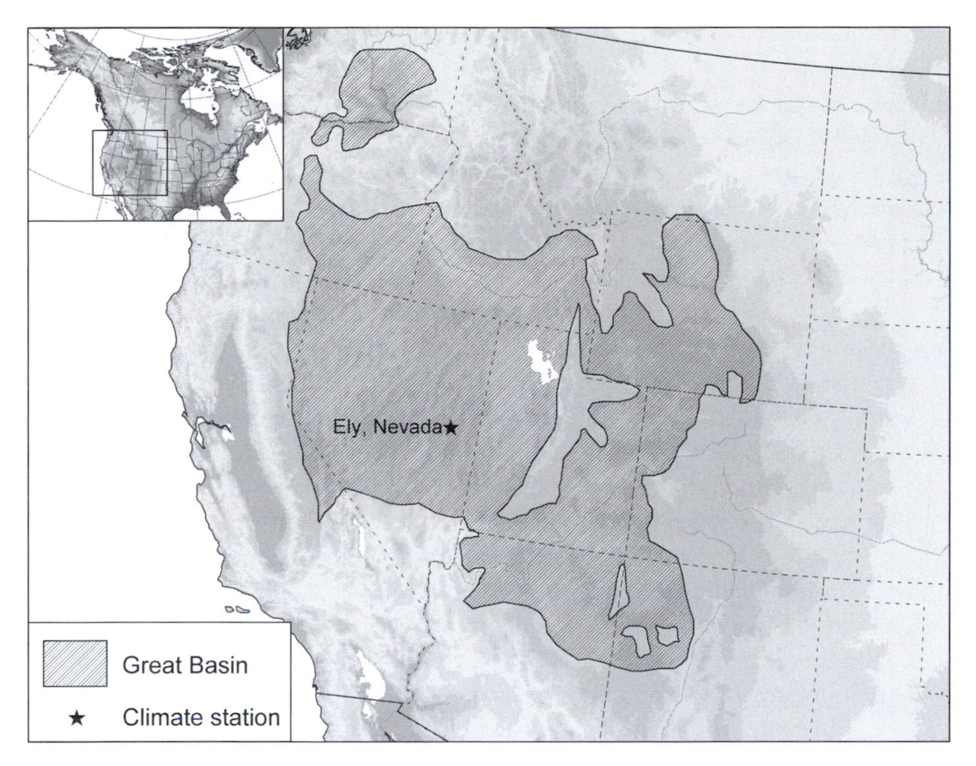

Figure 3.3 The Great Basin Desert is primarily in Nevada and adjacent states, but similar vegetation exists on the Columbia Plateau, on the Colorado Plateau, and in the Wyoming Basin. *(Map by Bernd Kuennecke.)*

the Wasatch Mountains and, before irrigation projects diverted the flow, ended at Sevier Lake, now dry except during rare flood events. The Colorado River drains a small portion of southern Nevada, and the Pit River crosses the Cascades in northwestern Nevada. In eastern Washington and Oregon, the Snake and Columbia Rivers carry water from the Rocky Mountains to the Pacific Ocean. The North Platte River also gets water from the adjacent Rocky Mountains and drains eastward through the Wyoming Basin.

Many of the playas owe their origin to continental glaciation. When glaciers covered much of eastern North America, the climate in the west was wetter than it is now. Many lake beds that are now dry were part of an interconnected river system. As the climate changed and arid conditions of today developed, evaporation lowered surface levels until lakes became isolated. Most dried up completely, but several salty lakes remain. Glacial Lake Bonneville in Utah, 20,000 mi^2 (51,800 km^2) and more than 1,000 ft (305 m) deep, was the forerunner to Great Salt Lake, the extremely salty remnant that was left as water evaporated. Other glacial lake remnants include Pyramid Lake, Walker Lake, Humboldt Sink, and Carson Sink, all remnants of Glacial Lake Lahontan in western Nevada.

Bonneville Raceway

The landscape of the Bonneville Salt Flats, more than 30,000 ac (12,140 ha) in northwestern Utah is so flat and barren that the area is used as a race track. Speeds of more than 600 mph (965 kph) have been attained.

The Great Basin has a continental climate, intensified by high elevations, with both diurnal and seasonal temperature extremes. Daytime temperatures in summer average 85° F (30° C), and nights drop to 40°–50° F (4.5°–10° C). Overnight frost frequently occurs until May and begins again in October. High temperatures in winter average around freezing or slightly above, but may not rise above freezing all day. Winter nights are normally 15° F (−10° C) or lower. An exceptionally cold Arctic airmass can drop temperatures to −30° F (−35° C)

The Great Basin is arid because it is in the rainshadow of the Sierra Nevada and Cascade Range, which block rain-bearing westerly winds. The Rocky Mountains prevent incursions of Great Plains cyclonic storms from the east. The region, particularly in the southeast, receives occasional summer thunderstorm activity originating from the Gulf of Mexico. Annual precipitation ranges 6–16.5 in (150–420 mm), but it is mostly less than 10 in (250 mm). One-half of the annual precipitation falls as snow, which is important in replenishing soil moisture. Although winter precipitation is more common in the west and summer rain is more common in the east, the Great Basin has no distinct wet or dry season.

The most common plants of the Great Basin are spineless evergreen shrubs with an understory of perennial grasses. In general, shrubs dominate on fine-textured or rocky soils, and grasses are more common on deeper loam or sand. Species diversity is low, and each plant community usually has only one dominant shrub. Microphytic crusts of mosses, lichens, and algae commonly cover the ground between shrubs. Cacti and succulents are less significant than in warm deserts, but some cholla, prickly pear, and yucca grow where soils are sandy. Plant communities fluctuated frequently during the Pleistocene as glacial and interglacial periods altered both temperature and precipitation. Shrubs that originated in cold-temperate environments include sagebrush, saltbush, and winterfat. Warmer climate dominants are rabbitbrush, blackbrush, hopsage, and horsebrush.

The indicator plant is big sagebrush, a long-lived shrub (up to 100 years) that dominates on deep soils, and gives the landscape a grayish-green cast. It grows 3–6 ft (1–2 m) tall, widely spaced with an open canopy. Smaller shrubs less than 1.5 ft (0.5 m) high, such as black sagebrush, low sagebrush, and silver sagebrush, are common on shallow soils with a high clay or rock content. Smaller sagebrush species also replace big sagebrush where soils are intermittently flooded. Big sagebrush has both deep (up to 6 ft, 2 m) and shallow roots, allowing it to capture soil moisture from several levels. Because it is evergreen, it conducts photosynthesis all year whenever moisture and temperatures are suitable, allowing it to extend the growing season. Photosynthesis is limited during the summer because stomata are closed during the hottest part of the day. The plant has two types of leaves. New ephemeral leaves are produced in spring to take advantage of moisture from snowmelt. These larger leaves are shed as heat and moisture stress increase, leaving only smaller, tougher ones. Except when summer is too dry, the plant flowers in fall. Germination takes place in late winter or early spring when moisture and temperatures are favorable. An environmental disadvantage is that it is unable to resprout after a fire. In most areas that have been degraded by fire or grazing, native shrubs, such as rabbitbrush, Mormon tea, horsebrush, and broom snakeweed, as well as prickly pear cactus, increase in numbers and coverage because of their ability to regenerate after burning.

Several major plant communities occur according to climate and substrate. Found primarily in the north—the Columbia-Snake River Plateau, northwestern Nevada, and Wyoming—the Sagebrush Steppe community dominated by big sagebrush originally had an extensive cover of bunch grasses. The most important and widespread is bluebunch wheatgrass, but other perennial grasses exist according to geographic area. Idaho fescue is found in the northwest; needlegrass is in the southwest; and, because of more summer precipitation, Great Basin wild rye grows in the east. Much of the original shrubland has been converted to agriculture and the native grasses have been replaced by imports such as cheatgrass.

The Great Basin Sagebrush community dominates drier regions in Nevada and on the Colorado Plateau (see Figure 3.4). Big sagebrush is again dominant, but shrubs are shorter, less than 3.3 ft (1 m) high, and less densely spaced. Because of aridity, grasses are less abundant and herbaceous plants grow in the slightly wetter

Figure 3.4 Sagebrush shrublands, shown here near the Snake Range in Nevada, are the dominant vegetation on Great Basin alluvial fans. *(Photo by author.)*

Cheatgrass

Accidentally introduced into North America, probably mixed in packing material or in crop seeds, cheatgrass from southwestern Asia has become a widespread environmental problem. This annual plant germinates in the fall and spends winters as a seedling. In spring, it outcompetes native grasses for soil moisture and has succeeded in replacing them in many parts of the western United States. The plants become dry in summer, increasing the potential for range wildfires. Although the grass now provides important forage for both domestic and native animals, the sharp awns can pierce and seriously damage mouth, nostrils, eyes, and even intestines.

microclimate beneath rather than between shrubs. In response to precipitation patterns, grass species change from cool-season grasses on the west to warm-season grasses in the east. At higher and wetter boundaries, the sagebrush communities intermingle with trees of Utah juniper, single-leaf pinyon, and large shrubs of mountain mahogany and oak scrub. In Wyoming, the transition is to Great Plains grasslands.

Saltbush-Greasewood communities, dominated by the goosefoot family, grow on salty playas and flats at lower valley elevations. They are also found on nonsaline desert pavement east of the Sierra Nevada where it is too dry for sagebrush. Three concentric rings of halophytic vegetation outline the playas according to availability of water. Shrubs most common in the drier outer circle are shadscale, greasewood, and spiny hopsage. A smaller but still important shrub is winterfat. Salt-tolerant grasses such as inland saltgrass, alkaligrass, and alkali sacaton grow where groundwater is closer to the surface. In the inner-most ring, springs may keep the soil moist, and the main plants are also halophytes, such as seepweed and glassworts. Nothing grows in the dried salt crust in the center of large playas. Blackbrush communities are typical of the lower elevations where the Great Basin and Mojave deserts merge. Usually less than 1.5 ft (0.5 m) high, the shrub is found on bajadas underlain by caliche, a layer of calcium in the soil. It shares the slopes with few plants other than an occasional yucca and prickly pear and occasional grasses, such as galleta, Indian rice grass, and three-awn.

The few sand dune areas in the Great Basin support a more diverse plant community than the saline flats of playas. Shifting dunes occur in Silver State Valley northwest of Winnemucca and Sand Mountain in the Carson Desert, both in western Nevada. Water soaks into the permeable sand where it remains to be tapped by deep-rooted plants. Indian rice grass is the most common perennial bunchgrass, and other plants such as fourpart horsebrush can sustain partial burial in dunes.

The only trees in the Great Basin, willows and cottonwoods, grow along major waterways. In many areas, native trees have been displaced by introduced salt cedar and Russian olive. No riparian community occurs along minor dry washes.

Pinyon-juniper woodland occurs at higher and wetter elevations above the desert scrub, and higher mountains may support boreal plant communities and even alpine tundra, wetter "islands" with 25–45 in (635–1,100 mm) of precipitation rising above the desert (see *Arctic and Alpine Biomes* in this series).

Although many plants have spines or aromatic substances that reduce the palatability of leaves, many large browsers have adapted. Big sagebrush is the main food of mule deer and elk. Mule deer are year-round residents, while elk spend summers in adjacent mountains and winter on the sagebrush plains and bajadas. Other large ungulates are poorly represented. Pronghorn are a unique American genus and not true antelopes (see Figure 3.5). Congregating in small herds, they are curious and often let humans approach quite closely. The animal's hairs are hollow, with large air cells that insulate from both extreme heat and cold, suiting it to a continental climate with annual temperature extremes.

Feral horses and burros still roam the western deserts, especially in Nevada. Both animals damage the natural ecosystem by trampling and grazing, which can destroy native vegetation and cause erosion. They also contribute to the spread of nonnative species by carrying seeds in their dung or hair, and the weight of large horses can cause burrows of small animals to collapse. Both compete with native animals such as bighorn sheep, quail, some lizards, and small mammals for food and water. Burros especially are well adapted to desert conditions, and can walk 15 mi (24 km) without water in temperatures over 100° F (38° C). Like a camel, it can rehydrate rapidly when water is available. However, their hooves and numbers churn up mud and foul water holes. The animal is seemingly oblivious to extremes of temperature and is adaptable in diet, eating anything from cottonwood saplings to prickly pear cactus.

Climatic Transplants

Several species of Russian thistle are weedy shrubs that colonize disturbed sites. Seeds of the plant were accidentally introduced in the late 1800s mixed in bags of imported crop seed. Russian thistle does well in the Great Basin because it is native to Asia in a similar cold desert climate. Each shrub produces many seeds that are actually embryonic plants. Their means of distributing seeds give the plant its name, tumbleweed. When the seeds are mature, the entire dried plant breaks from its root and blows about in the wind, depositing seeds wherever it goes. Seeds can germinate in temperatures 32°–104° F (0°–40° C), a great advantage in a mid-latitude climate. Another introduced chenopod from Kazakhstan in Asia, saltlover (*Halogeton glomeratus*), has become a problem since the 1930s because it is poisonous to sheep. It produces two types of seed, one that germinates quickly and one that can remain dormant for years.

Small mammals are plentiful, and rodents can be seed eaters, browsers, or omnivores. Black-tailed jackrabbits are the most abundant. Sagebrush provides cover for several small animals, such as sagebrush chipmunk, Townsend's ground squirrel, and sagebrush vole. Desert woodrats (packrats) are common. The large-headed kangaroo mouse is restricted to sandy areas, while the canyon mouse lives in rocky areas. Many ground squirrels in two genera include soft-haired ground squirrel and antelope ground squirrel. The Great Basin pocket mouse and several other small rodents are centered in but not restricted to the Great Basin. Many small mammals burrow to escape both heat and cold, and Townsend's ground squirrel aestivates when food is scarce in mid-summer.

The grasshopper mouse is an unusual genus among desert rodents. A small mouse, 4 in (10 cm) long and less than 2 oz (55 g), it is a predator. Although it can and does eat seeds and plants, it prefers a diet of grasshoppers, scorpions, beetles, moths, and other invertebrates. It will also attack and kill other rodents such as

Figure 3.5 Pronghorn are desert-adapted large mammals found in the Great Basin and adjacent grasslands. *(Courtesy of Shutterstock. Copyright: Patsy Michaud.)*

pocket mice and voles. Although no other rodents in the world's deserts are carnivores, hedgehogs in the Old World and some marsupials in South America and Australia that also feed on rodents may fill a similar niche.

Mammal predators on these small animals are coyotes, badgers, and an occasional bobcat, all feeding primarily on rodents. Bears can occasionally be seen in the sagebrush steppes.

Many birds live in the Great Basin Desert. Turkey Vultures and ravens eat carrion. Common raptors like Golden Eagles, hawks, and owls prey primarily on rodents. Sagegrouse, characteristic ground birds, are particularly associated with sagebrush. The bird relies on sagebrush in winter, but requires other food for better nutrition. The Chukar Partridge, a pheasant introduced from Pakistan as a game bird, occupies rocky habitats and eats introduced plants from its home territory—Russian thistle and cheatgrass. They generally do not interfere with or displace native Sagegrouse because they thrive in less hospitable environments. The most common hummingbird is the Broad-tailed Hummingbird. The saline lakes of Nevada, as well

Chisel-Toothed Rat

The chisel-toothed kangaroo rat is especially adapted to not only survive but thrive in saltbush flats of the Great Basin. Instead of the pointed incisors that are found in all other species of kangaroo rats, the lower incisors are squared-off and shaped like a carpenter's wood chisel. It does not store and eat seeds, but depends on the succulent saltbush instead. Before eating the leaves, the rat uses its flattened teeth to scrape off the salty residue. It is the only North American rodent that is able to eat saltbush.

as Great Salt Lake in Utah, with broad marshes and shallow lagoons, attract a variety of water birds, including gulls and many species of ducks and geese. Pinyon Jays are common where pinyon pines grow, slightly above the sagebrush desert.

Reptiles are less diverse than in warm deserts. A large spotted leopard lizard (5.5 in, 14 cm long) feeds on insects and caterpillars, but will also eat other lizards, snakes, and small mammals. The Great Basin collared lizard, also spotted and slightly smaller, can be distinguished by its black collar and preference for rocky locations. The fairly common sagebrush lizard is largely confined to sagebrush areas, while the brown-shouldered lizard lives among both rocks and sagebrush looking for insects. Two species of horned lizards are represented. Common snakes include the western racer and gopher snake, both nonpoisonous, and the Great Basin rattlesnake. Almost no amphibians are in the Great Basin except for the spadefoot toad. Similar to Couch's spadefoot toad in warm deserts, it uses its feet to dig into the mud where it waits out the dry period. Several subspecies of horned lizards, gopher snakes, and rattlesnakes occur in this biome.

Desert Shrimp

Great Salt Lake and Mono Lake harbor a tiny, 0.25 in (6 mm) long, brine shrimp (*Artemia* spp.), adapted to the high salt content of the water. Brine shrimp are an important part of the food chain for gulls, but other visiting waterfowl such as pelicans, herons, cormorants, and terns prefer what they can find in fresh water.

Population explosions of insects can quickly defoliate the sagebrush because the ecosystem is so little diversified. These insects include a webworm (*Aroga websteri*) and Mormon crickets (*Anabrus simplex*).

South America

Patagonia. Extending from 40° to 50° S, Patagonia is the only mid-latitude desert that borders the east coast of a continent (see Figure 3.6). Dry because it is in the rainshadow of the Andes Mountains to the west, it is also influenced by the cold Falkland Current on the east coast. It is a cool semidesert without extreme temperature changes. Plateaus and hills of both sedimentary and volcanic origin are high in the west, 2,500–4,000 ft (760–1,200 m), but slope gently toward the Atlantic Ocean where they end in abrupt cliffs. Most rivers are deeply incised into narrow valleys, and plateau surfaces are coarse textured or gravelly. Almost half is desert, sparsely covered by low shrubs, and 20 percent is semiarid shrub and grass-steppe. Because of strong winds, most of the shrubs are rounded hemispheres with a cushion appearance. Because the region has been heavily grazed by domestic animals since the early 1900s, the landscape is altered. Little is known about the original vegetation because no good prior descriptions exist.

Patagonia lies in the belt of the Southern Hemisphere Westerly Winds, which are consistently strong. Winter is the wetter season because of cyclonic storms. Precipitation decreases eastward, from 12–20 in (300–500 mm) at higher elevations in the west down to 6 in (160 mm) in the lower elevations in the east. It is slightly

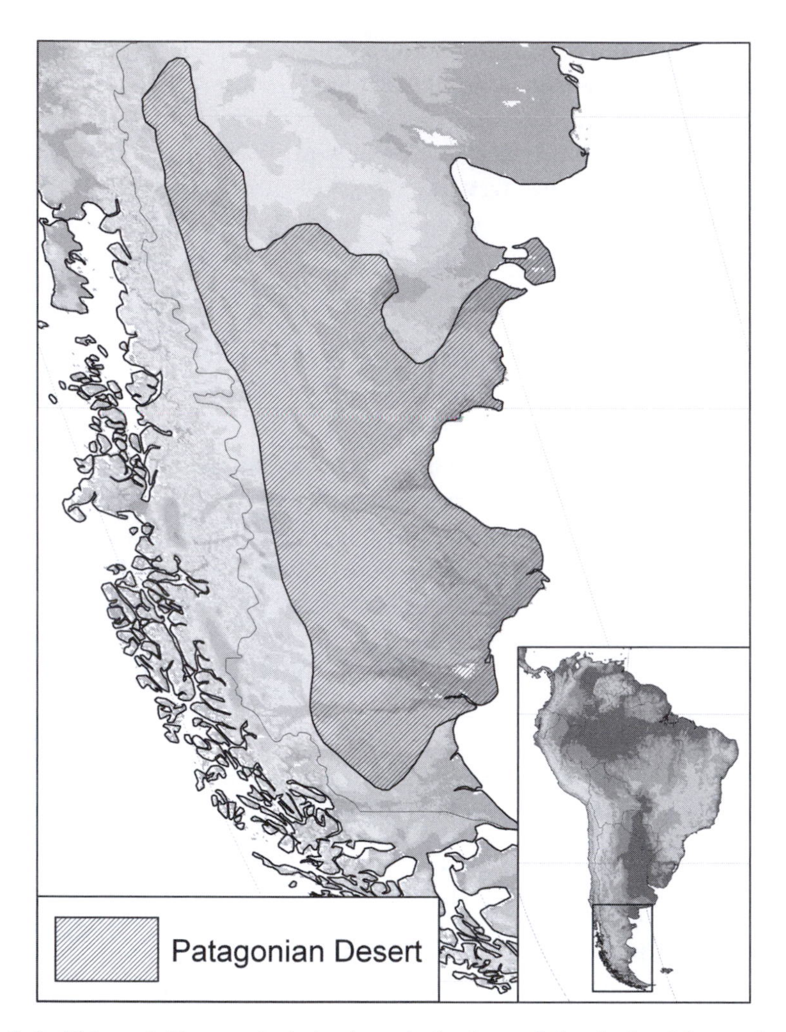

Figure 3.6 Although Patagonia is in the rainshadow of the Andes Mountains to the west, it extends to the Atlantic coast. *(Map by Bernd Kuennecke.)*

wetter, however, 8 in (200 mm), directly on the east coast. Annual variation in all localities can be significant. Because of the narrow continent and maritime influence, temperature changes little from summer to winter. Patagonia normally lacks high seasonal temperatures that are common in other mid-latitude deserts. Summers average 60°–70° F (15.5°–21° C), but daytime highs rise to 80° F (26.5° C), and only occasionally reach 100° F (38° C). Winters are only slightly below freezing, but extreme lows can drop to 20° F (6.5° C). Except for mild coastal regions, snow or frost is possible in any month. Summer drought is exacerbated by strong winds that promote evaporation.

Although three vegetation regions are recognized, two cover only a small amount of territory, either paralleling the Andes or bordering the east coast. (Few plants have English common names.) The Occidental (western) subdivision is a narrow strip along the Andes only 60–75 mi (100–120 km) wide. Because of its higher elevation near the mountains, this wetter semidesert is characterized by grasses. Tussock grasses, especially needlegrass, with spiny leaves dominate. Other important grasses include bluegrass, barley, and fescue. Areas between grass tussocks may be occupied by cushion-like shrubs up to 3 ft (1 m) high, predominantly *Mulinum spinosum, Adesmia campestris,* and *Senecio filaginoides.* Low perennial herbs beneath both tussocks and shrubs are mostly geophytes, primarily rhizomes rather than bulbs. Annuals are uncommon. This region is the southern-most extent of the cactus family, represented by three genera, all with different growth habits. *Mainhuenia* consists of closely packed spiny segments forming a broad, low cushion or shrub, 3 ft (1 m) in diameter and 8 in (20 cm) high. *Austrocactus* is a short cylindrical cactus up to 2 ft (0.6 m) tall, also with long spines. *Pterocactus* survives with a swollen root or underground caudex, its stems covered with many short spines. Most plants are actively growing all year, flowering at the beginning of summer after winter rainfall. A narrow zone bordering the ocean, the San Jorge Gulf district is characterized by dissected plateaus where vegetation varies with aspect and landform. *Trevoa patagonica* and *Colliguaya integerrima* shrubs, with an herb layer of needlegrass and other grasses, form a dense cover (60 percent) on slopes. Severe winds on the plateau sculpt these shrubs and cushion plants. *Larrea ameghinoi*, the southern-most species of creosote, forms a compact wind-sculpted carpet layer.

Covering most of the Patagonian Desert, the Central district is the most arid part. Grasses are less common. The shrub *Nassauvia glomerulosa,* in the sunflower family, is the most characteristic and dominant plant, in places replaced by *N. ulicina.* The northern part, in Chubut and southern Rio Negro Provinces, has two vegetation types. Plains, plateaus, and hills more than 1,300 ft (400 m) are dominated by wind-sculpted shrubs of *Chuquiraga avellanedae* (also in the sunflower family), *Nassauvia glomerulosa,* and *N. ulcina,* with needlegrass and bluegrass. Groundcover is sparse, usually less than 35 percent. Other shrubs, such as *Prosopis denudans* (a mesquite) and boxthorn, occur occasionally but are frequently absent, leaving low cushions of *N. glomerulosa* that resemble rounded rocks on the soil surface to dominate the landscape. Saltbush and seaheath shrubs grow in salty lowlands at 650 ft (200 m). Badlands support the endemic *Ameghinoa patagonica,* also in the sunflower family. The southern part of the Central district, in Santa Cruz, is similar to the north but without *Chuquiraga avellanadae.* It is replaced by *Verbena tridens,* which can form thickets of shrubs 2.5–3 ft (0.75–1 m) high on several landforms, including alluvial plains, rocky slopes, and muddy coastal flats (see Plate X). On low plateaus, 650–1,000 ft (200–300 m), near the Atlantic coast, *Verbena* is associated with *Nardophyllum obtusifolium, Berberis cuneata,* and Chilean boxthorn in an open shrubland with bunchgrasses, cushion plants, and perennial herbs.

Because of the cold and arid conditions, the flora of Patagonia is closely related to the Andes, especially the Puna at 11,000–15,000 ft (3,300–4,500 m) (see *Arctic and Alpine Biomes* in this series). Several dominant genera are common to both regions.

Indicator animals of Patagonia are the mara and pichi. About 28 in (70 cm) long with a short tail, maras are the largest rodents in the Patagonian arid grasslands and desert, where they eat grasses and other herbaceous plants (see Figure 1.6b). They superficially resemble jackrabbits but are related to capybaras and guinea pigs in the family Caviidae. They can hop like rabbits but also walk normally and bounce on all four feet at once. They can be fast, up to 28 mph (45 kph) for short distances. Mated pairs roam the desert grassland together, the male always on guard to protect the female against male rivals and predators. Diurnal, they spend much of the day in the sun and shelter in burrows at night. Although not endangered, numbers are decreasing due to habitat destruction and competition from the introduced European hare. Pichi is a dwarf armadillo, about 12 in (30 cm) long with a 5 in (13 cm) tail. Active at night, its defensive behavior is to pull its legs underneath its body. With its scaly plates in direct contact with the ground, a predator cannot dislodge it from even a shallow depression.

Most rodents, such as grass mice, leaf-eared mice, and coneys, are small. Leaf-eared mice are characterized by large ears. Coneys, also called bunny rats, are mouse-like rodents that are viewed as agricultural pests because they can eat their body weight in grasses during a single night. The only large ungulate is the guanaco, whose numbers have been greatly reduced by domestic animal grazing.

All predators have low populations. Red fox and Argentine gray fox both depend on rodents for food. Pumas are occasional visitors to the desert area, and two small wild cats are about the size of a domestic cat. Little is known about the Pampas cat except that it is found in a variety of habitats in addition to desert scrub where it hunts small mammals at night. It will also take penguin eggs on the Atlantic coast. Geoffrey's cat has a more limited distribution in woodlands and scrublands and is characterized by spotted fur. Unlike the Pampas cat, which is a ground dweller, Geoffrey's cat sleeps in trees where it may feed on birds, small mammals, and lizards. Both cats have been hunted for their fur. Patagonian weasel, hog-nosed skunk, and an opossum are also common predators.

Birds are predominantly cursorials, meaning they prefer to run rather than fly away from danger. Typical are Darwin's Rhea and Patagonian Tinamou. It is possible that strong winds inhibit flying; Darwin's Rhea has lost the ability. Primarily vegetarian, eating plants, seeds, and roots, rheas will also catch insects and lizards. They are capable of running 37 mph (60 kph) and have several evasive measures, such as a zig-zag path, to avoid predators. Birds of prey include Black-chested Buzzard Eagle, Crested Caracara, Chimango Caracara, Great Horned Owl, falcons, and hawks, but none are exclusive to Patagonia (see Figure 3.7). Buzzard Eagles are large, with a wingspan of 30 in (80 cm) and can be identified while flying

Mara Nurseries

Although they are well developed at birth, young mara, called pups, are kept together in a communal den for two to three months. The parents periodically return to the den so the mother can nurse the offspring. She locates her pups by scent, rejecting any pup not her own, and the male drives off other adults while she is tending to her babies.

(a) (b)

Figure 3.7 Two common raptors in Patagonia: (a) Crested Caracara. *(Courtesy of Shutterstock. Copyright: Bob Blanchard.)* (b) Chimango Caracara. *(Photo courtesy of Keith Sauer.)*

overhead by the white underside. Crested Caracaras, also known as Mexican Eagles, are even larger, weighing up to 3.5 lb (1.6 kg) and with wingspans of 4 ft (1.2 m). This bird is distinguished by its black-and-white pattern and a large orange hooked beak. They feed primarily on carrion but are opportunistic and will take small mammals, reptiles, nesting birds, fish, and insects. Although it prefers large animals because of its size, the Andean condor occasionally can be seen eating carrion.

Typical sea birds, such as plovers, sand pipers, cormorants, terns, petrels, and albatross, congregate where the desert meets the rocky cliffs of the Atlantic Ocean. An unusual addition to a desert environment is the Magellanic Penguin population, which lives in large colonies along the Atlantic coast. They prefer to nest in burrows where soil is deep, but will also nest in shallow surface depressions or under shrubs. Shrubs provide protective cover from predators as well. Although the female lays two eggs of equal size, the adults give preference to the first chick that hatches and the second often fails to survive. Commercial fishing has caused a decline in populations by limiting the penguins' food supply and inadvertently catching the birds in trawling nets. Oil spills also kill many birds.

Typical reptiles include several swift lizards and two geckos. The Patagonian pit viper, which is endemic to Argentina, is found in sandy and rocky areas, including beaches. Although it averages only 18–30 in (45–75 cm), it can grow up to 3.3 ft (1 m) long.

Asia

Mid-latitude Asian deserts at 36° to 45° N stretch across the continent from 50° to 120° E

Rhea Fatherhood

Male rheas, not the females, care for offspring. After an elaborate courtship display, the male mates with several females, who then deposit eggs in his nest. Over a period of several weeks, he may accumulate up to 30 eggs, which he then incubates for 35–40 days. The father continues to care for the chicks after hatching and is extremely protective of the young, even adopting lost chicks into his family group.

(see Figure 3.8). Two regions are distinct, especially in terms of climate. The west-central region includes the Karakum and Kyzylkum deserts in Turkmenistan, Uzbekistan, and southern Kazakhstan east of the Caspian Sea. The north-central region covers the Tarim Basin and the Dzungarian Basin in China and the Gobi Desert along the border of China and Mongolia. In the north-central area, the aridity is exacerbated by the strong high-pressure system that dominates in winter. A part of the monsoon system, it blows bitterly cold, dry airmasses over much of the continent. Because this region is dry in winter and spring, plant growth does not occur until after summer rains. The highest latitudes get summer cyclonic storms blown by Polar Easterlies from east to west. The Tien Shan and Pamir Mountains create a natural climatic boundary between north-central and west-central Asia. West-central Asian deserts, from the mountains west to the Caspian Sea in the area formerly called Turkestan, are neither as cold nor as dry. The climatic regime is Mediterranean, where winter precipitation exceeds summer rain. The driest region in mid-latitude Asia is in the center, especially the Takla Makan in the Tarim Basin, with little winter or summer precipitation. The best-studied regions in Middle Asia are in the former Soviet Union; the least studied are in Iran and Afghanistan.

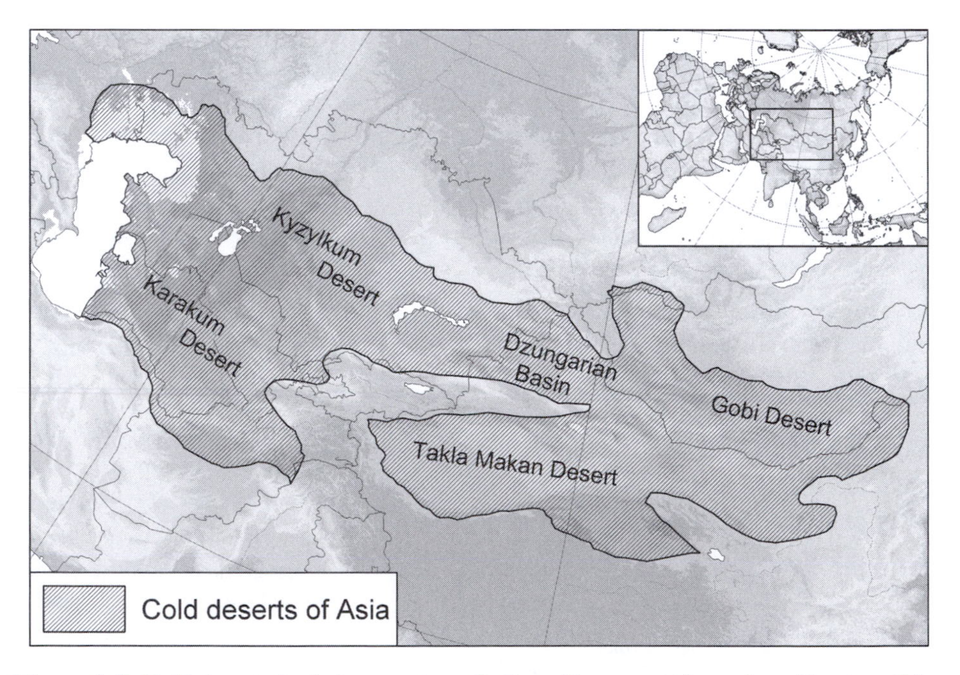

Figure 3.8 Cold deserts in Asia are primarily found in mountain-enclosed basins. *(Map by Bernd Kuennecke.)*

West-central Asia—Karakum and Kyzylkum deserts. The Karakum and Kyzylkum deserts extend from the Caspian Sea east to the Tien Shan Mountains at roughly 35° to 45° N. They are separated from the Takla Makan in China by the Tien Shan Mountains northeast of the Pamir Knot, a major mountain group of the Himalayan system. Major geomorphic units of the Karakum are the limestone Ustyurt Plateau, in the northwest bordering the Caspian Sea, and the southern sand deserts. Foothills at the base of mountains in the south and east are covered by loess, a fertile silty soil. Clay flats, river floodplains, and saline depressions also occur in limited areas. Uplift of mountains in the south and east isolated this region from the rest of Asia, and due to biotic relationships with both the north and south, this area houses the richest desert complex in Eurasia. The Karakum, the most studied and well known, lies in Turkmenistan between the Caspian Sea and the Amu Darya River. The Kyzylkum is northeast of both the Caspian Sea and the Amu Darya River in Uzbekistan and southern Kazakistan.

Both deserts have a variety of landscapes, including stony mountains, sand and gravel plains, bajadas, plateaus, canyons, and dunes, but 80 percent of the Karakum is erg (sand dunes). Salt and clay playas cover only 10 percent of the Karakum. Saline flats are found near the Caspian and in more localized depressions. Playas, created by seasonal spring streams flowing into depressions where the surface is clay rather than salt, are called takyrs. Clay patches and shifting sand support no vegetation. High winds carrying loose sand sculpt rocks into ventifacts, and high shifting dunes (10–12 ft, 3–4 m) are common. Dunes change direction according to monsoon wind flows, moving northeast toward the Pamirs in summer and southwest in winter. Groundwater may be available beneath the dunes. Stabilized sand ridges can be several miles (kilometers) long and up to 300 ft (100 m) wide and 200 ft (60 m) high. On a much smaller scale, shrubs trap sand, forming sand hills called nebkas. Some oases can be found at the edges of the valleys close to surrounding mountains.

The Karakum is still volcanically active, with thermal phenomena such as mud craters. Many highly mineralized hot springs have water too salty and laden with iron oxides to be potable. Most of the region between the Caspian Sea and the Amu Darya River, the Karakum, is black sand. Sands are called "black" only because they are relatively fertile. In contrast, the Kyzylkum is covered with red sand. The desert names are derived from the Uzbek language, "kara" meaning black sand and "kyzyl" meaning red sand. The extensive dune areas are the remains of the ancient Tethys Sea from Cretaceous times, of which the Aral and Caspian Seas are remnants.

In the geologic past, the Caspian Sea was connected to the Black Sea. More recently, during the Pleistocene, it was larger; evidenced by shell beach accumulations found up to 100 mi (160 km) away. Now, landlocked and a center for interior drainage, it continues to shrink, and the soil is too salty for plant life.

A Dying Sea

The Karakum and Kyzylkum deserts are crossed by two exotic rivers, the Amu Darya and Syr Darya, that empty into the landlocked Aral Sea. Diversion of river water for irrigation has caused the Aral Sea to continually shrink in size. Most of the native plants and animals, including fish that were the basis for a once-thriving fishing industry, have been unable to survive the increased salinity. Environmental consequences are more far-reaching, however, including soil contamination and an increase in polluted sediments that are picked up and blown by the wind to other localities, even worldwide. Oases that formerly depended on a higher water table have now gone dry.

Because the Tien Shan and Pamir Mountains partially protect the region from dry Siberian winds, west-central Asia receives winter precipitation from the Atlantic, with amounts decreasing eastward. Showing Mediteranean affinities, most precipitation in the Karakum falls from cyclonic storms in winter and spring, with 4 in (100 mm) per year. The foot of the mountains on the southwestern border with Iran receives up to 8 in (200 mm). Wet soil in spring promotes spring growth of plants. Almost no rain falls in summer, causing many plants and animals to go dormant or at least slow growth. In the Kyzylkum to the north, precipitation is more evenly distributed all year, averaging 5 in (125 mm), but what little rain falls in the long, hot summers evaporates almost immediately. Dust storms caused by unequal surface heating are frequent, about 60 days per year.

Temperatures show continental influence, and winter temperatures vary according to latitude. In the southern parts of desert, especially the Karakum, winters are short, with only occasional light snow. Average low temperatures in January hover near freezing, 30° F (−1° C). Snow is possible from December to February, but prolonged snow cover rarely occurs because winter thaws are common. The northern desert, Kyzylkum, is both cooler and slightly wetter than the Karakum. Temperatures are below freezing for four to five months, and January mean minima are 15°–20° F (−6.5° to −9.5° C). Because winds from the north are not blocked by mountains, cold Siberian air incursions occur several times each winter, occasionally dropping temperatures to −15° F (−26° C). Sudden weather changes are common in spring due to cyclonic storms between Polar and Tropical airmasses. Within a few days, temperature can change from 77° F (25° C) to freezing. Frost is possible until April. Summers are hot in both deserts. Most days average over 80° F (26.5° C), and 100° F (38° C) daytime highs are common. The diurnal range is extensive, as much as a 35° F (20° C) difference from day to night. On extremely hot days, the surface may be 180° F (82° C). Hot airmasses from Iran often bring dust storms to the Karakum. Areas close to and downwind of the Caspian Sea show some marine influence, with more moderate temperatures.

Most of the Karakum has few or no plants, due to salt, clay, or sand. The white salt desert areas are barren, but the black sand areas support some grasses because of higher fertility. No plants can take hold on shifting sand dunes. All plants in the Karakum and Kyzylkum have tiny leaves or no leaves. Because rain comes in late winter in west-central Asian deserts, spring growing and blooming plants are most important. About 100 annuals and geophytes (bulbs) depend on winter moisture for spring bloom, and about 50 more are summer bloomers. Bulbs, such as tulips, irises, and lilies, are prominent. Similarly, rhubarb regenerates from rhizomes. Ephemeral species of grass and annuals in the mustard and sunflower families dominate in March and April, but dry up by the end of May. The composition of ephemerals in any year depends on temperature and precipitation patterns. (Few plants have English common names.)

Perennial plants are strongly associated with soil types. Approximately 400 species in west-central Asia grow on gypsum-rich soils, especially on the limestone Ustyurt Plateau. Many genera, such as false spirea shrubs and *Niedzwedzkia*, and *Borszczowia* herbs, are endemic. Species of beancaper, spider flower, glasswort, and *Nanophytum* are also endemic. Other dwarf shrubs, several of which are thorny or spiny, include *Artemisia* species. Other *Artemisia* species are herbaceous. The dominant community of *Artemisia-Salsola* has more species and is floristically different from that of Kazakhstan farther north. Tar is a common community dominant, along with *Artemisia* and several ephemerals of bulbous bluegrass, carex sedges, and other annuals, particularly at the foot of mountains where water is close to the surface of bajadas.

Salty Water

Water from the Caspian Sea spills over into Kara-Bogaz-Gol, a bay on the east side. Intense heat on the bay evaporates so much water, especially during the hot summers, that the surface becomes several feet lower than the Caspian Sea, encouraging the flow of more water from the Caspian to the bay. As water evaporates, mineral salts continue to accumulate in and around the bay. The salts are noxious sodium sulphate, not sodium chloride (table salt). In winter, the sodium sulphate crystallizes at temperatures below 42° F (5.5° C), giving the water a whitish tinge. The salts redissolve with the return of warm summer temperatures. Fish caught in the current from the Caspian Sea are killed by excessive salts in the bay. Soils are salty even inland from the Caspian Sea because wind blows salt-laden air eastward and high temperatures pull salt to the soil surface through capillary action.

Sand deserts, but not shifting dunes, support many species, more than half of which are endemic. West-central Asia is the center of distribution for *Calligonum,* with 30 species of trees and shrubs. The genus is rare elsewhere. Only one species grows in the Sahara, and only a few inhabit the Caucasus Mountains, Iran, and Mongolia. Trees, either leafless or with tiny leaves, are dominant on sand. Photosynthesis takes place through the green stems. The southern Karakum has many tree and tall shrub species. Two species of saksaul (Chenopod family), white and black, grow in sandy soil in the southeastern Karakum, and the shrubby white saksaul tree is an indicator species for this desert. Growing with sedges on stablized sands, it can be 25 ft (7.5 m) tall. It is often eaten by sheep, but survives by sprouting from its roots. White saksaul has small, scale-like leaves, but black saksaul has none.

The roots of the endemic sand acacia extend 50 ft (15 m), allowing it to reach deep moisture levels in slightly mobile sands. These common trees may be up to

30 ft (9 m) high, but the trunks are only 3–10 ft (1–3 m) tall. The top consists of long branches. Each year when it is too cold or too dry, the shoots or upper branches fall off and new ones emerge the following season. Other small trees, 15–30 ft (5–9 m) tall, include the endemic *Eremosparton flaccidum* in the pea family and two species of *Calligonum* in the buckwheat family. Russian thistle at 10 ft (3 m) and *Ephedra strobilaceae* at 5 ft (1.5 m), both endemic, are also common shrubs. Subshrubs, where the upper portions die back during adverse times, include species of *Artemisia* and *Smirnovia turkestana*, an endemic legume. *Carex physodes* is an important forage plant that forms a turf similar to grass. This sedge begins growing in fall when winter rains start and can reach 15 in (40 cm) high. In areas of thin sandy soils, white salsola and endemic species of *Artemisia* dominate. Many annuals, one-third of which are spring bloomers, thrive on stable sand.

Several genera, especially Russian thistle, seepweed, and saltbush, are found on saline soils with shallow groundwater. Widespread chenopods such as glasswort and *Halocnemum* have adapted to high concentrations of chlorides. Most halophytic species are succulent. Black saksaul is an important source of firewood along rivers and in salty alluvial plains. Salt crusts have little to no vegetation.

While halophytes survive on salty plains, nothing except dessication-tolerant algae (*Desertialgeta*), lichens (*Desertilichineta*), and cyanobacteria grow on the cracked clay surfaces of takyrs. They are mostly barren. Nonsalty floodplains seasonally fed by rain or snowmelt in the mountains support forests of poplar, willow, and Russian olive. Reeds are found on areas that hold water for a longer time. At the margins of the floodplains where flooding does not occur, salt cedars depend on groundwater.

Vegetation on loess that covers mountain foothills in the south and east is strictly ephemeral, dominated by annuals of bulbous bluegrass and thick-stemmed sedge. Species composition changes with geographic location. The landscape, seemingly barren for 10 months, becomes a closed meadow in spring, with perhaps 45–50 species, depending on temperature and rainfall. These ephemeral meadows are used for livestock grazing and provide good soils for irrigated agriculture.

The southern mild winter and early spring is responsible for a change in dominance of plants between the Karakum and the Kyzylkum farther north. Many Karakum plants have affinity to southern deserts, while plants in the Kyzylkum are a mixture of European and Mongolian origin. The Mongolian elements are farther north in Kazakhstan where a physical connection to the Dzungarian Basin exists. Many chenopods occur in these deserts, with 100 species of *Artemisia* alone.

The Kyzylkum, which is mostly sand, marks a transition from northern to southern floras. Because of mountain building and isolation, a large number (approximately 30 percent) of the Kyzylkum flora, both genera and species, is endemic. Perennial semishrubs of saltworts and *Artemisia* are common, especially on clay soils. Stony soils have white salsola and tar. Sandy soils support psammophitic subshrubs such as winterfat and several *Artemisia* species, along with shrubs of *Calligonum aphyllum, Ephedra lomatolepis*, and psammophitic wheatgrass. Spring ephemeral flora is not as rich as in the southern deserts, but tulips are prominent. Halophytic shrubs and herbaceous saltworts and seepweed are all found on salty soils.

Animals are either well adapted to desert conditions or small enough to need little food or space for shelter. Because few species can tolerate the summer heat, most small animals seek refuge in underground burrows where temperature is lower and humidity is up to five times higher than at the surface. Lizards need only dig a few inches into loose sand to find cooler conditions. An additional advantage to digging, especially in clay substrate, is that it churns the soil and allows plants to take root. Most creatures are nocturnal. Many small mammals live on metabolic water, and some can drink water with high salt content. The fauna has a high degree of endemism, especially in the sandy areas. Characteristic animal components are rare and disappearing, and several threatened or endangered species are found only in nature preserves. Little detail is known about animals in the Kyzylkum Desert, but they may be similar to those in the Karakum.

Populations of several large ungulates—including saiga antelope, wild sheep, and onager (wild ass)—grazed the desert before widespread hunting with guns. Now, they are rarely seen. The remaining large animals are goitered gazelle, which spend winters grazing on the sedges, and wild boar, which migrate in spring from floodplain forests along the Amu-Darya River to find bulbs. The most common desert mammals are long-eared hedgehog, long-quilled hedgehog, and tolai hare (see Figure 3.9). Long-eared desert hedgehogs dig burrows beneath shrubs, where they live alone, curled up in a spiky ball while sleeping. They prefer insects, but will also eat eggs, vegetables, and even lizards. At a maximum length of 10.5 in (27 cm) with a 2 in (5 cm) tail, they are small animals. Their long ears help to dissipate heat in hot summers, and sharp spines protect them from predators. They are nocturnal and may travel as far as 5.5 mi (9 km) during the night in search of food. The tolai hare is a brownish-gray animal about 20 in (50 cm) in length with long ears. Common throughout Central Asia, it prefers a shrubby environment where it eats mainly grass and seeds in summer, changing to a bark diet in winter.

The deserts support a variety of rodents, including gerbils, jirds, and several genera of jerboas. Two common jerboas, rough-legged and comb-toed, resemble kangaroo rats in both appearance and habits. The comb-toed jerboa is found in sandy areas under bushy vegetation such as sand acacia. Stiff bristles on the hind toes help it dig burrows through sandy soil. Unlike most other jerboas that have more than one exit to their burrow, the comb-toed jerboa does not. If danger threatens, the small animal digs an escape route as needed. It is nocturnal and may dig a new burrow each day. The front legs are short, while the longer rear legs give the jerboa the ability to make jumps 3.3 ft (1 m) high and 10 ft (3 m) in length. In December, the jerboa digs a deeper, more permanent burrow and goes into hibernation until February when ground temperatures again rise above 64° F (18° C).

Gerbils are active all year, storing food in complex burrow systems. They eat rhizomes of sedges and all parts of black saksaul. The great gerbil, the largest of the

Figure 3.9 Long-eared hedgehogs are found in both warm and cold deserts of Asia, including the Arabian, Karakum, Takla Makan, Dzungarian Basin, and Gobi. *(Photo courtesy of Bj'örn Jordan, Breeding Centre for Endangered Arabian Wildlife, Sharjah.)*

species at 8 in (20 cm) not including the tail, lives in mountain foothills of sand and clay deserts. Their burrows have several chambers as much as 8 ft (2.5 m) beneath the ground surface, where they live in family groups and large colonies. They eat a variety of plant material and can become pests in agricultural areas. Other rodents include long-clawed ground squirrel and porcupines in black saksaul thickets.

Predators include red fox, common to many biomes in the Northern Hemisphere, and two cats about the size of a house cat. The sand cat lives in sandy areas where saksaul trees house nesting birds, although the cat is not adept at climbing or jumping into trees. Special adaptations to sand include long, thick hairs that protect the inner ear from blowing sand and wiry fur on the soles of their feet that give them better traction. They are nocturnal and have an exceptional sense of hearing, able to detect prey moving underground. Food includes rodents, birds, lizards, and even spiders and poisonous snakes. Shallow burrows in sand allow them to escape summer heat during the day. The rare sand cat has become part of the illegal pet trade. In contrast to the sand cat, Pallas' cat lives in rocky desert areas where it sleeps in cavities within the rocks. Its favorite food is small

Baby Hedgehogs

Born with only a sparse covering of soft spines, baby long-eared hedgehogs mature rapidly. The spines grow four times their intial length within five hours after birth, and the babies have a full set of coarse spines after only two weeks. Although nursed by their mother, the young are able to eat solid food after just three weeks.

rodents. Unlike the pupils of other cats, which form slits, the pupils of the Pallas' cat are round.

Predators in the Kyzylkum also include steppe ferret and corsac fox. With its slim body, the ferret can enter rodent burrows to catch its prey. Widespread throughout the deserts and semideserts of central and northern Asia, the corsac fox is slightly smaller than the red fox, about 20 in (50 cm) long with a 12 in (30 cm) bushy tail (see Figure 3.10). They are more social than most foxes, sometimes forming small hunting packs, perhaps family groups, in winter. They do not have fixed territories and may move south to avoid snowy or icy conditions. Not fast runners, they catch rodents at night by jumping into the air and pouncing on their prey.

One of the few year-round bird residents is the Great Tit, which feeds on insects. Also an insect eater, the Lesser Whitethroat is a common warbler that winters farther south and spends only summers in Asia. Common desert birds also include insectivorous wheatears, seed-eating Black-billed Desert Finch, and Streaked Scrub-warbler. The Desert Lark, common in stony areas, eats both seeds and insects and nests in rock crevices on the ground. Larger birds are Black-bellied Sandgrouse and Cream-colored Courser, both primarily ground birds. Several raptors, including Golden Eagle, prey primarily on rodents. A major scavenger is the omnivorous Brown-necked Raven, which eats a variety of carrion, snakes, and grasshoppers. A small scavenger, only 33 in (85 cm), the Egyptian Vulture also eats eggs and preys on small mammals. Saksaul Jay and MacQueen's Bustard are rare but still found.

Figure 3.10 Corsac fox is a small predator in several cold Asian deserts, including the Takla Makan, Dzungarian Basin, and Gobi. *(Courtesy of Shutterstock. Copyright: Eric Gevaert.)*

Several species of agama lizards are typical of west-central Asia, including several toad agamas, so named because their flattened head resembles that of the horned lizard found in North America. These lizards are common in both sandy and rocky areas, and their toes have fringes that provide traction in sand. Gecko genera include naked-toe and even-fingered geckos. Skink geckos are also common. Other reptiles include Chernov's snake-lizard, black-eyed lizard, and the larger—up to 45 in (120 cm)—desert monitor lizard. Typical snakes are arrow snake and cobra. Rarely seen, the desert tortoise is inactive most of the year, emerging from its burrow only in late spring when fresh shoots of annuals begin to grow. It thereby escapes both the hot summer and the cold winter.

North-central Asia. North-central Asia is a series of basins separated by high mountain ranges. Drainage is primarily to the interior, forming extensive alluvial fans and bajadas at the base of mountains. Snowmelt from the high mountains may create rivers at the periphery of the basins, but these rivers do not reach the sea. Basin interiors are either occupied by extensive sand dunes or salty lake flats. Although each basin has a distinctive character, they share many plant species. Typical of sandy deserts are *Caragana* shrubs and sweetvetch forbs. High plateaus of sand and gravel are dominated by several shrubs, including bean-caper, Russian thistle, joint pine, glasswort, and *Artemisia,* often with different species in different desert basins. Salty locales have *Kalidium*, a chenopod shrub, and salt cedar. Gypsum and clay deserts are less prominent than in west-central Asia. The northern part of the region has flora related to the Mongolian region, while the southern part is more Tibetan. Some areas have been more studied, while little detail is known about others.

North-central Asia—Tarim Basin—Takla Makan Desert and Turpan Basin. The Tarim Basin covers 155,000 mi^2 (400,000 km^2) roughly between 35° and 45° N in western China. It is bounded on three sides by high mountains, the Tien Shan in the north, the Pamir Mountains in the west, and the Kun Lun Mountains and Tibetan Plateau in the south. The eastern side is open where the Tarim Basin adjoins the Mongolian Plateau. Elevations are highest in the west, 4,500 ft (1,400 m), gently sloping down to 2,500 ft (780 m) in the east. Stony alluvial fans that slope down from the base of the surrounding mountains are more extensive in the south because more rain in the Kun Lun Mountains causes more runoff. Although the basin is an area of little rainfall and interior drainage, several oases, such as Kashgar, occur around its periphery where springs emerge from alluvial fans. The west and north sides are watered by the Tarim River, which flows from west to east for about 1,200 mi (2,000 km) before emptying into Lop Nor salt lake. Seasonal glacier and snowmelt from the mountains and a low gradient has caused the river to develop a wide, braided floodplain, 50–60 mi (80–100 km), with shifting channels. Water depth may be 33 ft (10 m). The majority of the basin (85 percent) is covered by large shifting sand dunes 330–660 ft (100–200 m) high, the Takla Makan Desert.

However, groundwater flowing through the alluvium may be less than 5 ft (1.5 m) beneath the sand. An eastern subdivision of the Tarim Basin is the Turpan depression, where two extensively irrigated oases, Turpan and Ha-mi, produce grapes and other fruit. The deepest part of the Turpan depression is 505 ft (154 m) below sea level.

The climate is extreme for several reasons. The interior location bounded by high mountains makes the region the most arid in Asia. Winter and spring are dry because the strong Siberian high-pressure system prevents entry of moisture-bearing winds. Summer rainfall comes from the east through the gap in the surrounding mountains. Therefore, the western, higher-elevation part of the basin at the base of the Pamirs receives some orographic rainfall. Annual precipitation throughout the region averages 0.4 in (10 mm) in the east, increasing to 2.2 in (55 mm) at Kashgar in the west. The region is strongly continental in terms of temperature. Although July temperatures average 75°–80° F (24°–27° C), maxima can be more than 105° F (40.5° C) with only 2–3 percent relative humidity. China's record high temperature, 118° F (47.6° C), was recorded in the Turpan Depression. Winters are cold, averaging 15°–20° F (−6.7° to −9.5° C) in January, but because the area is subject to Siberian Arctic airmasses, absolute minima can be much lower. China's record low temperature was also recorded in this area. Winds strong enough to disrupt transportation are common. They are associated with flow around the Siberian High Pressure in winter and downslope flow (katabatic winds) from surrounding mountains in summer. Dust clouds up to 14,750 ft (4,500 m) high can last for weeks or months, often reducing visibility to less than 0.6 mi (1 km), and sometimes to only 160–330 ft (50–100 m). The dust is deposited as loess on lower mountain slopes in the western part of the basin.

Plant diversity is low. Only 120 plant species, and no endemics, grow in the Tarim Basin. Winters with little to no rain leave soils too dry for many annuals. Four major vegetation types exist. The gravel slopes of the alluvial fans at the base of mountains encircling the basin support only a few dwarf shrubs of joint pine, bean-caper, *Gymnocarpus, Sympegma,* glasswort, and *Reaumuria,* with a cover of less than 5 percent. The shifting sand dunes of the Takla Makan, which means "place from which there is no return," are largely barren. Some stunted psammophytes (plants adapted to sand), however, such as scrubby salt cedar or black saksaul trees, and shrubs of *Nitraria schoberi, Calligonum reborowski,* and boxthorn, occur sporadically. Herbs may include *Karelinia caspica* (in the sunflower family) and tall three-awn grass. The sand desert here supports several psammophytes that are also found in west-central Asia, but the Takla Makan has none in common

Grapes and Raisins

The dry interior of Asia may seem like an odd place to grow grape vines that are more usually found in temperate climates. Fields must be irrigated, but the dry, sunny summers are ideal for naturally drying the grapes into raisins. Winter low temperatures, however, are beyond the tolerance of the plants. To keep the plants from freezing and dying, even though they are dormant in winter, farmers slightly bury each long vine in the soil, which provides enough insulation that the plants survive harsh winters.

with the closer Gobi Desert. In some sites between dunes where the water table is close to the surface, salt cedar shrubs and reeds may grow. Vegetation in old river channels and deltas with salty soils is similar to that of the sand dunes but also includes seepweed and saltlover annuals. The salt-tolerant black saksaul is a dominant shrub at the drier edges of the Tarim River riparian zone. Lop Nor dry lake is barren salt crust. In contrast to the sparse vegetation on the sand dunes, river floodplains and oases at the edges of the basin often support continuous forests of poplar and elm. Other common trees include seaberry, salt cedar, and Russian olive. Reeds are found growing in standing water. Much of the original forest landscape has been converted to irrigated agriculture.

In spite of the aridity and sparse vegetation, the Tarim Basin maintains small populations of wild Bactrian camels and Asian wild asses, also called onager. Bactrian, or two-hump, camels were once widespread in Asian deserts, but only 500 wild camels are estimated to currently live in the Takla Makan, primarily east of Lop Nor (see Plate XI). The domesticated population numbers about 2 million. Although larger, up to 2,000 lb (900 kg), they share many characteristics, such as tolerance to heat and lack of water, with dromedary camels, but can also withstand cold winter temperatures. Their body temperature can drop as low as 86° F (30° C), and in winter they grow a long, shaggy coat that is then shed in spring. Like their warm desert counterparts, they can utilize brackish water if necessary. They are usually found in herds of 6–20 animals led by a single male. Elsewhere in China these animals have been extirpated.

Most animals occupy the periphery of the basin, closer to the rivers, rather than the center of the sand dune region. Tarim red deer take shelter in the reeds along the marginal rivers where desert beaver also live. Wild boar also frequent thickets in river valleys. The rare Siberian deer lives in the Tarim River floodplain. Herds of goitered gazelle may occasionally be seen in open spaces. Long-eared hedgehogs, midday gerbils, and Northern three-toe jerboas are common small animals. The Tarim hare is endemic. Tufted Lark and Tarim Jay are the most common birds, but several others, such as Rufous-tailed Shrike, Common Starling, Collared Turtle Dove, and White-browed Chinese Warbler, are also frequently seen. Depending on snowfall, Pallas's Sandgrouse sometimes migrate south in winter. Red fox and corsac fox are common predators, primarily hunting rodents for food. The Steppe Eagle preys on rodents, lizards, and snakes but also will eat carrion. The Qinghai sand lizard is common.

North-central Asia—Dzungarian Basin. The Dzungarian Basin, bounded by the Tien Shan Mountains on the south and the Altai Mountains on the north, is west of the Gobi Desert and north of the Tarim Basin, roughly 45° to 48° N. Elevations are 1,600–3,300 ft (500–1,000 m). Wetter than the Tarim Basin, precipitation is evenly distributed throughout the year, with slightly more falling in summer. Urumqi, in the south at the base of the Tien Shan Mountains, receives 10 in (250 mm) per year. The center of the basin is drier, although no data are available.

The flora and major vegetation are similar to west-central Asian deserts, dominated by saksaul, but north-central Asian (Mongolian) elements are also found in this region. Typical plants are shrubs—glasswort, tar, white saksaul, black saksaul, and Russian thistle—with few annuals. The northern edge of the basin is bare rock and rubble, deposits on the alluvial fans at the base of the Altai Range. The southern edge is also rocky slopes just north of the Tien Shan Mountains. The central part, which is the largest area, is sand desert with saksaul, while the high plateaus in the east support *Artemisia* and Russian thistle shrubs. In most of the basin, both species of saksaul are the most widespread plants, growing on both sand and rocky surfaces. In the eastern-most limit of the basin, however, their habitats become distinct. White saksaul is found on sand. Black saksaul, which is more typical of the Gobi Desert, occupies rocky soils, along with *Ephedra przewalskii*. Tulips and wild rhubarb are typical bulbs. Black saksaul also dominates saline soils where sand and alluvium merge, in association with *Reaumuria soongorica,* salt cedar, and winterfat.

The northern and northwestern regions have plants typically found in the Kyzylkum Desert of Kazakhstan, such as saksaul trees and shrubby tar, *Artemisia gracilescens, A. terrae-albae,* and *A. arenaria.* The true Mongolian elements, such as *Caragana leucophloe* and *Calligonum mongolicum,* are found in the east. The lowest part is the Ebi Nor Basin, a sandy and salty region with white saksaul, tall three-awn grass, *Ephedra przewalskii,* glasswort, and *Artemisia borotalensis.* Little is known about the center of this region.

The most abundant group of animals is rodents, including pikas, hamsters, and several species of ground squirrels and jerboas. The one endemic species is Cheng's jird. Ungulates that may be present include saiga antelope and goitered gazelle. Wild Bactrian camels and wild boar may still exist. Major predators are marbled polecat and corsac fox. Little is known about the birds of the region, but they are probably similar to those of adjacent deserts. Henderson's Ground Jay is common. The Steppe Eagle is a large raptor that feeds primarily on carrion, although it will also take rodents and small birds (see Figure 3.11). Found in several central Asian deserts, it is migratory, wintering in either Africa or India. Two significant reptiles are the gobi gecko and the plate-tailed gecko.

North-central Asia—Gobi Desert. The Gobi Desert lies in Inner Mongolia in China and straddles the border with the country of Mongolia, roughly 40° to 50° N in central Asia. The word Gobi means pebbly plain in Mongolian and refers to both desert and steppe (grassland). The landscape of high plateaus, 3,300–4,300 ft (1,000–1,300 m), is pebbly because fine silt and sand were blown away, leaving desert pavement. The fine material was carried long distances by Westerly winds and deposited as loess in China east of the Huang Ho River.

The annual precipitation of 5 in (125 mm) falls predominantly in summer because the region is under strong influence of the Siberian high-pressure cell in winter. The western region is driest and may not experience rain all year. Unlike other central Asian deserts that are in basins sheltered by high mountains, the Gobi is open in the north to cold Arctic winds. Even though January averages only 0° F (−18° C), clear winter skies admit high levels of solar radiation that frequently raise daytime temperatures above freezing. The thin snow cover fails to wet the soil. The snow sublimates into the dry winter air rather than melting. Summer rain also fails to penetrate the compact rocky soil and results in runoff and erosion.

The primary plants of the Gobi Desert are low chenopod shrubs, species of glasswort, saksaul, Russian thistle, *Sympegma,* and *Nanophytum*. Shrubs in other families include *Reaumuria* (tamarisk), *Nitraria* (bean-caper), *Caragana* (pea), *Calligonum* (buckwheat), and *Artemisia* (sunflower) (see Figure 3.12). The most characteristic shrub is baglur, widespread on gravel in all subdivisions of the Gobi. Black saksaul is the most common plant in sandy areas. The semidesert or desert-steppe, just north of the desert zone, is a transition to grassy steppes. Most common are needlegrass communities with lily bulbs. Annuals begin growth in early summer with the first rains. Oases are few and small, with sparse stands of poplar trees and willow species. Salty soils support herbaceous plants such as reeds, jiji grass, silverweed, seepweed, glasswort, and oakleaf goosefoot. Sandy nebkas at the edges of oases have shrubby tamarisk, boxwood, black saksaul, and *Nitraria sibirica.*

Figure 3.11 Although it migrates in winter, the Steppe Eagle is common to all the cold Asian deserts where it sometimes preys on small birds. *(Courtesy of Shutterstock. Copyright: center, Andrey Ushakov; inset, Eric Gevaert.)* Henderson's Ground Jay is found in both the Dzungarian Basin and the Gobi Desert. *(Photo courtesy of Ts. Dashzeveg.)*

Przewalski's Horse

The takhi, also called Przewalski's horse, is the ancestor of domestic horses. Extinct in the wild since the late 1960s, it has been the subject of several international efforts to preserve the species. Breeding of captive populations, initially only 13 animals, was successful, and more than 60 'wild' horses now live in Mongolia.

Subdivisions of the Gobi Desert share many basic characteristics, plants, and animals and vary only in detail. The Eastern Gobi lies between 40° and 46° N along the Mongolia-China border. The northern part is steppe like, dominated by needle-grass or peashrub and *Artemisia* shrubs. Different plant communities develop according to slope aspect and type of soil. The Gobi-Altai is a region of desert mountains southwest of Ulan Bator with zones of typical desert and desert-steppe vegetation on the lower slopes. The Western Gobi, with only 0.7 in (18 mm) of rainfall a year, is one of the driest deserts in Central Asia. The climate is extremely continental. Temperatures can change 54° F (30° C) between day and night and 126° F (70° C) from winter to summer. In general the Western Gobi is hillier, but the western-most extent, the Dzungarian Gobi, is a plain with many salty dry lakes that get seasonal water from the Altai Mountains. The Large Lake District in western Mongolia lies in a basin between the Altai Mountains to the southwest and the Hangayn Nuruu Mountains to the northeast. Although in rainshadow with little rainfall, the region has both freshwater and salt

Figure 3.12 Widely spaced shrubs are typical of the Gobi Desert, but in summer, the landscape may be covered by ephemeral bulbs, such as wild onions. *(Photos courtesy of U. Bayarsaikhan.)*

Fossils

Miles of rocky landscape support little plant or animal life today, but the geologic past supported many different animals. The sedimentary rocks are rich in fossils of mastodons, rhinoceros, boars, and even earlier, dinosaurs and eggs. In 1923, a nest of fossilized eggs was discovered in the Gobi Desert. Because of its association with dinosaur bones, it was the first indication of how dinosauers reproduced—a significant scientific discovery.

lakes, fed by runoff from the mountains. It is also much colder in winter, down to a minimum of −54° F (−48° C). Both the Dzungarian Gobi and Large Lake District are significant because they have flora from both the Dzungarian Basin and west-central Asia, particularly tar, *Artemisia terre-albae, Anabasis aphylla,* and others. Vegetation in the Lake District changes according to salinity.

The Gobi is home to some rare animals, such as Mongolian kulan, saiga antelope, goitered gazelle, marbled polecat, and wild Bactrian camels. The wild Przewalski horse has been reintroduced. Rodents are the most common mammal, more in the desert-steppe and fewer in the desert. Particularly plentiful are several genera and species of jerboas, gerbils, and dwarf hamsters, each in different habitats. Mongolian jirds live in family groups of 15–20 animals, often led by a dominant male. Although the fur is thin, oils help to absorb sunlight and maintain body temperature. The animals, however, become inactive during the hottest and coldest parts of the day or year. They spend most of the day feeding on *Artemisia, Salsola,* and grasses. Souslik, a type of ground squirrel, and pika are found in desert-steppe regions but not in the deserts. The corsac fox and marbled polecat both prey on the abundant rodents.

Characteristic birds include the increasingly rare Houbara Bustard. Pallas's Sandgrouse, Henderson's Ground Jay, and Chukar are commonly seen ground birds. The Greater Plover feeds on insects and crustaceans in salty lakes in summer, where it also breeds, but it winters farther south. Lammergeier, also known as Bearded Vulture, feeds on fresh carrion, preferring bone marrow. The bird will carry bones upward and then drop them to break them open. Cinereous Vulture, also a scavenger, is a large bird—3.3 ft (1 m) long with a wingspan of 9 ft (2.75 m). It can weigh up to 27.5 lb (12.5 kg). The Steppe Eagle is another common raptor and carrion eater.

Falconry

Saker Falcons can dive at 200 mph (320 kph) to capture ground-dwelling rodents. Although the falcons have no natural enemies, they are a favorite of Middle Eastern falconers, who trap the birds as they migrate in winter from the northern deserts to the Middle East. Juvenile females were formerly preferred, but due to increasing scarcity, both adults and juveniles are now caught and sold, a practice that threatens the viability of breeding population in the wild. Houbara Bustards, the falcons' preferred prey, also have become threatened. Trapped in their Middle Eastern wintering grounds, the bustards are used to train the falcons.

The Gobi Desert has few reptiles. *Eremias* species and *Phrynocephalus versicolor,* a toad-headed agama, are common in both desert-steppe and desert habitats, but *Agama stoliczkana* is restricted to granite areas of the desert only. In spite of low nighttime temperatures, the plate-tailed gecko, also known as a frog-eyed gecko, is nocturnal, able to remain active with a body temperature considerably cooler than that of diurnal lizards.

Further Readings

Internet Sources

Biological Informatics Office of the U.S. Geological Survey. n.d. "Geographic Perspectives, Great Basin." http://greatbasin.nbii.gov/portal/server.pt.

The Encyclopedia of Earth. n.d. "Central Asia Northern Desert." http://www.eoearth.org/article/Central_Asian_northern_desert.

The Encyclopedia of Earth. n.d. "Central Asia Southern Desert." http://www.eoearth.org/article/Central_Asian_southern_desert.

One Earth Adventures. n.d. "People of the Wind and Sand: A Trek across the Gobi Desert." http://www.oneearthadventures.com/gobi/index.htm.

United Nations Environment Programme. n.d. "Deserts as Corridors." http://www.unep.org/geo/GDOutlook/052.asp.

Appendix

Biota of the Cold Desert Biome (arranged geographically)

North American Cold Deserts

Some Characteristic Plants of the Great Basin Desert

Trees	
Russian olive	*Eleaganus* spp.[a]
Utah juniper	*Juniperus utahensis*
Single-leaf pinyon pine	*Pinus monophylla*
Salt cedar or Tamarisk	*Tamarix* spp.[a]
Shrubs	
Low sagebrush	*Artemisia arbuscula*
Silver sagebrush	*Artemisia cana*
Black sagebrush	*Artemisia nova*
Big sagebrush	*Artemisia tridentata*
Shadscale	*Atriplex confertifolia*
Winterfat	*Ceratoides lanata*
Rabbitbrush	*Chrysothamnus nauseosus*
Blackbrush	*Coleogyne ramosissima*
Mormon tea	*Ephedra nevadensis*
Spiny hopsage	*Grayia spinosa*
Broom snakeweed	*Gutierrezia sarothae*
Russian thistle	*Salsola* spp.[a]
Greasewood	*Sarcobatus vermiculatus*
Fourpart horsebrush	*Tetradymia tetrameres*
Large leaf succulents	
Narrowleaf yucca	*Yucca angustissima*
Navajo yucca	*Yucca baileyi*

Cactus	
Buckhorn cholla	*Opuntia acanthocarpa*
Beavertail prickly pear	*Opuntia basilaris*
Plains prickly pear	*Opuntia polyacantha*
Grasses and forbs	
Western wheatgrass	*Agropyron smithii*
Bluebunch wheatgrass	*Agropyron spicatum*
Three-awn grass	*Aristida* spp.
Cheatgrass	*Bromus tectorum*[a]
Inland saltgrass	*Distichlis spicata*
Great Basin wild rye	*Elymus cinereus*
Idaho fescue	*Festuca idahoensis*
Saltlover	*Halogeton glomeratus*[a]
Galleta grass	*Hilaria* spp.
Indian rice grass	*Oryzopsis hymenoides*
Alkaligrass	*Puccinellia nuttaliana*
Pickleweed or Glasswort	*Salicornia* spp.
Alkali sacaton	*Sporobolus airoides*
Thurber's needlegrass	*Stipa thurberiana*
Seepweed	*Suaeda* spp.

Note: [a]Introduced.

Some Characteristic Animals of the Great Basin Desert

Herbivores	
White-tailed antelope ground squirrel	*Ammospermophilus leucurus*
Pronghorn	*Antilocapra americana*
Elk	*Cervus elaphus*
Soft-haired ground squirrel	*Citellus mossis*
Chisel-toothed kangaroo rat	*Dipodomys microps*
Feral burro	*Equus asinus*
Feral horse	*Equus caballus*
Sagebrush chipmunk	*Euatamias minimus*
Sagebrush vole	*Lagurus curtatus*
Black-tailed jackrabbit	*Lepus californicus*
Large-headed kangaroo rat	*Microdipodops megalocephalus*
Desert woodrat or Packrat	*Neotoma desertorum*
Mule deer	*Odocoileus hemionus*
Great Basin pocket mouse	*Perognathus parvus*
Canyon mouse	*Peromyscus crinitus*
Townsend's ground squirrel	*Spermophilus townsendii*
Carnivores	
Coyote	*Canis latrans*
Bobcat	*Lynx rufus*
White-bellied grasshopper mouse	*Onychomys leucogaster*

Birds	
Chukar Partridge	*Alectoris chukar*[a]
Golden Eagle	*Aquila chrysaetos*
Great Horned Owl	*Bubo virginianus pacificus*
Western Red-tailed Hawk	*Buteo jamaicensis*
Turkey Vulture	*Cathartes aura*
Sagegrouse	*Centrocercus urophasianus*
Common Raven	*Corvus corax*
Pinyon Jay	*Gymnorhinus cyanocephalus*
Broad-tailed Hummingbird	*Selasphorus platycercus*
Reptiles and amphibians	
Western racer	*Coluber mormon*
Great Basin rattlesnake	*Crotalus viridis lutosus*
Great Basin collared lizard	*Crotaphytus bicinctores*
Long-nosed leopard lizard	*Gambelia wislizeni*
Short-horned lizard	*Phrynosoma douglasi*
Desert horned lizard	*Phrynosoma platyrhinos*
Great Basin gopher snake	*Pituophis catenifer deserticola*
Great Basin spadefoot toad	*Scaphiopus intermontanus*
Sagebrush lizard	*Sceloporus graciosus*
Sideblotched lizard	*Uta stansburiana*

Note: [a]Introduced.

South American Cold Deserts

Some Characteristic Plants of the Patagonian Desert

Shrubs	
In the Pea family	*Adesmia campestris*
Saltbush	*Atriplex* spp.
In the Berber family	*Berberis cuneata*
In the Sunflower family	*Chuquiraga avellanedae*
In the Euphorbia family	*Colliguaya integerrima*
Seaheath	*Frankenia patagonica*
Creosote bush or Jarilla	*Larrea ameghinoi*
Boxthorn	*Lycium ameghinoi*
Chilean boxthorn	*Lycium chilense*
In the Carrot family	*Mulinum spinosum*
In the Sunflower family	*Nardophyllum obtusifolium*
In the Sunflower family	*Nassauvia glomerulosa*
In the Sunflower family	*Nassauvia ulicina*
Mesquite	*Prosopis denudans*
In the Sunflower family	*Senecio flaginoides*
In the Buckthorn family	*Trevoa patagonica*
Verbena	*Verbena tridens* = *Junellia tridens*

Cactus	
Austrocactus	*Austrocactus* spp.
Maihuenia	*Maihuenia patagonica*
Pterocactus	*Pterocactus* spp.
Grasses and forbs	
In the Sunflower family	*Ameghinoa patagonica*
Fescue grass	*Festuca* spp.
Barley	*Hordeum* spp.
Bluegrass	*Poa* spp.
Needlegrass	*Stipa humilis*
Needlegrass	*Stipa speciosa*

Some Characteristic Animals of the Patagonian Desert

Herbivores	
Grass mouse	*Akodon* spp.
Mara or Cavy	*Dolichotis patagonum*
Guanaco	*Lama guanicoe*
European hare	*Lepus europaeus*[a]
Leaf-eared mouse	*Phyllotis* spp.
Coney or Bunny rat	*Reithrodon* spp.
Carnivores	
Hog-nosed skunk	*Conepatus humboldtii*
Puma	*Felis concolor*
Pampas cat	*Leopardus colocolo*
Geoffrey's cat	*Leopardus geoffreyi*
Opossum	*Lestodelphys halli*
Patagonian weasel	*Lyncodon patagonicus*
Red fox	*Pseudolopex culpaeus*
Argentine gray fox	*Pseudolopex griseus*
Pichi or Armadillo	*Zaedyus pichiy*
Birds	
Great Horned Owl	*Bubo virginianus pacificus*
Black-chested Buzzard Eagle	*Geranoaetus melanoleucus*
Chimango Caracara	*Milvago chimango*
Crested Caracara	*Polyborus plancus*
Darwin's Rhea	*Pterocnemia pennata*
Magellanic Penguin	*Spheniscus magellanicus*
Patagonian Tinamou	*Tinamotis ingoufi*
Andean Condor	*Vultur gyphus*
Reptiles and amphibians	
Patagonian pit viper	*Bothrops ammodytoides*
Darwin's gecko	*Homonota darwini*

(*Continued*)

Borelli's gecko	*Homonota borellii*
Swift lizards	*Liolaemus* spp.

Note: [a]Introduced.

Asian Cold Deserts

Some Characteristic Plants of the Karakum Desert

Trees	
Sand acacia	*Ammodendron conollyi*
In the Buckwheat family	*Calligonum arborescens*
Russian olive	*Eleaganus angustifolia*
In the Pea family	*Eremosparton flaccidum*
Black saksaul	*Haloxylon ammondendron*
White saksaul	*Haloxylon persicum*
Poplar	*Populus* spp.
Willow	*Salix* spp.
Salt cedar or Tamarisk	*Tamarix* spp.
Shrubs	
Glasswort	*Anabasis* spp.
Artemisia	*Artemisia arenicola*
Artemisia	*Artemisia diffusa*
Artemisia	*Artemisia dimoana*
Artemisia	*Artemisia kemrudica*
Saltbush	*Atriplex* spp.
In the Goosefoot family	*Borszczowia* spp.
In the Buckwheat family	*Calligonum* spp.
Joint pine	*Ephedra strobilaceae*
In the Amaranth family	*Halocnemum strobilaceum*
Tar	*Nanophytum erinaceum*
White salsola	*Salsola arbusculae*
Russian thistle	*Salsola richteri*
In the Pea family	*Smirnovia turkestana*
False spirea	*Spiraeanthus* spp.
Bean-caper	*Zygophyllum* spp.
Bulbs and rhizomes	
Fox-tail lily	*Eremurus* spp.
Tuberous geranium	*Geranium tuberosum*
Iris	*Iris longiscapa*
Iris	*Iris songarica*
Rhubarb	*Rheum spp.*
Tulip	*Tulipa sogdiana*
Grasses and forbs	
In the Sunflower family	*Amberboa* spp.
Brome grass	*Bromus* spp.
Thick-stemmed sedge	*Carex pachystylis*

Sedge	*Carex pysodes*
Spider flower	*Cleome* spp.
In the Sunflower family	*Koelpinia* spp.
In the Mustard family	*Malcomia* spp.
In the Begonia family	*Niedzwedzkia* spp.
Bulbous bluegrass	*Poa bulbosa*
Pickleweed or Glasswort	*Salicornia herbaceae*
Seepweed	*Suaeda* spp.

Some Characteristic Animals of the Karakum Desert[a]

Herbivores	
Rough-legged jerboa or Northern three-toed jerboa	*Dipus sagitta*
Onager or Wild ass	*Equus hemionus*
Jerboa	*Eremodipus* spp.
Goitered gazelle	*Gazella subgutturosa*
Porcupine	*Hystrix hystrix*
Tolai hare	*Lepus tolai*
Jird	*Meriones* spp.
Wild sheep	*Ovis orientalis*
Comb-toed jerboa	*Paradipus ctenodactylus*
Great gerbil	*Rhombomys opimus*
Saiga antelope	*Saiga tatarica*
Three-toed pygmy jerboa	*Salpingotus heptneri*
Long-clawed ground squirrel	*Spermophilopsis leptodactylus*
Wild boar	*Sus scrofa*
Carnivores	
Sand cat	*Felis margarita*
Long-eared hedgehog	*Hemiechinus auritus*
Pallas' cat	*Otocolobus manul*
Long-quilled hedgehog	*Piracohinus hypomelas*
Red fox	*Vulpes vulpes*
Birds	
Desert Lark	*Ammomanes deserti*
Golden Eagle	*Aquila chrysaetos*
Steppe Eagle	*Aquila nipalensis*
MacQueen's Bustard	*Chlamydotis macqueenii*
Brown-necked Raven	*Corvus ruficollis*
Cream-colored Courser	*Cursorius cursor*
Egyptian Vulture	*Neophron percnopterus*
Wheatear	*Oenanthe deserti*
Great Tit	*Parus major*
Saksaul Jay	*Podoces panderi*

(*Continued*)

Black-bellied Sandgrouse	*Pterocles orientalis*
Streaked Scrub-warbler	*Scotocerca inquieta*
Lesser Whitethroat	*Sylvia curruca*
Reptiles and amphibians	
Southern even-fingered gecko	*Alsophylax laevis*
Kaspischer's even-fingered gecko	*Alsophylax pipiens*
Black-eyed lizard	*Eremias nigrocellata*
Naked-toe gecko	*Gymnodactylus caspius*
Cobra	*Naja naja*
Chernov's snake-lizard	*Ophiomorus chernovi*
Spotted toad agama lizard	*Phrynocephalus macalatus*
Khentau toad agama lizard	*Phrynocephalus rossikowi*
Strauch's toad agama lizard	*Phrynocephalus strauchi*
Arrow snake	*Psammophis lineolatus*
Skink gecko	*Teratoscincus scincus*
Desert tortoise	*Testudo horsfeldi*
Desert monitor lizard	*Varanus griseus*

Note: [a]May also occur in the Kyzylkum Desert.

Some Characteristic Plants of the Kyzylkum Desert

Trees	
Black saksaul	*Haloxylon ammondendron*
White saksaul	*Haloxylon persicum*
Shrubs	
Glasswort	*Anabasis aphylla*
Wormwood	*Artemisia arenaria*
Artemisia	*Artemisia gracilescens*
Artemisia	*Artemisia gurganica*
Artemisia	*Artemisia santolina*
Artemisia	*Artemisia songarica*
Artemisia	*Artemisia terrae albae*
Saltbush	*Atriplex* spp.
In the Buckwheat family	*Calligonum aphyllum*
Winterfat	*Ceratoides papposa*
Joint pine	*Ephedra lomatolepis*
In the Goosefoot family	*Halocnemum strobilaceum*
In the Goosefoot family	*Kalidium folitum*
Tar	*Nanophytum erinaceum*
White salsola	*Salsola arbusculae formis*
Bulbs and rhizomes	
Tulip	*Tulipa greigii*
Tulip	*Tulipa sogdiana*

Grasses and forbs	
Wheatgrass	*Agropyron fragile*
Saltwort	*Climacoptera* spp.
Saltwort	*Petrosimonia* spp.
Seepweed	*Suaeda* spp.

Some Characteristic Plants of the Takla Makan Desert

Trees	
Russian olive	*Eleaganus* spp.
Black saksaul	*Haloxylon ammondendron*
Seaberry	*Hippophae rhamoides*
Poplar	*Populus diversifolia*
Salt cedar or Tamarisk	*Tamarix* spp.
Elm	*Ulmus pumila*
Shrubs	
Glasswort	*Anabasis* spp.
Artemisia	*Artemisia* spp.
In the Buckwheat family	*Calligonum reborowski*
Peashrub	*Caragana* spp.
Joint pine	*Ephedra strobilaceae*
In the Pink family	*Gymnocarpus* spp.
In the Goosefoot family	*Kalidium* spp.
Boxthorn	*Lycium aphyllum*
In the Nitraria family	*Nitraria schoberi*
In the Tamarisk family	*Reaumuria* spp.
Russian thistle	*Salsola* spp.
In the Amaranth family	*Sympegma regelii*
Bean-caper	*Zygophyllum* spp.
Grasses and forbs	
Saltlover	*Halogeton glomeratus*
Sweetvetch	*Hedysarum* spp.
In the Sunflower family	*Karelina caspica*
Reed	*Phragmites communus*
Tall three-awn grass	*Stipagrostis pennata*
Seepweed	*Suaeda* spp.

Some Characteristic Animals of the Takla Makan Desert

Herbivores	
Bactrian camel	*Camelus bactrianus*
Siberian deer	*Capreolus pygargus*
Desert beaver	*Castor fiber birulai*

(*Continued*)

Tarim red deer	*Cervus elaphus yarkandensis*
Northern three-toe jerboa	*Dipus sagitta*
Onager or Wild ass	*Equus hemionus*
Goitered gazelle	*Gazella subgutturosa*
Tarim hare	*Lepus yarkandensis*
Midday jird	*Meriones meridianus*
Wild boar	*Sus scrofa*
Carnivores	
Long-eared hedgehog	*Hemiechinus auritus*
Corsac fox	*Vulpes corsac*
Red fox	*Vulpes vulpes*
Birds	
Steppe Eagle	*Aquila nipalensis*
Rufous-tailed Shrike	*Lanius isabellinus*
Desert Finch	*Rhodopechys obsolete*
White-browed Chinese Warbler	*Rhopophilus pekinensis*
Collared Turtle Dove	*Streptopelia decaocto*
Common Starling	*Sturnus vulgaris*
Pallas's Sandgrouse	*Syrrhaptes paradoxus*
Reptiles and amphibians	
Qinghai sand lizard	*Phrynocephalus vlangalii*

Some Characteristic Plants of the Dzungarian Basin Desert

Trees	
Black saksaul	*Haloxylon ammondendron*
White saksaul	*Haloxylon persicum*
Salt cedar or Tamarisk	*Tamarix* spp.
Shrubs	
Glasswort	*Anabasis aphylla*
Glasswort	*Anabasis salsa*
Wormwood	*Artemisia arenaria*
Artemisia	*Artemisia borotalensis*
Artemisia	*Artemisia gracilescens*
Artemisia	*Artemisia terrae albae*
In the Buckwheat family	*Calligonum mongolicum*
Peashrub	*Caragana leucophloea*
Winterfat	*Ceratoides papposa*
Joint pine	*Ephedra przewalskii*
In the Goosefoot family	*Kalidium* spp.
Tar	*Nanophophytum erinaceum*
In the Tamarisk family	*Reaumuria soongorica*

White salsola	*Salsola arbusculae*
Salsola	*Salsola rigida*
In the Amaranth family	*Sympegma regelii*
Bean-caper	*Zygophyllum* spp.
Bulbs and rhizomes	
Rhubarb	*Rheum* spp.
Tulip	*Tulipa* spp.
Grasses and forbs	
Sweetvetch	*Hedysarum* spp.
Tall three-awn grass	*Stipagrostis pennata*

Some Characteristic Animals of the Dzungarian Basin Desert

Herbivores	
Bactrian camel	*Camelus bactrianus*
Ground squirrel	*Citellus* spp.
Northern three-toed jerboa	*Dipus sagitta*
Onager or Wild ass	*Equus hemionus*
Goitered gazelle	*Gazella subgutturosa*
Cheng's jird	*Meriones chengi*
Mongolian pika	*Ochotona pallasii*
Dzungarian dwarf hamster	*Phodopus* spp.
Saiga antelope	*Saiga tatarica*
Wild boar	*Sus scrofa*
Carnivores	
Long-eared hedgehog	*Hemiechinus auritus*
Marbled polecat	*Vormela peregusna*
Corsac fox	*Vulpes corsac*
Birds	
Chukar Partridge	*Alectoris chukar*
Steppe Eagle	*Aquila nipalensis*
Greater Plover	*Charadrius leschenaultii*
MacQueen's Bustard	*Chlamydotis macqueenii*
Saker Falcon	*Falco cherrug*
Lammergeier or Bearded Vulture	*Gypaetus barbatus*
Henderson's Ground Jay	*Podoces hendersoni*
Common Starling	*Sturnus vulgaris*
Pallas's Sandgrouse	*Syrrhaptes paradoxus*
Reptiles and amphibians	
Gobi gecko	*Cyrtapodion elongatus*
Plate-tailed gecko	*Teratoscincus przewalskii*

Some Characteristic Plants of the Gobi Desert

Trees	
Black saksaul	*Haloxylon ammondendron*
Downy poplar	*Populus diversifolia*
Willow	*Salix* spp.
Salt cedar or Tamarisk	*Tamarix ramosissima*
Shrubs	
Glasswort	*Anabasis aphylla*
Baglur	*Anabasis brevifolia*
Fringed sagebrush	*Artemisia frigida*
Artemisia	*Artemisia rutifolia*
Artemisia	*Artemisia terrae albae*
In the Buckwheat family	*Calligonum mongolicum*
Peashrub	*Caragana bungei*
Peashrub	*Caragana leucophloea*
Joint pine	*Ephedra* spp.
In the Goosefoot family	*Kalidium folitum*
Boxwood	*Lycium ruthenicum*
Tar	*Nanophytum erinaceum*
In the Nitraria family	*Nitraria sibirica*
In the Tamarisk family	*Reaumuria soongorica*
Russian thistle	*Salsola passerina*
In the Amaranth family	*Sympegma regelii*
Bean-caper	*Zygophyllum* spp.
Bulbs and rhizomes	
In the Lily family	*Allium mongolicum*
In the Lily family	*Allium polyrrhizum*
Grasses and forbs	
Jiji grass	*Achnatherum splendens*
Oakleaf goosefoot	*Chenopodium glaucum*
Sweetvetch	*Hedysarum* spp.
Reed	*Phragmites australis*
Silverweed	*Potentilla anserina*
Glasswort or Pickleweed	*Salicornia* spp.
Needlegrass	*Stipa gobica*
Needlegrass	*Stipa orientalis*
Seepweed	*Suaeda* spp.

Some Characteristic Animals of the Gobi Desert

Herbivores	
Jerboa	*Allactaga* spp.
Jerboa	*Alactagulus* spp.
Dwarf hamster	*Allocricetulus* spp.

Mongolian kulan	*Asinus hemionus*
Bactrian camel	*Camelus bactrianus*
Jerboa	*Cardiocranius* spp.
Souslik or Ground squirrel	*Citellus erythrogenys*
Ratlike hamster	*Cricetulus* spp.
Jerboa	*Dipus* spp.
Przewalski's horse or Takhi	*Equus przewalskii*
Goitered gazelle	*Gazella subgutturosa*
Long-eared hedgehog	*Hemiechinus auritus*
Mongolian jird	*Meriones unguiculatus*
Mongolian pika	*Ochotona pallasii*
Hamster	*Phodopus* spp.
Gerbil	*Rhombomys* spp.
Saiga antelope	*Saiga tatarica*
Jerboa	*Salpingotus* spp.
Carnivores	
Pallas' cat	*Felis manul*
Marbled polecat	*Vormela peregusna*
Corsac fox	*Vulpes corsac*
Birds	
Cinereous Vulture	*Aegypius monachus*
Chukar Partridge	*Alectoris chukar*
Steppe Eagle	*Aquila nipalensis*
Greater Plover	*Charadrius leschenaultii*
Houbara Bustard	*Chlamydotis undulata*
Saker Falcon	*Falco cherrug*
Lammergeier or Bearded Vulture	*Gypaetus barbatus*
Henderson's Ground Jay	*Podoces hendersoni*
Pallas's Sandgrouse	*Syrrhaptes paradoxus*
Reptiles and amphibians	
Agama lizard	*Agama stoliczkana*
Lizard	*Eremias* spp.
Toad-head lizard	*Phrynocephalus versicolor*
Plate-tailed gecko or Frog-eyed gecko	*Teratoscincus przewalskii*

4

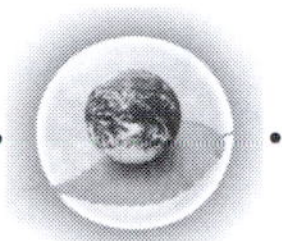

West-Coast Fog Deserts

Deserts occupy coastal areas in a number of world locations. Parts of the Sahara, Arabian, and Southwest Asian deserts are adjacent to the ocean, specifically around the Red Sea and Persian Gulf. Like their inland counterparts, coastal deserts in those regions experience little cloud cover, rain, or fog; the primary difference is somewhat milder temperatures and higher humidity. This chapter focuses on west-coast deserts that have frequent fog as well as mild summer and winter temperatures, all caused by cold ocean currents offshore. Cold currents bring water from poleward locations toward the Equator. Between approximately 8° and 33° latitude in both hemispheres, cold currents are close to the west coasts of continents. The cold water is intensified where the cold current turns westward out to sea, causing upwelling of deeper, even colder seawater. The west coasts of Baja California, Peru, Chile, and southwestern Africa are especially affected. It may seem odd to talk about foggy deserts, but the key concept is that little rain falls. Most plants and animals must be adapted to dry conditions in spite of the occurrence of fog.

Climate

These cool, coastal deserts have little rainfall because they experience a temperature inversion that causes fog. Normally, temperature is lower at higher altitudes, but in an inversion, the opposite is true. It is cold at the surface and temperature increases with altitude. Inversions may result from different phenomena, but the most common cause in these coastal deserts is advection. Advection refers to horizontally moving air, or simply wind. Water evaporates into the warm air, especially in summer when both the air and the ocean are warmer. Westerly winds blow the warm, humid air over the cold current. The lower layer of the warm air becomes cooler because of contact with the cold current, causing an advection inversion, with cold air underneath warm air. Water vapor in the cooler air over the cold current then condenses into fog, and westerly winds blow both the cooler air and fog eastward onto the land. The upper air contains little water vapor, and because ground temperatures are not hot, no convection can carry moist air from the surface upward to create clouds.

Inland areas may have foggy nights because of reradiation of solar energy absorbed during the day. Radiation from the Earth's surface at night transfers energy back to space, cooling the air at ground level and creating a radiation inversion. If air temperatures near the ground become cool enough, water vapor condenses into liquid droplets, forming fog. Where mountains are close to the coast, moist air forced to rise up the slopes may create an orographic or upslope fog. The condensation, or fog, hugs the ground rather than forming higher clouds because the cool air is stable, wanting to sink rather than rise. The garua of Peru is an example of upslope fog. Farther inland away from moderating effects of the ocean and cold current, 30–60 mi (50–100 km) or more, temperatures are higher and humidity is lower. No fog can form because it is too warm, and the climate makes a transition to a warm desert. The poleward portions of west-coast deserts have the most fog, less occurs toward the Equator, and the fog may be either at ground level or slightly higher (low clouds).

In spite of being tropical or subtropical in latitude, west-coast deserts are cool all year, 60°–70° F (15°–21° C), with only a slight seasonal change (see Figure 4.1). They are cool both because of the direct influence of the cold current and the frequent fog which blocks much of the sun's radiation. With increasing distance inland, climate becomes more continental and temperatures more extreme. Temperatures average 80° F (26.5° C) for the warmest month and 60° F (15.5° C) for the coolest month. The lowest temperatures reached for both locations are generally above freezing, particularly along the coasts.

West-coast fog deserts generally have a seasonal pattern in what little rain that does fall. Poleward regions experience a winter maximum, while the equatorward regions experience a summer maximum. The central portions of these deserts are more variable both in rainfall amount and seasonality. During the warmest season, some inland areas may have convectional storms caused by higher summer temperatures.

Because of predominantly cool conditions, most plants and animals have little need to adapt to high temperatures. The exceptions are biota inhabiting inland areas. Aridity and salinity are still desert factors, however, and many plants and animals depend on fog drip for water requirements.

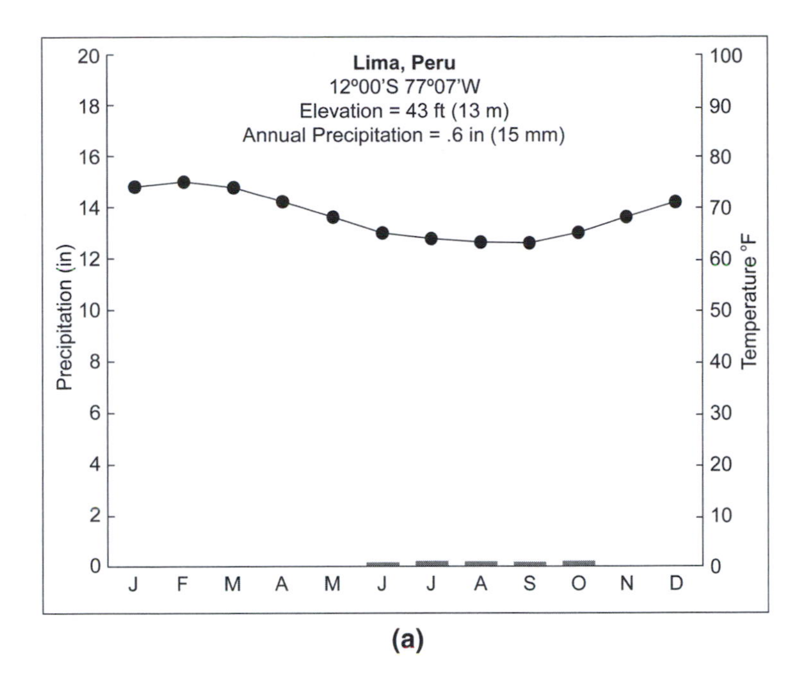

(a)

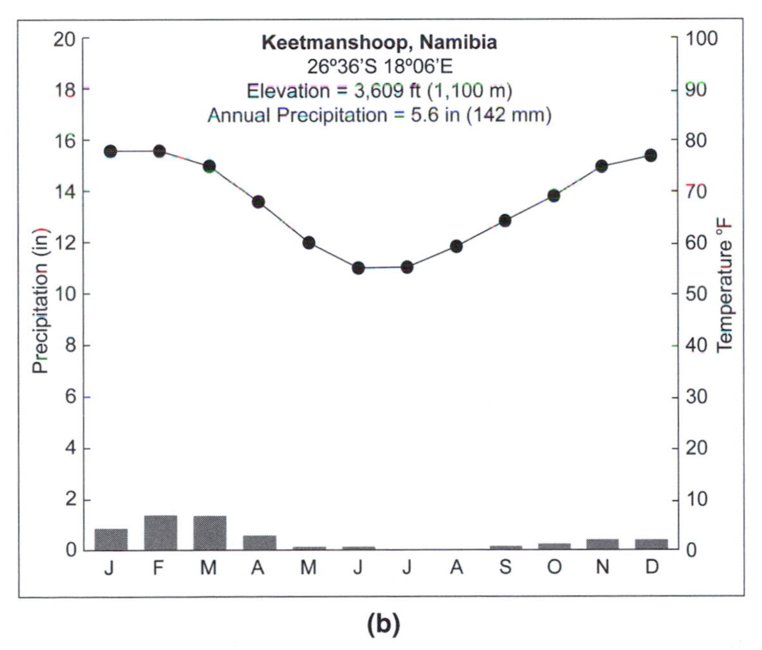

(b)

Figure 4.1 (a) The temperature regime in Lima, Peru, is typical of coastal desert locations, moderated by the ocean. (b) Keetmanshoop in Namibia has greater temperature variation because it is in a more continental location. Both have low rainfall. *(Illustration by Jeff Dixon.)*

Regional Expressions of West-Coast Fog Deserts

North America

Sonoran Desert—Vizcaino subdivision. The Vizcaino subdivision of the Sonoran Desert at 26° to 30° N on the west coast of Baja California shares many genera and even species with the rest of the Sonoran Desert but is set apart because of the prevalence of coastal fog (see Figure 4.2). Depending on winds and terrain, the distance fog extends inland from the coast is variable, 3–40 mi (5–65 km). In contrast to the rest of the Sonoran, which is dominated by small trees and columnar cacti, the Vizcaino is dominated by large leaf succulents, species of *Agave, Yucca,* and *Dudleya.* Baja has a high incidence of endemism, a result of its isolation as an island arc or peninsula during the recent geologic past. More than 20 percent of plant species are endemic.

The combination of the subtropical high pressure and cold coastal current provides little chance for rainfall, less than 4 in (100 mm) per year, despite proximity to the ocean. Rain from sporadic cyclonic storms in winter and early spring is most significant, but is extremely variable from year to year. Occasional summer rains may be related to rare west-coast hurricanes. Because the landscape is open to the west, nightly fogs lasting until mid-morning extend inland up to 3,300 ft (1,000 m) elevation or up to 4 mi (6 km) during spring and summer. Fog or high humidity in some places may extend as much as 30 mi (50 km) inland. July and August are the foggiest months because the Pacific Ocean is warmest in summer, making a bigger contrast with the cold current. The amount of moisture provided by fog is hard to quantify, but fog drip to the soil and direct absorption by plants partly offset the meager rainfall. Regardless of whether fog occurs, a strong coastal wind affects vegetation, either restricting some plants to the lee sides of hills and sand dunes or stunting and shaping their growth. Elephant trees, for example, are misshapen on the windy coast but grow as erect trees inland. In some places, the windward side of a hill may be bare or covered only with lichens.

Compared with continental deserts at this subtropical latitude, temperatures are mild because of the coastal location, cold current, and west winds that carry the ocean's influence inland. Mean summer temperatures consistently average 10° F (5° C) lower than the rest of the Sonoran Desert. Summer means in the Vizcaino are 72°–80° F (22°–27° C). Winter temperatures between 52° and 65° F (11° and 18° C) are wamer than inland Sonoran Desert locations.

A marked coast-to-inland temperature and humidity gradient affects the flora. Fruticose lichens are prominent from the coast to 40 mi (65 km) inland, where they are replaced by foliose and crustose lichens and higher plant lifeforms. The epiphytic bromeliad *Tillandsia recurvata* (also called ball moss although it is not a moss) is particularly abundant on the foggy coast. Because soil aridity, wind, and salt spray restrict growth of most plants, epiphytic lichen communities are well developed on cliffs and steep slopes facing the coast. Other common lichens include

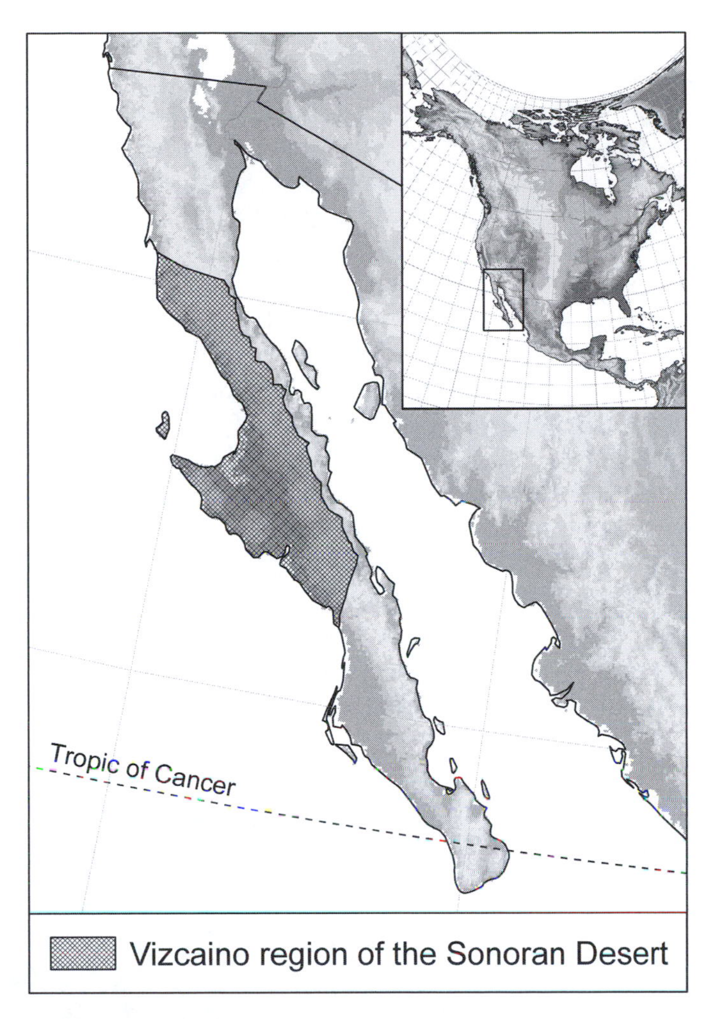

Figure 4.2 The foggy part of the Sonoran Desert, the Vizcaino, is primarily close to the west coast in Baja California. *(Map by Bernd Kuennecke.)*

Roccella spp. and other genera in the family Roccellaceae, as well as *Niebla* spp. and *Ramalina* spp. in the family Ramalinaceae. The Ramalinaceae family is most diverse. *Teloschistes* species of lichen are also significant. The introduced ice plant from coastal southwestern Africa does well here, attesting to similarity of climate.

Most of the Vizcaino Desert is broad sandy valleys, gently sloping bajadas or plains, and low hills, with an occasional volcanic tableland or cinder cone. Extensive areas have alkaline soils and sparse vegetation. The Vizcaino is characterized by leaf succulents, especially maguey, siempreviva, and datillo. Twenty-three species of *Agave* are found in Baja, and the Vizcaino is the center of distribution of several, such as blue agave, maguey, and *A. avellanidens,* which are frequently dominant in their respective communities. Depending on type of soil, several species of bursage grow with agaves, giving it the designation of Agave-Ambrosia desert. Several species of both large and small cacti are also abundant.

Although the Vizcaino region has uniform vegetation for miles, several distinct communities grow according to distance from the coast, substrate, and permeability of the soil. Visual dominants of the region are cardon, boojum (also called cirio), elephant tree, agave, and datillo (see Figure 4.3). Cardon, growing up to 70 ft (21 m) tall and weighing as much as 25 t, is the largest cactus in the world. Boojum is conspicuous because of its height (15–50 ft, 4.5–15 m) and unusual growth. Its thick stem, 1–3 ft (0.3–1 m) in diameter, sprouts short thorny branches, 1–2 ft (0.3–0.6 m) long, from base to top. Like its relative the ocotillo, boojums are drought-deciduous, developing leaves when enough rain falls and shedding them during drought. Elephant trees are short and squat, with fat trunks and short branches. Datillo is a tree-size yucca that can be 23–33 ft (7–10 m) high; it needs deep roots for support. In contrast, maguey, an agave, is abundant in the north and along the coasts where its shallow, wide-spreading root system is well suited to extracting moisture from fog drip.

Typical plants found inland, farther from the fog, are shrubs of San Diego goldeneye, jojoba, bush buckwheat, and creosote bush, along with the leaf succulents datillo and desert mescal. Cholla and large cacti also occur. Extremely arid inland

Figure 4.3 Typical plants in the Vizcaino subdivision of the Sonoran Desert in Baja California include the tall boojum trees, and cacti such as pitaya agria (left), senita (center), and large cardon (right, in background). *(Photo by author.)*

regions support only small shrubs such as bursage, allscale, creosote bush, boxthorn, and the cactus pitaya agria. Except for annuals, grasses are largely absent. In response to winter rainfall, most annuals are winter growers.

Plants that are rare in the north become more abundant to the south where boojum, cardon, maguey, desert mescal, and magdalena bursage are dominants. The south has many barrel cacti and senita columnar cacti. Torote trees, ocotillo, and elephant trees also increase in numbers toward the south. On basaltic soils near the central part of the Vizcaino near Punta Prieta is an agave-boojum community dominated by low blue agaves and tall boojums, creating an open woodland. Blue agave is the most common agave in Baja and is almost restricted to the Vizcaino. Boojum is found only in this subdivision and in a localized area on the Gulf of California coast in mainland Mexico. Distributions of two species of ocotillo overlap in the central Vizcaino, illustrating the seasonal precipitation trend. The common northern species *Fouquieria splendens* flowers after winter rains, while *F. diguetii* in the south flowers after summer rain. The dominant plant on the Vizcaino Plain is datillo, in association with magdalena bursage. The salty coastal flats in the southern half of the Vizcaino are dominated by low halophytic shrubs of Palmer's frankenia, and saltbush. No agaves, other shrubs, or trees grow on salty soils. After a rare rain, several species of annuals, such as *Dyssodia anthemidifolia*, sand verbena, woolly plantain, and three-awn grass, may appear.

The Vizcaino shares many mammal, bird, and reptile genera or species with other North American deserts, especially the Sonoran, but because of its relative isolation, distinct differences also exist. Common shared mammals include kit fox, coyote, black-tailed jackrabbit, woodrat, and Merriam's kangaroo rat. Hunting may have decimated mule deer and desert bighorn sheep populations. Birds include Harris Hawk, Cactus Wren, Bendire's Thrasher, Burrowing Owl, Gila Woodpecker, and Gilded Flicker. Reptile examples include desert iguana, zebra-tailed lizard, banded gecko, and two types of horned lizards. Endemic mammals are Baja California rock squirrel and two species of kangaroo rat, San Quintin and Vizcaino. California Quail is not found in the rest of the Sonoran Desert, although it extends north into other habitats in California. Endemic reptiles include orange-throated whiptail, coastal whiptail, and red diamond rattlesnake. In contrast, many animals characteristic of the Sonoran Desert are absent from the Vizcaino.

South America

Extending from southern Ecuador to northern Chile, 5° to 30° S, parts of the South American west-coast deserts are some of the driest regions of the world because they are in the rainshadow of the Andes Mountains and are affected by the cold Humboldt Current (see Figure 4.4). The influence of the temperature inversion over the Humboldt Current extends as far as 60 mi (100 km) inland. In many places, the region is almost barren of vegetation except along stream channels or where fog is trapped.

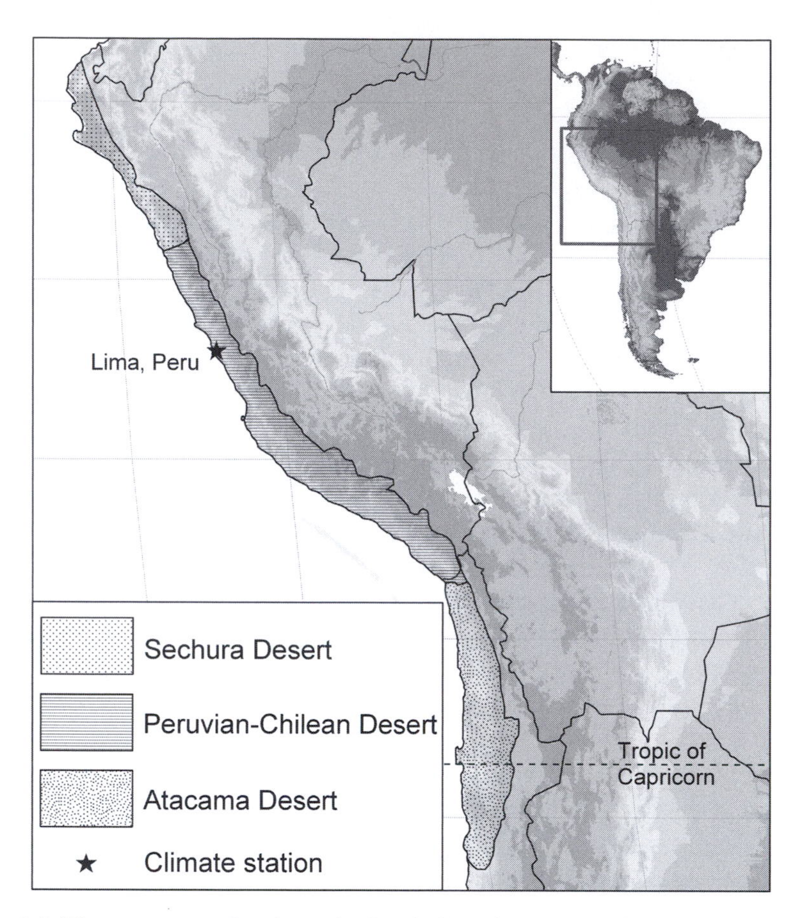

Figure 4.4 The west-coast fog desert in South America extends from southern Ecuador to northern Chile. *(Map by Bernd Kuennecke.)*

Annual precipitation averages less than 2 in (50 mm), and in some places rain rarely falls. Trujillo, Peru, averages 0.2 in (5 mm), and Iquique, Chile, is even drier, with 0.05–0.1 in (1–2 mm). Three major desert subdivisions are recognized, according to climate and vegetation. North of 8° S is the Sechura Desert where rain occurs only during a December El Niño event, when warm water displaces the normally cold ocean current. The warm water prevents development of an inversion. With higher temperature, higher humidity, and instability of air, the normally dry coast experiences thunderstorms. Runoff from the Andes also supplements local rainfall, especially during an El Niño year. In the Peruvian and Chilean fog deserts, 8° to 20° S, the dominant moisture source is fog, called garuas in Peru and camanchacas in Chile. Garuas extend 20–30 mi (30–50 km) inland and may envelope valleys up to 2,300–3,500 ft (700–1,100 m) above sea level. South of 20° S, winter cyclonic storms produce only sparse rainfall in the Atacama Desert, and coastal mountains prevent fog from penetrating far inland. Although vegetation differences are associated with these precipitation regimes, cactus species are dominant in all three regions.

In spite of the tropical latitude, temperatures are moderated by the coastal location and fog. The warmest month (March) averages only 75° F (24° C), and the coolest (September) averages 65° F (18° C). High temperatures during the day, however, frequently reach 80° F (27° C), and the highest temperature recorded is more than 90° F (32° C). In this maritime environment, summer and winter have little variation.

Sechura Desert. The Sechura Desert extends 200 mi (320 km) from southern Ecuador to 8° S in northern Peru and 60–90 mi (100–150 km) inland. It has no fog but experiences winter rain every 5–12 years, caused by the El Niño countercurrent. The landscape is generally flat, with extensive plains, sand dunes, and low hills. Coastal saline soils have various beach grasses and halophytes such as saltgrass, dropseed grass, and glasswort. The coast in southern Ecuador, where it is slightly wetter, is called a tree desert because of the tree-size, multibranched columnar cactus of *Armatocereus cartwrightianus, Pilocereus tweedyanus,* and *Monvillea* species. The tallest cactus in Peru is *Neoraimondia arequipensis*, growing to 30 ft (9 m) tall on rocky hills and west slopes at 1,000 ft (300 m). Sand dunes are generally barren. Stands of honey mesquite were formerly widespread, but most have been cut for fuel. Other trees include paloverde and other green-bark phreatophytes. Some coastal mountain valleys have willow species.

El Niño

A cyclical event every 5–10 years that alters weather patterns throughout the northern hemisphere, El Niño refers to a change in water temperature and currents in the Pacific Ocean near the Equator. Because it usually occurs around Christmas time, it was given the Spanish name in honor of the Christ Child. Under normal conditions, the Trade Winds blow strongly from east to west along the Equator and warm surface water is pushed in an equatorial current all the way across the Pacific Ocean to Indonesia. The removal of surface water in the eastern Pacific allows colder water from depth to upwell off the coast of South America. The cold water both prevents cloud formation and promotes fog formation, creating the foggy Peruvian-Chilean Desert. The warmer water in Indonesia promotes thunderstorm activity and torrential rainfall. For unknown reasons, when the Trade Winds weaken, warm water is not pushed westward across the Pacific, and an equatorial countercurrent from west to east develops. The result is that warm water replaces the cold water normally found off the west coast of South America. The warm water promotes instability, and the normally dry Peruvian-Chilean Desert experiences intense thunderstorms. Indonesia undergoes a drought because the water there is not as warm as usual. This reversal of currents affects wind and pressure patterns far removed from the equatorial Pacific, but the exact patterns are not yet known.

Peruvian-Chilean Desert. Fog and fog-adapted vegetation are typical of the Peruvian-Chilean Desert coast from 8° to 20° S in southern Peru and extreme northern Chile as far south as Iquique. Fog dominates in winter due to upwelling of cold water, which both cools and stabilizes the air. Fog is less common in summer because the warmer land does not allow condensation to occur. Hillsides and lower portions of gorges between sea level and 3,500 ft (1,100 m) trap fog and support isolated plant communities called lomas (meaning small hills) in an otherwise barren landscape. As westerly winds force the fog against the coastal mountains, the low cloud may produce fog drip or drizzle, capable of wetting only the surface soil. Fog does not occur at higher elevations because the stable upper air prevents the fog from rising.

Fog is most intense at night and may clear by mid-morning. Although moisture from fog is not absorbed directly by most plants, a small amount soaks into the soil where it can then be utilized by roots. Fog moderates the microclimate by reducing air temperature and intensity of sunlight during the day. Increased humidity reduces moisture lost during transpiration and also reduces heat loss at night.

Perennial terrestrial bromeliads are found in this region, from near Trujillo, Peru, south to Iquique, Chile (see Figure 4.5a). They are most dense in the Peruvian Desert. *Tillandsia,* found in mats and pure stands, is strictly a New World genus. Of the higher plants, they are unusual in their ability to absorb moisture from the air by means of fine hairs called trichomes. Roots are irrelevant for water intake and

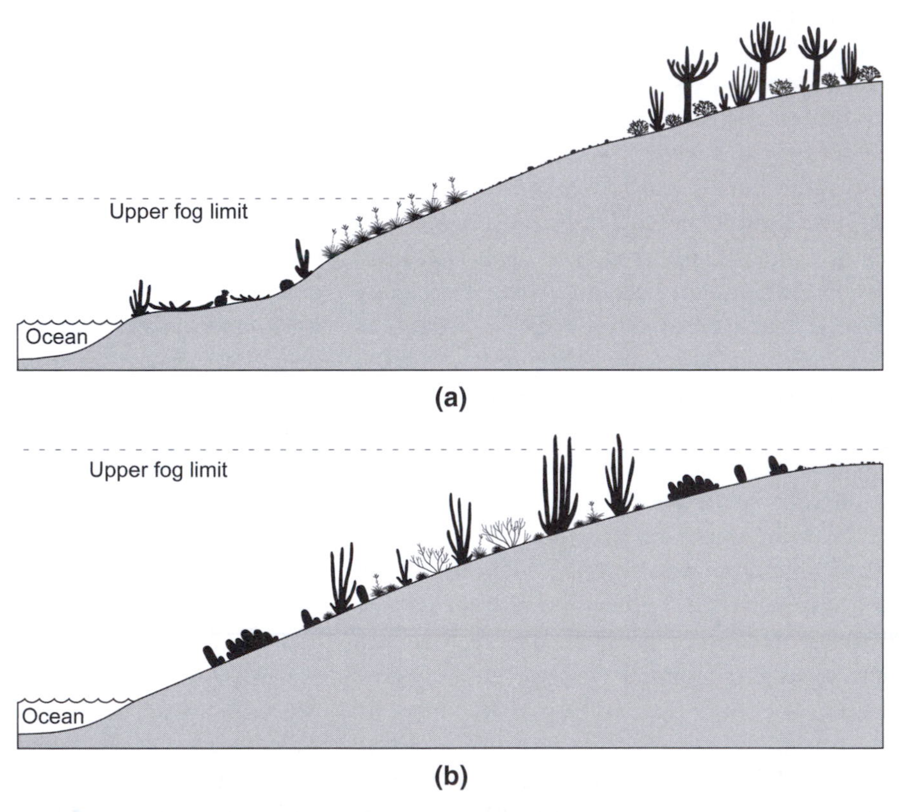

Figure 4.5 (a) Foggy lomas in the Peruvian coastal desert support various types of fog-adapted cacti at lower elevations, changing to the bromeliad *Tillandsia* near the top of the fog zone. A barren landscape above the fog gives way to a cactus desert, where some orographic precipitation occurs. (b) Lomas in the Atacama Desert support distinct bands of vegetation, primarily *Copiapoa* and *Eulychnia* cacti, and bromeliads according to density of fog. Nothing can grow above the fog zone. *(Illustration by Jeff Dixon.)*

only serve to anchor the plant to the ground. *T. latifolia* is most common, but several species occur. Common lichens in the lower fog zone are species of *Teloschistes*.

Cactus lomas, where species of cactus adapted to fog dominate, occur in more southern areas of coastal Peru and extreme northern Chile. *Haagocereus* spp., a columnar variety that grows prostrate, is common in sandy areas. Only the tip of the cactus is erect, and the stem may be covered with *Cladonia* and *Teloschistes* lichens. Soil cacti, *Pygmaeocereus rowleyanus* in Peru and *Neochilenia* species in Chile, are unique to this fog desert. Soil cacti shrink into the soil during drought. Most of the plant is beneath the surface as thick succulent tubers, making it hard to see except when flowering. Fine roots spread out near the surface to absorb fog drip. Because fog lomas are isolated from one another by barren desert, the majority of the flora in a loma may be endemic.

Above the winter fog level near the coast but below the higher mountain slopes is a strip or valley of barren rock desert. Humidity is low, sunlight is intense, and surface temperatures can be 160° F (70° C). Nothing grows. At slightly higher elevations, 3,300–6,600 ft (1,000–2,000 m), east of the rock desert, occasional orographic precipitation supports "forests" of several columnar cactus. Species vary with latitude, but dominants are *Neoraimondia arequipensis* (endemic to Peru), *Espostoa melanostela, Armatocereus procerus, Haageocereus aureispinus,* and *Browningia candelaris. Melocactus* is common, along with occasional long-spine acacia and paloverde trees. Many endemics are restricted to isolated valleys.

Although both Peru and Chile have fog lomas, their floras are distinct. Northern Chile has a flatter coastal plain and fewer coastal mountains to trap incoming fog. The barren and inhospitable landscape prevented migration of species between Peru and Chile.

Atacama Desert. The Atacama Desert, which merges with the Peruvian-Chilean Desert in the north, extends from Arica (18° S) south to La Serena (30° S). It is one of the driest regions in the world. Ninety percent of the landscape is barren of higher plants, and not even halophytes grow on many salt pans. Average precipitation from winter cyclonic storms is less than 0.1 in (0.03 cm), and many areas have never recorded rainfall. It becomes slightly wetter toward the south and at the base of the mountains.

Coastal ranges that rise abruptly, almost from the water's edge up to 3,000–3,500 ft (900–1,000 m), determine which areas are foggy. Except where the mountains are cut by east-west valleys, fog is confined to the coast. The fog is usually not on the ground but at an elevation of 1,000–2,600 ft (300–800 m), resulting in distinct bands of vegetation depending on density of fog (see Figure 4.5b). *Copiapoa* and *Eulychnia* are the most common plants in the foggy Atacama. Several species of the short columnar cactus *Copiapoa* (named for the nearby city of Copiapó) grow on the fringes of the fog zone, both below and above the densest fog. Several species of *Eriosyce*, small cacti, are commonly found with Copiapoa in the drier areas. Bulbs such as Peruvian lily occur in the coastal fog zone where their shallow roots

Figure 4.6 *Euphorbia lactiflua* is a caudiciform shrub common in the foggiest zone of the Atacama Desert. *(Photo courtesy of Mark Muradian.)*

absorb fog that drips into the soil. *Eulychnia* species, tall columnar cacti endemic to Chile, extend throughout the foggy elevations. However, many of these large plants have been cut for firewood. In the lower fog zone, *Eulychnia* grows with *Puya boliviensis*. In the upper regions, it grows with *Copiapoa* (see Plate XII). The foggiest central zone supports a dense community of *Eulychnia* and *Euphorbia lactiflua*, a caudiciform shrub that is semisucculent (see Figure 4.6). The epiphytic bromeliad *Tillandsia geissei* grows on cactus and shrubs in the foggiest zones, as do various lichens and algae. *Eulychnia* spines may become red with a dense cover of the alga *Trentopohlia*. A terrestrial bromeliad, *Deuterocohnia chrysantha* also grows

Fog Forest

A unique wood loma, or fog forest, occurs in a narrow elevation zone above 1,600 ft (500 m) in Fray Jorge National Park in central Chile. Even though precipitation is only 6 in (150 mm), the trees extract an additional 60 in (1,500 mm) of fog drip from the wet air, perpetuating their unique ecosystem. An evergreen tree, tique (*Aextoxion punctatum*) dominates, growing with the bromeliad puya, columnar *Eulychnia* cacti, and shrubs (*Drymis winteri* and *Myceugenua corrafolia*). The shrubs and even the cacti are covered with moss and lichens. This "forest island" is an example of woodland lomas that were once more widespread as fog oases in the desert. Other wood lomas have *Acacia* species, *Eugenia ferreyrae, Caesalpina tinctoria, Capparis prisca,* and columnar cacti (*Trichocereus chiloensis*).

throughout the fog zone, although plants are severely stressed when growing in the drier *Copiapoa* areas. Shrubs include *Tetragonia maritima* and *Nolana mollis.*

Many *Copiapoa* species tilt north toward the sun, a response to foggy conditions. The tilt concentrates the sun's rays on the growing points of the plants. Decay is very slow in this extremely dry region. However, dead plants leave a white blot on the landscape as their tissues release high concentrations of salt or calcium.

The inland region, called the Atacama Plateau, and elevations above the fog are barren rocky desert with temperature extremes. They support mostly ephemeral vegetation and window lichens. Window lichens, buried in the soil, photosynthesize via gaps in leaf pigment and depend on dew for moisture. Most of the time the plateau is barren, but on rare occasions when it receives more than 0.75 in (20 mm) in winter (June and July) ephemerals come to life. Typical are *Cryptantha parviflora,* lupines, and a violet.

Few animals exist in the extremely dry habitats of South American west-coast deserts. Two large animals are the Sechura fox and guanaco. Guanaco is found in all three subdivisions, but Sechura fox is absent from the Atacama. The Argentine gray fox may be seen occasionally in all three regions (see Figure 4.7). Mice or rats in the genus *Phyllotis* are represented by a different species in each desert. The leaf-eared mouse is found in the Peruvian-Chilean Desert, and a closely related species, Darwin's leaf-eared mouse, is found in the Atacama. The Sechura Desert has the

Figure 4.7 Argentine gray fox is a common predator in several deserts of South America. *(Photo courtesy of Keith Sauer.)*

Sechura rat, which is endemic to Peru. The southern vizcacha rat is found in rocky, mountainous areas of the Peruvian-Chilean and Atacama deserts, where it feeds on grasses, mosses, and lichens.

Avian fauna includes small passerine birds, such as Coastal Miner in the Peruvian-Chilean Desert. It is absent, however, from the drier Sechura or Atacama. Cactus Canastero is found in the Sechura Desert. Several birds have restricted distributions in the Peruvian-Chilean Desert, including Chilean Woodstar, Thick-billed Miner, White-throated Earthcreeper, and Tamarugo Conebill. Migratory birds are more plentiful than residents, but Burrowing Owls can be found in all deserts. Because of the moisture from fog drip, lomas have more diversity in birds, such as Rufous-collared Sparrow, Blue-black Grassquit, Slender-billed Finch, and several hummingbirds, which arrive when plants are blooming or insect pupae are hatching. Loma birds are not found in the fog-free Atacama, which has few resident birds. Birds of prey and Turkey Vultures occasionally visit the deserts. Most birds, however, are coastal marine birds, such as Brown Pelican, Inca Terns, and gulls.

Endemic fauna include lava lizards in all three deserts, and Roedinger's lancehead viper, which is limited to Peru.

Flies, woodlice, carabid beetles, spiders (*Lactrodectes*), and scorpions (*Hadruroides lunutar*) are common in lomas, with different varieties or species in different locations.

Southwestern Africa—Namib-Karoo

The Namib-Karoo, from southern Angola to South Africa, is a large region with three distinct deserts, the Namib, the Succulent Karoo, and the Nama-Karoo (see Figure 4.8). Each of these can be further subdivided in terms of climate and biota. From north to south in Namibia, the Namib includes the Kaokoveld, Central Namib, and Southern Namib deserts. The Succulent Karoo in southen Namibia and the country of South Africa includes Namaqualand-Namib and the Southern Karoo. The Nama-Karoo, in both countries, is divided into Upper Karoo, Great Karoo, and Bushmanland. Karoo refers to dry shrubland. Three factors contribute to the aridity—the subtropical high-pressure cell, temperature inversions caused by local southwest winds over the cold Benguela Current, and easterly trade winds that warm adiabatically as they descend the Great Escarpment of Africa.

Although rainfall is low throughout the region, the Namib-Karoo straddles two seasonal precipitation regimes because of its north-south extent (14° to 32° S). The southern section has winter cyclonic storms, but a summer maximum is not reached until the Kaokoveld in the north. The transition zone, around Walvis Bay in Namibia, is the most arid in southwestern Africa, with no distinct rainy season. Rainfall in the Namib is sporadic, a major contrast with the reliable winter rain in the Succulent Karoo farther south. Coastal temperatures are moderate with little difference between winter and summer, but increasing distance inland causes more variation due to more continental influence.

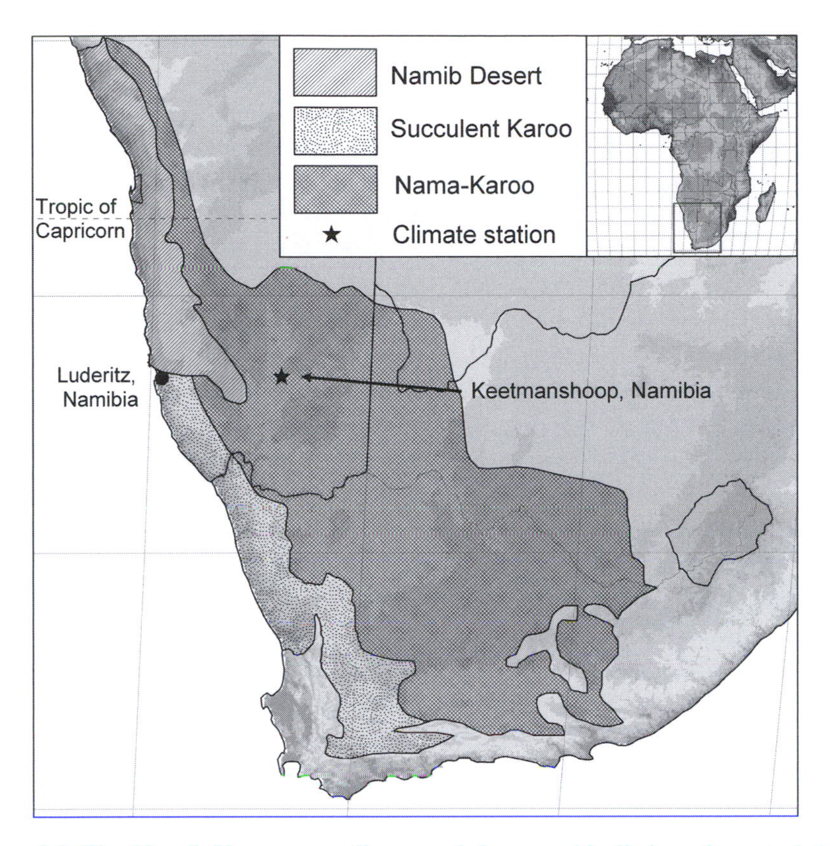

Figure 4.8 The Namib-Karoo, actually several deserts with distinct characteristics of climate and biota, extends from southern Angola to the Olifants River in South Africa. *(Map by Bernd Kuennecke.)*

Scientists believe that this desert area, the oldest on Earth, has existed for 15 million years. This long dry period has had a profound effect on biodiversity, and 50 percent of all plant species are endemic. Most plants have no English common names.

Namib Desert. The Namib Desert is a narrow coastal zone that stretches for 800 mi (1,300 km), from San Nicolai River in Southern Angola (14° S) south to Luderitz in Namibia (26° S). Bounded on the east by Africa's Great Escarpment and the Richtersveld Mountains, it is 50–90 mi (80–150 km) wide. Precipitation is less than 4 in (100 mm), variable from place to place and year to year, with some places receiving less than 1 in (25 mm). The major moisture source for most plants and animals is fog. Vegetation is sparse or nonexistent, especially in the sand dunes between Walvis Bay and Luderitz.

The northern area of the Namib Desert, from southern Angola south to the Uniab River in Namibia (14° to 20° S), is the Kaokoveld, a narrow coastal strip between the Atlantic and the escarpment. The region receives occasional summer thunderstorms,

Skeleton Coast

The area between the Kunene River and Swapkomund, primarily gravel flats or sand dunes, is called the Skeleton Coast because of numerous shipwrecks caused by dangerous currents and dense fog. The primarily barren desert offered no means of survival for marooned sailors. Dry river valleys extending from the inland highlands to the ocean are linear oases supported by underground water and occasional flooding, but they are infrequent.

and fog may extend up to 30 mi (50 km) inland. Temperatures are cool, with only a 4°–9° F (2°–5° C) temperature change from day to night. Although continental conditions gradually increase inland, the climate is still moderate. Little is known about the landscape or biota.

Most of the Kaokoveld is sand and gravel plains, but rugged hills, valleys, and sand dunes also exist. Gravel pavements along the coast may be covered with fruticose lichens, especially *Parmelia*, *Usnea*, and *Telochistes capensis.* Gravel plains away from the coast have dollar plant shrubs and *Stipagrostis* grasses (see Figure 4.9). The unique welwitschia is also found on inland gravel plains. Soils are salty, both close to the ocean and also where salty fog extends farther inland, supporting halophytes such as *Salsola zeyheri,* sea purslane, and alkali blite. The Kunene River, forming the border between Namibia and Angola, is the only perennial stream. Others are intermittent and choked by sand before reaching the sea. The Namibian part of the Kaokoveld is primarily dunes, which support a few shrubby plants such as *Salsola nollothensis* and *Merremia multisecta,* along with a few *Stipagrostis* and *Eragrostis* grasses. Little vegetation grows on the dunes in Angola, except for an occasional nara, a spiny shrub that traps sand.

Figure 4.9 The succulent dollar plant shrub is one of the few plants to survive on gravelly coastal flats in Namibia. *(Photos by author.)*

Many small leaf succulents, such as *Lithops ruschiorum, Sarcocaulon mossamedense,* and *Othonna lasiocarpa,* members of genera more common in the wetter Succulent Karoo, are found on rocky areas with more moisture. Greater diversity is found along dry riverbeds, perhaps because of the availability of groundwater, where shrubby leaf succulents are especially common.

From the Uniab River south to the town of Luderitz, the Namib is classified into two areas. Directly south of the Kaokoveld Desert, the Central Namib runs from the Uniab River south to the Kuiseb River near Walvis Bay. North of the Kuiseb River the landscape is gravel plains with occasional granite or limestone hills or low mountains. From the Kuiseb River south to Luderitz, the Southern Namib, the bedrock is covered by a thick layer of sand dunes.

In both subdivisions, rain is sparse and unpredictable, 0.2–3.4 in (5–85 mm) annually, most of which falls in a few rare events. The coast is driest, with a slight increase inland toward the base of the escarpment. Moisture in the Namib is provided by fog, not by rain. In general, incidence of fog decreases and rainfall increases slightly with distance inland.

The Central Namib has occasional summer rains, while the Southern Namib receives some winter rain. Two rare occurrences must coincide to cause summer rain in the Central Namib. For some reason, the temperature inversion is absent, allowing surface heating and convection, which, coupled with an influx of moist air from the Indian Ocean, generates thunderstorms. Winter rainfall in the Southern Namib is caused by cyclonic storms between cool air over the southern African plateaus and the maritime tropical airmass over the ocean. Cyclonic storms occur more frequently farther south over the Succulent Karoo and only sporadically in the Namib. At the other extreme, hot air occasionally drains downslope from the interior, heating adiabatically as it descends, lowering humidity and preventing even coastal fog.

Because of the coastal location and persistent fog, temperatures are mild with little daily or seasonal change. On the coast, daily mean temperatures are 60°–73° F (15°–23° C), with maxima not much higher. On the few days when an east wind descends the escarpment, adiabatic warming may raise the temperatures to 90°–100° F (32°–38° C). Temperatures along the coast may drop to 36° F (2° C) on rare occasions but are never low enough for frost. Inland, however, in the Inner Namib, temperatures are more extreme, possibly below freezing in winter and more than 100° F (38° C) in summer.

The Central Namib is well known and has a variety of habitats and plants. Even though most plants thrive in the foggy zone, only lichens and algae are true fog plants, which do not absorb water via their roots and depend directly on fog for moisture. Most plants cannot absorb moisture directly from the air and must take moisture through their roots as fog drip moistens the soil. Fruticose lichen fields and window algae are abundant on stony desert pavement areas in the coastal zone, and low, dark orange cushions of *Teloschistes capensis* can cover 40–60 percent of the surface. Others lichens are *Ramalina maculata* and black *Xanthoparmelia hyporbytida.* Many coastal lichens grow in the lee of stones and in crevices, protected from salt spray and sand blast. Window algae grow protected on the undersides of transparent stones that transmit light. Depressions on gravel plains are mostly bare except for colorful wanderflechten (wandering lichens), many of which are not attached to the rocks, rolling with the wind when dry. Lichen populations decrease inland as fog also decreases.

Rocky quartzite or marble areas support many genera and species of succulents (*Lithops, Othonna, Sarcocaulon, Pelargonium, Hoodia,* and others). Many succulents, especially Crassulaceae and mesems (Aizoaceae), conserve water by using the Crassulacean Acid Metabolism (CAM) method of photosynthesis. Halophytic

Hoodia

Superficially resembling cactus, hoodia is a genus of stem succulents in the milkweed family endemic to the Namib Desert (see Figure 4.10). Multistemmed plants can reach 3.3 ft (1 m) tall. Flowers are large and flesh-colored, with a strong odor of rotting meat. Although not proven to be effective, *Hoodia gordonii* has gained prominence as a potential appetite suppressant, a development that may threaten wild populations if they become extensively collected for medicinal use.

Figure 4.10 *Hoodia gordonii* is a stem succulent that has a growthform similar to a small columnar cactus, although they are not related. Long seedpods develop after the plant flowers. *(Photos by author.)*

shrubs such as dollar plant and *Salsola* trap sand into little hills called nebkas, where several varieties of mesembs grow (see the sidebar Mesembs or Vygies). Salt-tolerant shrubs and camel thorn acacia trees sparsely outline dry stream channels.

The Southern Namib is predominantly shifting sand dunes in an area 200 mi (320 km) north to south and 75 mi (120 km) east to west. Dunes up to 1,000 ft (300 m) high are stopped in their northern advance by vegetation at the Kuiseb River. Salty soils prevail along the coast, but the sands are largely barren. Even inland, wherever it is foggy, soils are brackish because each fog droplet carries salt with it. Surface water is nonexistent except on rare occasions when dry river beds flow. Because the sand dunes have no groundwater reserves, they support few plants. Dollar plant, a spiny shrub called nara, and two grass species are found only at their edges.

The desert farther from the coast has little fog and no lichens. The vegetation is similar to that of the Southern Namib, *Stipagrostis* grass, and the landscape appears barren until it rains. Perennial grasses reemerge to form a dense sea of plants with no space for forbs. Rocky areas have milkbush shrub. Camel thorn acacias, salt cedar, mustard tree, and the herbaceous introduced tobacco plant form dense stands along the Swartkop and Kuiseb Rivers.

Farther inland, the Great Western Escarpment rises to 3,000 ft (900 m), either with an abrupt elevation change or as a 20-mile (32 km) wide irregular dissected zone. This rocky region in the eastern part of the Central Namib has a unique plant assemblage of low trees with thick succulent bases, or caudices. Leaves on short stems are drought-deciduous. With short but large trunks and pale papery bark that reflects solar radiation, these plants morphologically resemble elephant trees of the Sonoran Desert but are not related. Typical are *Commiphora* species, *Euphorbia guerichiana, Moringa ovalifolia,* and three *Cyphostemma* species (see Figure 4.11a). Also in

Welwitschia

Welwitschia is a signature plant of the Namib Desert (see Plate XIII). This gymnosperm is endemic to the Namib and the Kaokoveld in the transition zone between the coast and Inner Namib. It is the only sclerophyllous xerophyte in the Namib and is not a fog plant. Fog rarely reaches that far inland, and welwitschia leaves cannot absorb moisture from the air. Depending on conditions, they have the ability to use CAM. Plants grow widely separated in broad flat channels on gravel plains. Floods can moisten soil to a depth of 5 ft (1.5 m), where moisture can remain for years. On rare occasions with sufficient rainfall, seed germinates within three weeks. The seedling first sends down a carrot-like taproot to deeper sources of moisture, eventually reaching 60 ft (18 m) in depth. Two leathery leaves grow 4–8 in (10–20 cm) per year, the only two leaves the plant will produce. They continue growing from the base, not from the tip, and may be up to 10 ft (3 m) long and 12 in (30 cm) wide, even though frayed and broken. After many years' exposure to the desert elements, the two long leaves are split and tattered by sun, wind, and windblown sand, resulting in a 3 ft (1.5 m) high tangle. It may take 25 years for the first flower to appear. Individual plants live for 1,000–2,000 years, and the largest may be 2,500 years old.

Diamonds

The extensive sand dunes along the southwestern African coast, from Walvis Bay in Namibia south to the Orange River in South Africa, are rich in diamonds. Little is known about the biota of these regions because, with few exceptions, the mining companies prohibit access.

Figure 4.11 The caudiciform growthform is common in many Namib-Karoo plants. (a) *Cyphostemma* stores moisture in its succulent base, and its waxy bark reflects excess sunlight. (b) Halfmens tilt their growing point northward so that the low winter sun is concentrated on the new leaves. *(Photos by author.)*

this location is the resurrection plant, a small woody shrub that can be completely desiccated but revives with rain.

Succulent Karoo. The Succulent Karoo, from Luderitz (26° S) south to the Olifants River (32° S) and extending approximately 20–60 mi (30–100 km) inland from the coast, is the southern part of the greater Namib-Karoo. A subdivision, the Southern Karoo, occupies separate inland basins farther south. It is a desert shrubland with winter rainfall caused by cyclonic storms. Aridity on the coast is moderated by fog and cooler temperatures. Annual precipitation ranges from only 0.75 in (20 mm) in the drier northwest to more than 16 in (400 mm) on the escarpment. Unlike most other deserts, rainfall is reliable in both season and amount. Long droughts are rare. Most of the region receives less than 6 in (150 mm) a year, supplemented by heavy dew and fog in autumn and winter, particularly within 10 mi (16 km) of the coast. Measurable fog drip is significant, up to 5 in (130 mm). The higher peaks on the escarpment, which are above the fog, have different vegetation. Dew is an important moisture source, especially inland where fog is infrequent.

Dew, however, fails to form in summer when temperatures are too high for condensation to take place.

Temperatures are mild. On the coast, mean minima in winter are 46° F (8° C), and frost is rare. Inland, minimum temperatures drop to 40° F (4° C), but only the high peaks of the Kamiesberg Mountains have frost and occasional snow. Cold winter weather is sometimes interrupted by berg (mountain) winds. These winds originate from high pressure inland on the Plateau and warm adiabatically as they flow downslope. Summer temperatures are rarely more than 77° F (25° C) along the coast, but increase inland, and may exceed 100° F (38° C) in the eastern Richtersveld Mountain region and in the Knersvlakte.

The Succulent Karoo has two major subdivisions—Namaqualand-Namib and the Southern Karoo. Namaqualand-Namib, located on the foggy coast and eastward to the escarpment, receives a small amount of winter rain. The Southern Karoo, farther inland and farther south, is characterized by spring and autumn rain and a lack of fog. The landscape of the Succulent Karoo is varied, from coastal sand dunes and gravel flats to bare rock uplands and granite dome mountains on the escarpment. Major vegetation is small leaf succulents in many families and genera. Only two perennial rivers cross the Succulent Karoo, the Orange River in the North and the Olifants River in the South. They both provide local water sources and serve as important corridors for migration of both plants and animals. Both Succulent Karoo regions can be further subdivided according to landforms and vegetation.

Succulent Karoo Vegetation. The Succulent Karoo is distinctive from other deserts for several reasons. It supports the greatest botanical diversity of all deserts, with more than 5,000 species of higher plants, especially in the sunflower, grass, iceplant, lily, and figwort families. It has the richest concentration of succulent plants in the world, including leaf succulents, miniature forms, and geophytes (bulbs). Typical species are in the Mesembryanthemaceae (mesembs, called vygies in South Africa) and Crassulaceae families. Mesems, *Crassula, Tylecodon, Haworthia, Aloe, Stapelieae,* and *Euphorbia* are particularly diverse.

Many shrubs have succulent leaves, a trait that is less important in the rest of the world's deserts. Approximately 1,700 species of leaf succulents grow here, 700 being dwarf forms, including several genera of stone plants, so called because their appearance mimics stones. Although the Chihuahuan Desert is also characterized by leaf succulents, the plants there are much larger. In contrast to the Sonoran Desert, which is dominated by cactus stem succulents, the Succulent Karoo has only 130 species of stem succulents (such as *Euphorbia, Tylecodon, Pelargonium*, and stapeliads), none of which are cactus. The Succulent Karoo is also unique for its bulb flora. No other desert in the world has such a diversity of bulbs. It has 630 species of geophytes, including amaryllis and the genera *Lachenalia, Moraea,* and *Romulea.* Although annuals are abundant, 390 species, they are only 10 percent of the total flora, in contrast to other deserts where annuals may account for more than 30 percent. The lower prominance of annuals is because other lifeforms are more

Mesembs or Vygies

Formerly a distinct family but now a succulent subdivision of the family Aizoaceae, Mesembryanthemaceae, shortened to mesembs and called vygies in South Africa, are also known as flowering stones and ice plants. Leaf structure, flower color and form, types of seeds, and size all exhibit great variation (see Plate XIV). Leaves are generally small, on short shoots, or are reduced to hemispheres like *Lithops* and *Pleiospeilos,* or even slightly split spheres like *Conophytum.* Flowers are many petaled and aster like, not large but showy. When blooming, flowers often completely cover the tiny plants. Mesembs are found in many different habitats, including rocky crevices, silty flats, saline soils, sand, and desert pavement, but need well-drained substrate. Although centered in southwestern Africa, isolated species occur in St. Helena, Madagascar, North Africa, and Arabia. The few species in Australia, New Zealand, and the west coasts of the Americas were introduced. Adopted as garden plants in mild, winter-rain climates, common ice plants are often used for soil stabilization. The greatest variation in both species and genera of mesembs is found in the Richtersveld Mountains, which have, for example, 55 species of *Conophytum* and 51 species of *Ruschia.* Many species are rare or threatened with extinction due to illegal plant collecting and habitat destruction from grazing, mining, and urbanization. Because many mesembs have a limited distribution, any loss is significant.

numerous. Unlike the Sonoran Desert where trees codominate the landscape with stem succulents, the Succulent Karoo has only 35 species of trees. Some, however, are impressive tree succulents, such as quiver trees (*Aloe* spp.) and halfmen (*Pachypodium namaquanum*), and caudiciforms such as *Commiphera.* The Succulent Karoo communities are very species rich. On a local scale, 10,750 ft^2 (1,000 m^2) plots average 74 species, almost double the number for the Sonoran Desert, the most species-rich desert in North America. On a regional scale, the Succulent Karoo has almost four times the number of species found in winter-rain North American deserts.

Almost 40 percent of species are endemic to the region, including 80 genera and hundreds of species, particulary in the ice plant, euphorbia, crassula, caltrop (bean-caper), sunflower, and purslane (moss rose) families. One-sixth to one-third of all species are found only in limited local areas. In contrast, disjunct distributions of related plants occur in Kenya, Somalia, and Yemen.

The rich flora is predominantly due to many small succulent shrubs and bulbs, newly evolved, closely related species. Evolution is facilitated by sexual reproduction of large populations with short lifespans. A large population will have a large gene pool, and sexual versus vegetative reproduction creates new combinations. Short lifespans ensure that many generations increase the potential for crossing of genes. (Fruit flies are used in experiments to illustrate evolutionary change for the same reasons.) Catastrophes such as droughts also divide populations, isolating them so they can develop independently. Plants dependent on wind to disperse seeds, such as crassula, stapeliads, *Othonno,* and *Senecio,* are less likely to have local endemics because the seeds travel long distances and counteract isolation. Plants capable of vegetative reproduction, such as crassula, also have less speciation and less local endemism. Because they have long lifespans and their seeds are dispersed by birds, tree species are also less likely to evolve independently. The Succulent Karoo has an abundance of small plants, which can colonize extreme habitats that would not support larger plants.

Although plants in southwestern Africa are generally faced with similar desert needs to withstand aridity, heat, solar radiation, and salinity, specifics of their environment make their adaptations distinct. Most plants grow during the rainy winter under conditions with less solar radiation and cooler temperatures. Winds can also be strong.

Water Recycling

Mesembs have a unique way of recycling moisture in their tissues. Moisture from older leaves is absorbed into new ones as the old leaves dry up. Many, such as *Conophytum, Argyroderma,* and *Lithops,* have only two fat leaves at a time. The new pair develops at the base of the old, reabsorbing the moisture until the old leaves are a papery shell, protecting the young developing leaves within.

Many miniature succulents evolved in the Succulent Karoo in response to fog, dew, and shallow soils. Unlike sporadic thunderstorms in summer-rainfall deserts, winter rain in southwest Africa is widespread, gentle, and reliable in amount, season, and type. Fog and dew are even more reliable than rain. Small succulent, many-branched shrubs that grow close to the ground are in a perfect position to catch dew. Most roots are shallow and widespread, also to quickly absorb any fog drip, dew, or rain. The reliable source of moisture allows small succulents to evolve because the plants need only to store enough water until the next season. In contrast, large succulents of summer-rainfall deserts, such as columnar cactus and agaves in the Americas or euphorbias and aloes in other parts of Africa and Eurasia, must store water to last more than one season. Deeper-rooted and larger plants replace small succulents where fog or dew is rare or soils are too deep. On deep, porous sand, water quickly penetrates beyond root depth. During droughts, which may occur every 10 years, a massive die-off of small succulents occurs because their life cycle is so closely tied with reliable rainfall.

Geophytes, any type of underground storage unit such as a bulb, corm, tuber, or rhizome, are also related to the predictable water regime. Their water storage is underground and they have no leaves in summer. Most flower in winter and spring just after winter rains, but some, including all amaryllids, grow only leaves at that time. After the leaves have shriveled and dried in summer, the bulb uses stored energy to send up a stalk with large showy flowers. The advantage is that if the bulb does not gain enough energy from its leaves to both flower in summer and grow new leaves the following season, it will delay flowering. Rather than being erect and sword-shaped, many leaves are broad, flat, and prostrate on the soil surface. This characteristic is almost unique to the winter-rain bulbs of southern Africa and may serve to absorb more dew at ground level. Some amaryllids cool their leaves below air temperature at night, forcing dew to form, which then soaks into the surrounding soil. Many lilies and irises have tightly coiled or twisted leaves. Leaves of several species are marked with purple or reddish streaks or patterns, but no explanation for these distinctive traits is yet known. Bulbs account for 16 percent of the total Namaqualand flora, which is 5–10 times higher than in other winter-rain deserts. The largest families are iris, hyacinth, oxalis, and amaryllis.

Plants with Windows

Many plants in the Succulent Karoo have translucent, pigment-free portions of the leaves, called windows, a trait almost exclusive to South African winter-rain deserts. During dry seasons, the roots of window plants contract and pull the plant into the ground, with only the top of the small leaves showing. The windows let the sun penetrate deeper into the cell, allowing the plant to continue photosynthesis even though little is exposed to the elements. Windows are commonly seen in *Fenestraria, Frithia, Conophytum, Lithops,* and *Haworthia* genera as well as in some algae and lichens. The patterns seen on the leaves are variations in the amount of pigment near the surface and chlorophyll zones inside the leaf.

Most Namaqualand plants are capable of two kinds of photosynthesis, C_3 on cooler winter days and CAM in drier conditions. Most annuals grow in the wetter and cooler winter.

Succulent Karoo plants must contend with both too much energy receipt in summer and too little in winter. When clear skies and higher sun angle in summer raise temperatures, particularly at ground level, low-growing plants need to keep their tissues cool. Many plants, such as *Crassula* species, have a red pigment in summer that reduces absorption of light. The tissues revert to green in winter. White plant surfaces and the white papery covering of old leaves on mesembs reflect radiation, as do the white quartz gravel flats where many tiny plants grow. The habit of many plants of retracting into the soil to avoid aridity during dry summers also exposes less plant surface to intense sunlight.

Winter is cooler because the sun is lower to the horizon, days are shorter, and skies are often cloudy or foggy, decreasing radiation receipt to about one-half that of summer. To maximize receipt of winter sun, many plants face north, orienting leaves and growth tips toward the sun. Most conspicuous is the tall stem succulent halfmen, which leans north so its rosette of leaves and buds at the top are better exposed to the sun (see Figure 4.11b).

Mesembs have tissue that is saltier than most plants. Because water moves from concentrations of less salt to more salt, salty tissue allows the plant to absorb slightly salty water either from the soil or from fog. Wind can be strong in the Succulent Karoo. In summer, south winds blast the Sandveld coast. In winter, hot berg winds may affect the entire area but especially the Richtersveld Mountains. Sandstorms with wind speeds up to 75 mph (120 kph) can occur several times a winter. Exhibiting a condition called psammophory, dwarf mesembs of *Psammophora* and *Arenifera* have sticky hairs on tender new leaves and stems. Sand sticking to these hairs serves as a barrier that protects the plant from abrasive action from windblown sand.

Because small plants have no excess tissue to lose to grazing animals and cannot resprout like grasses, several protection mechanisms have evolved. The major defense is chemical. Many mesembs have a layer of calcium oxalate crystals, which can impair kidney function in animals, near the leaf surface. Plants may have tannins that prevent digestion, glycosides that cause heart failure, and other toxins that cause diarrhea or blindness. Less severe toxins also make the plants unpalatable. Although several of these substances can be fatal to introduced livestock, many native animals have adapted. Tortoises, lizards, rodents, baboons, and birds depend on many Succulent Karoo plants for food. Four species of mole rats, a mole-like rodent, are especially well adapted to eat toxic bulbs. The prevalence of bulbs in inaccessible rock crevices may be a response to mole rat predation.

Various forms of mimicry that may fool a hungry animal are also common. *Crassula lycopodioides* looks like a dead stick, some *Anacampseros* species resemble bird droppings, *Lapidaria* and *Lithops* are hard to distinguish from stones, and *Psammophora* species are covered in soil or sand. Others may be hidden under larger plants and hard to find.

One-third of the Namaqualand flora are succulent species, and they are overwhelmingly endemic. Of the total 1,700 species of mesems, 99 percent are endemic to southern Africa. The most common succulents are widespread low, compact shrubs with succulent leaves. Most are less than 2 in (5 cm) tall, shallow-rooted, and evergreen. The most common shrubs, *Ruschia, Drosanthemum,* and *Leipoldtia,* are all mesembs. Some (*Othonna, Pelargonium, Sarcocaulon,* and *Tylecodon*) are also drought-deciduous in summer. Namaqualand is known for fields of miniature plants, many less than 0.4 in (1 cm), and some even smaller. Stem succulents are more common in the drier east where autumn thundershowers replace winter rain. The largest group of stem succulents is the stapeliads with 60 species. Common widespread stapeliad genera (*Trichocaulon, Quaqua,* and *Stapelia*) are usually small and hidden under shrub canopies. Also conspicuous are tree-size stem succulents. Because they have more water-storing capability, the few tall tree succulents such as halfmens and quiver trees (also called kokerbooms) are found in more extreme environments.

Most nonsucculent shrubs are evergreen, but some species of *Lycium* and *Dildelta spinosa* drop their leaves in summer. The largest genus is *Hermannia,* but strawflower and *Pteronia* are also common. The range of most nonsucculent shrubs extends beyond Namaqualand into the southern fynbos (chaparral) or east to the Nama-Karoo. Shrubs endemic to Namaqualand include daisies (*Pteronia, Osteospernum, Euryops*) and a pea (*Calliandra redacta*). Some shrubs will split down their main stem when they get too large, separating the plant into two individuals each dependent on its own root system. One of the smaller plants might have a better chance of survival during drought, whereas a single large one may not.

Nonsucculent trees are scarce and found mainly along water courses and in sites where runoff collects in the Hardeveld and Richtersveld landscapes. They are usually evergreen with sclerophyllous leaves, remnants of dry forests of past climates. Indicative of nonbrackish water, sweet thorn is widespread. Namaqua resin tree and *Rhus horrida* are endemic to Namaqualand. Graminoids are primarily grasses in dry locales and sedges aong water courses.

Succulent Karoo—Namaqualand-Namib. The Sperregebiet in southern Namibia, north of the Orange River, is a sandy diamond mine region that is little known. It is the Namib part of the Succulent Karoo. Vegetation includes low perennial shrubs with succulent leaves, mostly in the ice plant (mesemb), crassula, lily, and euphorbia families. Rocky outcrops in the coastal zone have low woody shrubs, such as succulent *Othonna furcata* and *Pelargonium* species and nonsucculent African daisies. Sandy areas support the nonsucculent woody shrub *Salsola nollothensis* and a spiky grass (*Cladoraphis cyperoides*). Lichens are abundant, especially the orange *Xanthoria turbinata.* Sand plains farther inland, where the spiny and leafless nara shrub forms hummocks, have low plant diversity. Farther inland, plants on the gravel plains are dense and shrubby with succulent dollar plant and *Euphorbia gummifera*, a succulent shrub 5 ft (1.5 m) tall.

Namaqualand, from the Orange River to the Olifants River, contains several physiographic regions. Rocks are primarily granite and gneiss, with some areas of sand and quartz gravel plains. The desert mountains near the Orange River are the Richtersveld, while the sandy coastal plain south of the river is the Sandveld. In contrast, the Hardeveld is the granite uplands on the Great Escarpment. The highest part of the Escarpment is the Kamiesberg Mountains, granite domes surrounded by the Hardeveld. The quartz plains in the south are the Knersvlakte.

Annual rainfall is generally less than 6 in (150 mm), but varies according to location (see Table 4.1). A significant change takes place from Succulent Karoo vegetation closer to the coast, where winter precipitation and fog dominate, to the inland Nama-Karoo, which is drier, with summer precipitation and no fog. The sandy coastal plain, the Sandveld, is wetter in the south and drier in the north. Gravel plains along the Orange River are dry. The central Hardeveld, at higher elevation, receives more orographic precipitation, and the Kamiesberg Mountains, at more than 5,500 ft (1,700 m), are the highest, wettest, and coldest region. In the Richtersveld, the west-facing high slopes are wet from cyclonic winter rain, while valleys and lower slopes are dry. Inland-facing slopes in the Richtersveld have summer rain and Nama-Karoo vegetation, with few species and less cover. The great variety of habitats, particularly in the Richtersveld, promotes a rich variety of plants.

Namaqualand has the richest flora of the Succulent Karoo, and the reliable rainfall is key to the richness of the biome. Prolonged drought is rare. The more than 3,000 species in Namaqualand are represented in more than 100 families and more than 600 genera. The presence and abundance of mesembs, irises, crassulas, tylecodons, and lachenalias distinguishes Namaqualand from other deserts where

Table 4.1 Precipitation Variation in Namaqualand

	Precipitation
Northern Sandveld	4 in (100 mm)
Southern Sandveld	6 in (150 mm)
Orange River Gravel Plains	2 in (50 mm)
Central Hardeveld	8 in (200 mm)
Kamiesberg Mountains	16 in (400 mm)
West-facing Richtersveld	12 in (300 mm)
Richtersveld Valleys	2 in (50 mm)

daisies, salt bushes, pea shrubs, and grasses dominate. In most of these families (mesembs, Crassulaceae, and stapeliads), all the species are succulent. Other families (sunflower) include succulent species, and others (iris and lachenalias) are mostly bulbs. The 10 genera containing the most species are also mostly succulents and bulbs.

Several broad vegetation types, or velds, in Namaqualand can be recognized, based on soil depth, texture, moisture, and temperature. The Afrikaans term veld refers to open grassy or low shrubby landscapes, and the prefix to the word provides a brief description. Only the main four (Strandveld, Vygieveld, Broken Veld, and Renosterveld) are addressed in this section. (The Fynbos community has more in common with the fynbos or chaparral biome.) Each veld, defined by plant community, has a unique assemblage of plants, and few are shared between velds. Most soils are shallow, a few inches (cm) to 1.5 ft (0.5 m), over impervious bedrock or a hardpan layer. An accumulation of calcium carbonate is locally called calcrete. A similar accumulation of silica is called dorbank. A deeper layer of sediment over an impermeable layer of calcrete or dorbank can store more water and thus support a more lush vegetation.

Strandveld is open shrubland, 1.5–6.5 ft (0.5–2 m) high, on the deep sand coastal plain. Species composition can include annuals, grasses, saltbush, dwarf mesembs, and bulbs according to age and depth of sand. Stunted by strong salty southwest winds, dominant plants in the coastal zone are a grass (*Cladophoris cyperoides*), small succulent shrubs of *Tetragonia fruticosa* and *Didelta carnosa*, a nonsucculent saltbush (*Salsola nollothensis*), and a creeping mesemb (*Amphibolia hutchinsonia*). Many dwarf mesembs grow where it is rockier. Because the sand is actively moving, dunefield vegetation is generally sparse. More variety is found in the tall strandveld on stabilized dunes slightly inland. Several species of shrubs, succulents, annuals, and bulbs, especially large-bulbed amaryllis, grow together in clumps up to 6.5 ft (2 m) high. Grassy strandveld also grows where dunes have been stabilized, but the grasses share the space with succulent-leaved *Othonna* shrubs.

Vygieveld, dominated by miniature succulents, such as mesembs and crassulas, is most widespread where soils are shallow and elevations are less than 1,000 ft (300 m). It occupies various types of rocky surfaces, including silty soils between the Hardeveld and the Sandveld at the base of the Escarpment, the quartz fields of Knersvlakte, gravel plains of the Orange River and the Richtersveld, and quartzite bedrock on the coastal plain (see Figure 4.12). Rainfall is less than 6 in (150 mm), but fog is frequent. Most of the region's succulents are found here, especially dwarf to small leaf succulent shrubs only 10–20 in

Lichen Fields

Alexander Bay at the mouth of the Orange River boasts the highest density of lichens in the world, a community similar to the foggy coast of Baja California. About 29 species of lichens and 49 species of higher plants, including several tiny succulents, thrive in the extremely foggy conditions. Water-repellent gypsum clay soil prevents infiltration of moisture and keeps the fog at the surface where it is used by plants. *Teloschistes capensis* is found only on gypsum substrate.

Figure 4.12 The most common vegetation type in the Succulent Karoo is shrubs with small, succulent leaves. *(Photos by author.)*

(25–50 cm) high. Species vary, but tiny plants are characteristic, with many local endemics. Vegetation in the quartz fields is sparse, covering only 5 percent of the surface, but because many plants are so small, 250 plants may grow in a 10 ft^2 (1 m^2) area. Each quartz field region has a distinct flora, and about 40 species are endemic to Knersvlakte alone. *Argyroderma, Conophytum, Oophytum, Phyllobolus digitatus*, several types of window plants, bulbs, miniature crassulas, and small *Tylecodon* are common.

Most of the miniature succulents are in the mild Succulent Karoo, where fog is common and temperatures are moderate. The exception is *Lithops* with its center of diversity in extreme environments on both sides of the Orange River and in the eastern Richtersveld. Summers are hot and dry, and rainfall is meager and not reliable, but *Lithops* manages to not only survive but also thrive.

Low mounds of earth, 16–115 ft (5–35 m) in diameter and called hueweltjies, were built by harvester termites. The organic matter stored by the termites and the now-resident burrowing animals such as aardvarks alters both the soil composition and texture, providing a local site for different plants. Where heuweltjies develop in silty soils over hardpan, dominant plants are small succulent *Ruschia, Drosanthemum, Tetragonia,* and *Othonna* shrubs.

Broken Veld is found on rocky escarpments throughout the Hardeveld and at the higher elevations in the Richtersveld where more rain falls. This is a rugged landscape of granite domes and boulders, with much variation in topography, runoff, and available water. The vegetation is generally taller, with fewer succulents.

Scattered tall shrubs or low trees 6.5–10 ft (2–3 m) "break up" the low succulent shrub layer of mesembs and *Euphorbias*, especially where runoff from the impermeable granite creates wetter pockets at the base of rock outcrops. In a transition from heuweltjie Vygieveld at lower elevations to Broken Veld, taller succulent shrubs, such as *Stoeberia frutescens, Rushia* species, and tortoise bush replace the low succulent shrubs. The trees may occur as scattered individuals or in dense thickets. Dominant trees on granite are Namaqua resin tree, *Rhus undulata,* smelly shepherd's tree, and African olive—all nonsucculent. The tree-like caudiciform *Tylecodon paniculatus* also grows on the rocky hills, along with several nonsucculent daisy shrubs. Succulent miniatures, bulbs, and annuals grow in cracks in the rocks. The unique tree succulents or caudiciforms halfmen, quiver tree, and bustard quiver tree, all endemic, grow as scattered individuals in this zone (see Plate XV).

On east-facing drier slopes with no fog, vegetation is less succulent and similar to the Nama-Karoo. *Stipagrostis ciliata* and Zulu fescue grasses form clumps among *Rhus undulata* trees, a cactus-like euphorbia (*Euphorbia virosa*), and several *Commiphora*, a caudiciform tree succulent.

Ornamental Plants

Several common garden or house plants are native to the deserts of southern Africa. Euryops daisy shrubs, with their evergreen leaves and large yellow flowers, are often used in landscaping because they require little care and tolerate heat and drought. The evergreen shrub *Osteosperma* and the annual *Dimorphotheca,* both called African daisy, brighten summer gardens with flowers of various colors. Ice plant (*Carpobrotus* and *Mesembryanathemum*) and a succulent called hearts-and-flowers (*Aptenia*) are common groundcovers in frost-free regions. *Amaryllis* bulbs produce beautiful lily-like flowers, either in the garden or as potted plants. Search the succulent and cactus section of your local home improvement store, and you'll find several potted South African succulents, such as *Kalanchoe, Crassula,* elephant's foot (*Portulacaria*), *Haworthia,* and even stone plants (*Pleiospeilos*)—often mislabeled "cactus."

Renosterveld is found in small upland areas of the Hardeveld and Richtersveld that receive 10–16 in (250–400 mm) of rainfall. (The vegetation type is also in the Little Karoo and Western Mountain Karoo, which are both part of the Southern Karoo.) Shrubs are taller, and vegetation is more dense than in the Broken Veld. Communities are dominated by tall evergreen shrubs, with few succulents. Most shrubs, such as Euryops daisy, *Pteronia* species, and *Stoebe plumosa*, are in the sunflower family, but wild rosemary also grows here. These sclerophyllous, nonsucculent shrubs are similar to those found in fynbos in the south. Thickets have trees of African olive, Namaqua resin tree, and wild peach. This subsection is distinguished by its many genera and species of bulbs, such as *Haemanthus, Babiana,* and *Ornithogalum.*

Dense forests of Cape willow, salt cedar, and Cape ebony dominate the riparian zone along the Orange River, which is fresh not brackish water. Small rivers support sweet thorn.

Succulent Karoo—Southern Karoo. The Southern Karoo has three regions. The Little Karoo is a shaly basin in the southeast enclosed by the Cape Fold Mountains.

The Western Mountain Karoo on the southwestern part of the Great Escarpment is shale, sandstone, and granite. The Tanqua Karoo is a stony basin between the Western Mountain Karoo and the Cape Fold Mountains. All regions are dominated by low-growing succulent-leaved shrubs, with few grasses, tall shrubs, or trees.

The Little Karoo, a rocky landscape at 1,000–2,000 ft (300–600 m), is extremely rich in succulents and endemics. Rainfall, distributed throughout the year, averages 6–12 in (150–300 mm), and summers are hot because of its inland location. Vegetation of the Little Karoo is similar to that of the drier eastern slope of the Broken Veld. The shale ridges and stony plains support trees along with low-succulent (*Crassula, Ruschia,* and *Tylecodon*) and nonsucculent (*Pteronia rhigozum* and *Osteospernum*) shrubs. Although succulent vegetation dominates, dwarf trees and shrubs are numerous. Succulents, particularly mesembs, dominate on drier flats; shrubby species are more common in rocky areas where water accumulates. Cape ebony is the principal shrub (or dwarf tree), but many small succulent shrubs, such as *Pelargonium ramosissimum* and *Sarcocaulon spinosum,* along with nonsucculent wild rosemary and *Pteronia pallens* also grow here. Runoff from stony hills concentrates in pockets of soil, creating varied habitats that contribute to endemism.

Although stony, the Western Mountain Karoo, has few solid rock outcrops. The gently rolling to steeply hilly landscape also has little soil. As the name implies, elevations are higher, 3,000–5,500 ft (900–1,700 m), and temperatures are cooler. The area receives 6–10 in (150–250 mm) of rain, with a slight winter maximum. Vegetation is a transition between Broken Veld and Little Karoo, with differences according to elevation. At higher elevations, it merges with Renosterveld and nonsucculent Broken Veld. Most typical are dwarf shrubs that grow unusually tall, up to 3 ft (1 m) high, where in other places the same species reach only 2–6 in (5–15 cm). The dominant shrub is nonsucculent *Pentzia spinescens,* with few succulents or perennial grasses. Lower and drier elevations support a more succulent karoo with many of the same species, but of normal height and in different proportions. *Salsola zeyheri* is more common, as are more mesembs.

The Tanqua Karoo along the valleys of the Tanqua and Doorn rivers is mostly flat, primarily 1,000–1,500 ft (300–450 m). Enclosed by mountains, the valley is in a rainshadow and receives less than 6 in (150 mm) of rain, primarily in winter. Although much of the vegetation has been degraded into barren shale by grazing, the natural landscape was dominated by short, stemless mesembs. Annuals and geophytes are numerous, and *Stipagrostis obtusa* grass can be abundant after a good rain. Natural landscapes that have been degraded by grazing or trampling to the extent that they have been invaded by species from adjacent more arid regions are called false karoo. Some of the original flora may still exist, but the dominance and composition has changed.

The Succulent Karoo habors many endemics, with no clear relationship with precipitation patterns. Endemic centers occur in both wet and dry areas. Rocky surfaces like quartzite, granite, and quartz fields support most of the endemics. Few

Table 4.2 Some Endemics of Namaqualand According to Centers of Endemism

Gariep	Kamiesberg	Van Rhynsdorp	Little Karoo
Juttadinteria[a]	*Babiana*[b]	*Argyroderma*[a]	*Cerochlamys*[b]
Arenifera[a]	*Moraea*[b]	*Oophytum*[a]	*Gibbaeum*[b]
Dracophyllus[a]	*Romulea*[b]	*Conophytum*[b]	*Zeuktophyllum*[b]
Fenestraria rhopalophylla[c]	*Lapeirousia*[b]	*Tylecodon*[b]	*Muirii*[a]
Lithops herrei[c]	*Cheiridopsis*[b]	*Crassula*[b]	*Glottiphylum*[b]
Euphorbia stapelioides[c]	*Conophytum*[b]	*Antimima*[a]	*Pleiospilos*[b]
Conophytum[b]	*Lithops*[b]		
Anacampseros[b]			
Euphorbia[b]			
Pachypodium namaquanum[c]			
Aloe pillansii[c]			
Aloe ramosissima[c]			
Aloe pearsonii[c]			
Portulacaria armiana[c]			
Portulacaria pygmaea[c]			

Notes: [a]Genus; [b]some species within genus; [c]species.

are found on uniform soils. Three centers of endemism are in Namaqualand-Namib and one is in the Southern Karoo (see Table 4.2).

The Gariep Center in Namaqualand-Namib extends from the mountains of the Richtersveld north into Sperregebiet. The topographic variety and climatic variations (fog, rainshadow, and winter and summer precipitation) create a variety of conditions and habitats that have given rise to 355 endemic species and three endemic genera. In the lichen fields, several species of lichens and higher plants are endemic, including tiny succulents. About 30 percent of the 55 *Conophytum* species are endemic to this area, and others include members of the geranium and milkweed families. The conspicuous tree succulents, such as halfmen and quiver trees are also found here. Also in Namaqualand is the Kamiesberg Center with 86 endemic species. Most are geophytes in the iris family and small mesemb succulents. The Van Rhynsdorp Center around the Knersvlakte in Namaqualand has 150 endemics, mostly dwarf succulents and geophytes growing in quartz gravel. *Antimima* is an edaphic endemic in the limestone gravels The Little Karoo Center in the Southern Karoo has 200–300 endemic species, mostly mesembs.

Nama-Karoo. With up to 12 in (300 mm) of rainfall, the Nama-Karoo, inland from both the Namib Desert and Namaqualand, is a wetter desert shrubland. It covers a large area of the South African Plateau in southern Namibia (where it is called Namaland) and in southwestern South Africa (where it is called Bushmanland and Upper Karoo). It also includes the Great Karoo, a large basin in South Africa at the base of the Plateau escarpment and north of the Cape Mountains. In contrast with most of the Succulent Karoo and particularly Namaqualand, this interior region receives summer rain from unpredictable and patchy thunderstorms. Because of its more continental location, summer temperatures can reach a maximum of 108° F (42 ° C) and frost is possible in winter (see Figure 4.1b). Many xerophytic dwarf shrubs in the sunflower family and short drought-deciduous, nonsucculent shrubs such as *Pentzia* and *Salsola* are typical. When precipitation is unusually high, short-lived annual grasses cover the ground. Before hunting and disease, these grasslands once supported herds of springbok and black wildebeest. Their habitat and much of the natural vegetation has been degraded by grazing.

The western part of the Nama-Karoo, Bushmanland, is the driest, with 2–8 in (50–200 mm) of rain each year. From a general elevation of 3,000 ft (900 m) in the north, the plateau gently slopes upward to 4,000 ft (1,200 m) in the south. Most drainage is north to the Orange River, but interior drainage basins also exist because of the aridity. The landscape is flat with few hills. It supports fewer shrubs and is grassier than the slightly wetter eastern part because grasses regenerate more quickly from seed than do shrubs after a long drought. Species of *Stipagrostis* are the major grasses, but some shorter grasses of *Eragrostis,* dropseed, and others also grow. Depending on composition of substrate, *Salsola* or *Pentzia spinescens* are common shrubs. Mesembs are more plentiful in rocky and hilly locales, and annuals and geophytes are abundant after good rains. *Ruschia* species occur on stony shales. The eastern part is the Upper Karoo, higher in elevation, 3,500–5,500 ft (1,050–1,700 m), and with more rain, 8–12 in (200–300 mm). Like Bushmanland, it is flat but also dotted with hills and low mountains. Substrate is stony (shale, sandstone, calcareous), but in places it may be covered with red loam. Floodplains along rivers are silty. Dominant grasses are *Eragrostis lehmanniana* and *Aristida congesta*. Nonsucculent shrubs include boxthorn, *Rhigozum trichotomum,* and *Rhus undulata.* A richer flora grows in stony areas, but mesembs are rare and the only significant succulent is the shrub *Ruschia ferox*.

Animals in the Namib-Karoo. Except in extreme desert environments, many animals are found throughout the Namib-Karoo. Most large mammals migrated via river valleys from the eastern savannas, and none are exclusive to the Namib or to the Succulent Karoo. Several animals have become locally extinct because of hunting by early settlers. Many formerly common large mammals, notably red hartebeest, Hartmann's zebra, and large predators such as cheetah, lion, and leopard, now remain only in parks or nature reserves. Endangered desert elephants, black rhinos, lions, and giraffes occasionally visit the Kaokoveld.

Various antelope are the dominant large herbivores. Gemsbok and springbok are the most common ungulates. The large gemsbok are well-adapted to the desert environment. Because they stop sweating when no water is available, their body temperature might soar to 113° F (45° C). The brain remains cool enough to prevent damage, however, because fine blood vessels at its base dissipate heat to the air. Congregating in herds up to 100 individuals, springbok are smaller grazing animals, weighing just 88 lb (40 kg). Although they will drink water if it is available, they usually obtain enough moisture from their diet. Their favorite foods are the succulent shrubs of the karoo. Both gemsbok and springbok are frequently hunted for their meat and skins. Steenbok is more common in the Nama-Karoo where it uses grasses and bushes for cover. Klipspringer, a small antelope just 22 in (55 cm) high and weighing only 40 lb (18 kg), inhabits rocky hillsides. Damara, or Kirk's dik-dik, is an even smaller antelope, 13.5 in (35cm) tall and 10 lb (4.5 kg). It lives in the driest parts of the region, depending on dew for water. Like the dik-dik, the crepuscular common duiker needs browse and cover and is independent of water. Burchell's zebra, formerly in both grasslands and desert, may now occasionally be found on plains or grasslands. They can go for five days without water.

Desert Horses

A herd of about 150 feral horses occupies the Nama-Karoo grasslands in the Central Namib between Aus and Luderitz. Different stories account for their origin. They may have been frightened away from a South African forces encampment by a German bombing event during World War I, abandoned by German troops, or escaped from farms. The horses have developed adaptations to desert conditions but still depend on a borehole (a well) that brings water to the surface, the only water source in the area. They can be seen from a covered shelter near the waterhole.

Burrowing animals, including mammals such as rodents but also reptiles and insects, are plentiful and varied. Ground squirrel, springhare, a mouse, porcupine, vlei rat, and shrew are common. Vlei rats lives in coastal nebkas, and elephant shrews prefer eastern plains. Brant's whistling rat, also a vlei rat, is found in Namaqualand. Sandy areas, where the grains are loose, can support only simple burrowing animals, such as insects or reptiles. More complex burrows or tunnels require something more solid. The hairy-footed gerbil selects patches of sand that are partly solidified by gemsbok urine. More stable soil is also found under grass tussocks and shrubs. Rock dassies, or hyrax, are found in rocky areas in all regions, in contrast to springhares, which prefer burrowing into sandy soils. Cape porcupines are widely distributed. Living in colonies, meerkats, also called suricate, are commonly seen members of the mongoose family (see Figure 4.13). Active during the day, one will stand guard on its hind legs while the others forage for insects, scorpions, and spiders. Small rodents also include pygmy mouse in rocky areas and golden mole in sandy areas. The common mole rat, using long claws to dig for worms and larvae underground, is widespread. Gerbils are found throughout the Namib-Karoo, with different genera or species occupying each region.

Typical savanna predators follow the prey. Black-backed jackal is common throughout the region and can often be seen on beaches scavenging for dead fish, seals, and other carrion. It also eats insects and hunts rodents and small antelope. Bat-eared fox is widely distributed, especially in the Nama-Karoo. After detecting invertebrates underground with its large ears, the mammal then digs them out for a meal. Although their major food is insects, the foxes will also hunt rodents and eat eggs. Caracal is widespread and common except in the driest desert; it avoids sandy areas. A smaller animal, weighing only 11 lb (5 kg), African wild cat is also

Figure 4.13 Meerkats in the Namib-Karoo are social burrowing animals that live in colonies. *(Courtesy of Shutterstock. Copyright: EcoPrint.)*

absent from the driest desert and prefers rocky areas with cover. Its diet is primarily mice and rats.

Other animals widely distributed except in the driest Namib Desert areas include both herbivores and carnivores. Warthogs eat grasses and use their tusks to dig out succulent bulbs. Cape hares are fast runners, up to 48 mph (75 kpm), and can leap long distances to avoid predation. They eat their droppings to obtain the most nutrition from their diet of plants and berries. Honey badgers are carnivores that feed primarily on insects and their larvae, rodents, birds, and lizards, using powerful claws to dig out their prey. They don't eat honey but will tear apart a beehive to get the developing bees. Mongoose are social animals, with several living together in complex burrow systems. They eat insects, small mammals, lizards, and eggs, and are preyed on by raptors, snakes, and jackals. The aardwolf, a relative of hyenas, digs out termites for food and is found wherever termite mounds exist, but not on the desert coast. Nocturnal hunters, such as bat-eared fox, aardvark, and brown hyena, take refuge in burrows during the day. Also absent from the Namib Desert are Chacma baboons. Common in most habitats, troops of up to 100 individuals can be seen along roadsides. They can be pests in agricultural areas.

Because of the lack of surface water, few birds are year-round residents. Ostriches are common, living in groups of up to 50 birds and eating primarily seeds and plants. Unlike other birds that have four toes on each foot, ostrich have only two. The nail of the larger toe is enlarged, becoming hoof-like, an adaptation that helps the bird run as fast as 40 mph (65 kph). Like many other desert animals, they have little need for free water, getting enough moisture from their food. Other nesting birds include Karoo Lark, which is endemic to the shrublands of southern Africa. The Pied Crow is common in several open habitats, where it survives on a variety of food—insects, eggs, seeds, carrion, and small mammals and birds. Present in all three desert areas, the Rock Kestrel is a small falcon that preys on rodents, small birds, and insects. Namib Desert Lark is restricted to dune areas in the Namib Desert. A seed-eater endemic to the Namib, Cinderella Waxbill, is a gray bird with a strikingly red bill and rump feathers. Several species of cursorial (adapted to running) bustards live in the desert and do not need free water. Ruppell's Korhaan, also called Ruppell's Bustard, lives on the fringes of the Namib, visiting the dunes after a rain.

Ostrich Eggs

After mating with only one male, the female ostriches in his harem use a communal nest, a simple pit scraped into the ground, which ultimately may hold as many as 60 eggs. Each egg weighs about 3 lb (1.4 kg). Females incubate the nest during the day and are relieved by the male at dusk. The sandy-colored females blend in with the ground during the day, while the darker male is less obvious at night. After hatching, the male typically defends and raises the chicks.

With more than 100 species, reptiles in the Namib-Karoo are especially diverse. Approximately half are endemic, including the Namba padloper tortoise, which is found only in the Sperregebiet, and the small Namaqualand speckled padloper in mountain areas. Other Namaqualand endemics include several spinytail lizards and three geckos. Many other reptiles, such as the geometric tortoise and the related karoo tent tortoise, have restricted ranges in the Succulent Karoo. In contrast, the leopard (or mountain) tortoise is widespread in grassland habitats, feeding on both grasses and succulents (see Figure 4.14a). Individuals can become quite large, up to 24 in (60 cm) long, and weigh up to 80 lb (36 kg). When he is ready for mating, the head and upper body of the male southern rock agama lizard become bright blue (see Figure 4.14b).The wedge-snouted sand lizard burrows into cooler layers of sand when surface temperatures rise too high. Peringuey's adder, a mildly venomous snake, is characteristic of Namibian dunes, moving with a side-winding motion. It hunts by burrowing into the dune with only eyes and tail tip exposed. A similar species, the Namaqua dwarf adder, is found in Namaqualand. Cape cobra is also found in the Karoo and desert regions. Two nonvenomous snakes include the southwestern shovel-snout snake, which digs through soft soil in search of reptile eggs, and the Karoo sand snake, which chases lizards on sandy flats. Of 15 amphibians, three frogs are endemic—Boulenger's short-headed frog, Namaqualand short-headed frog, and *Bufo robinsoni.*

Drinking Habits

The web-footed gecko gets water by licking fog that condenses on its head. The sand plated lizard gets water from eating wild melons in dunes. The Namib Desert beetle (*Onymacris unguicularis*) gathers fog droplets on its body by lowering its head and facing into the foggy wind. Grooves on its body and face channel the moisture down into its mouth. Other beetles (*Lepidochora discoidalis*) dig depressions in sand on the windward side of dunes and drink dew that collects.

The Namib-Karoo also has many invertebrate endemics, especially arachnids (spiders, scorpions, ticks), beetles, and stinging bees and ants. The monkey beetle is an important pollinator in the Karoo. Desert insects have typical adaptations to water scarcity. Some scorpions and a tick (*Ornithodoros savignyi*) may not need water for a year if

Figure 4.14 The Namib-Karoo supports a variety of reptiles, including (a) leopard or mountain tortoise and (b) southern rock agama lizard. *(Photos by author.)*

they are first satiated. Others exist on metabolic water from insects and prey or even from seeds.

The Kalahari is not climatically a desert. Sandy soils ensure a moisture supply that supports tree or shrub savanna. Refer to *Grassland Biomes* in this series.

Unique Small Deserts

Galapagos Islands. The Galapagos archipelago is located almost exactly on the Equator 600 mi (960 km) west of South America. Plants and animals evolved in isolation, and the island group is well known for unique and endemic species. Darwin first studied the biota here, taking note of species that evolved to fit various unfilled niches. The islands are entirely oceanic, meaning that they developed volcanically from the seafloor and have never been connected to any continent. Almost all of the flora originated from South America and was transported to the Galapagos Islands by birds or by rafting (floating on debris). More than 500 species of vascular plants are present, and more than 180 are endemic to the islands. Animal endemics include insects, land snails, finches, giant tortoises, iguanas, and rice rats.

The islands are desert because they lie in the Humboldt Current. From May to December, the cold waters, 66° F (19° C), cause cool temperatures, mist, and drizzling rain. Due to a shift in ocean currents, December to May is the hot, wet season. March can be as warm as 86° F (30° C) with up to 3 in (80 mm) of rainfall. During an El Niño event when the ocean stays warm, the marine ecosystem suffers. Without the upwelling of cold water, the ocean has fewer nutrients, which upsets the food chain. Land-based populations, however, increase because of more abundant rainfall.

Vegetation varies with elevation, but the arid zone with drought-tolerant, xerophytic species of cacti, trees, shrubs, and herbaceous plants generally extends up to 260–400 ft (80–120 m) in elevation. Dominant vegetation includes endemic cacti—the giant *Opuntia echios, O. helleri,* candelabra cactus, and lava cactus (see Figure 4.15a). Palo santo and Jerusalem thorn are typical drought-deciduous trees, along with shrubby specimens of Galapagos acacia, honey mesquite, and *Croton scouleri*. Higher elevations have both more rainfall and more fog, defining them as humid rather than arid zones. Several plant species have been introduced, threatening both native plant and animal life.

Best-known animals are marine iguana and giant tortoise, which has different subspecies on several of the islands (see Figure 4.15b). Land iguanas have also evolved, and lava lizards are distinct. The number of endemics increases when subspecies are considered. Sea birds, such as gulls, albatross, frigatebirds, and boobies depend on the sea for food but nest and breed on the desert shores. Land birds, especially Galapagos Mockingbird, Galapagos Dove, and several genera of finches, feed as well as nest on land. Depending on the bird, food includes lizards, insects, seeds, or even small birds. Many bird species are endemic. Mammals are few because of the distance from the mainland but include rice rats and bats.

Socotra. The Socotra archipelago, a chain of islands in the Arabian Sea at approximately 12° N and 54° E, has a unique biotic assemblage, especially on the island of Socotra itself. Although politically a part of Yemen, Socotra is geologically and biogeographically an extension of the Horn of Africa. Many species and some genera that were formerly widespread on the African mainland are now endemic to Socotra. The island is known for its biodiversity, caused by its isolation and local

Figure 4.15 The Galapagos Islands is famous for its many endemic species, including (a) the tree-size *Opuntia echios* and (b) giant tortoises. *(Photos by author.)*

microclimate variations. Of the 850 types of plants, about 250 species and 10 genera are endemic. The major landform is a limestone plateau 1,000–2,300 ft (300–700 m) high bounded by an abrupt escarpment down to a sandy or rocky coastal plain that almost encircles the island. The Hagghier Mountains, a granite and crystalline mountain mass, rises to 5,000 ft (1,500 m) in the northwest. Most endemics are on the limestone plateau and mountain slopes.

The island lies in the path of monsoon winds between Africa and Asia. From April to October hot dry winds originating in Africa carry no moisture and plants must withstand desiccating conditions. Beginning in November and lasting until March, the winds reverse, bringing unreliable wet monsoon flow from the northeast. Rainfall is low, about 6 in (150 mm) on the coastal plain. Clouds in the mountains act like fog, and even though it may not rain, deposition from mist and nighttime dew provide essential moisture. Because of its island location, temperatures are moderate compared with most tropical locations. On the coastal plain, maximum temperatures average 80°–100° F (27°–38° C), and minima average 63°–80° F (17°–27° C). Temperatures decrease with elevation.

The coastal plains are covered with deciduous shrub thickets of *Croton socotranus* with a few trees of *Dendrosicyos socotranus* and Christ's thorn jujube. *Dendrosicyos* is the only member of the cucumber family to grow tree size. The coastal foothills and limestone cliffs support the most common plant community, an open shrubland with many species but dominated by two endemic shrubs, *Croton socotranus* and *Jatropha unicostata.* A few caudiciform tree species, such as *Euphorbia arbuscula,* dragon's blood, *Commiphora,* and *Adenium socotranum,* stand taller above the shrubs. Most of the succulents have developed a globular or columnar shape (called caudiciform), with less surface area for water loss. A waxy surface both decreases transpiration and reflects solar radiation. Two of the more interesting plants are *Adenium socotranum*, sometimes called desert rose, and dragon's blood tree. The globular caudex of many adeniums is as large as a small car (see Plate XVI). Given enough moisture, leaves and flowers emerge from stubby stems. Dragon's blood tree, a large tree with rosettes of succulent leaves, is named for the blood-red resin used by ancient Greeks and Egyptians as incense, dye, and medicine. On the higher mountain slopes, lichens and cushion plants cover the rocks.

Only seven mammal species inhabit Socotra, and because of the difficulty of mammals migrating to island environments, all were introduced, except perhaps a bat (*Rhinopoma* spp.) and a shrew (*Suneus* spp.). Of 24 reptiles, 21 are endemic, illustrating the significance of isolation. Birds, however, are mobile, and only a few of the many species on the island are endemic. These include a starling, a sunbird, a sparrow, and the Socotra Golden-winged Grosbeak. In spite of seasonal water supplies, no amphibians are found. It is probable that they may have become extinct during extreme drought conditions in the past.

Although most of the human population is limited to the coastal plain, grazing and woodcutting for fuel have degraded the limestone plateau and mountain environments. Habitat is fragmented and many species are endangered.

Madagascar. Although the narrow coastal strip about 30 mi (50 km) wide from Morondava (20° S) on the west coast south to Cap Ste. Marie (25° S) on the south coast of Madagascar receives up to 18 in (450 mm) of annual rainfall, the region qualifies as a desert with a unique variety of drought-adapted plants. The southwest location places it in the rainshadow of the island, excluding rain-bearing northeast winds. Annual rainfall is unevenly distributed, and the year's total might fall during only one month of thunderstorms. Precipitation is sporadic and localized, and no rain may occur in an area for 12–18 months. Porous limestone bedrock or sandy soil retains little water, contributing to the aridity. However, high relative humidity, 60 percent near the coast, is important for fog and dew formation. Dew is so extreme in some places that natives collect it as a water source. Temperatures are generally not extreme, although maximum temperatures more than 100° F (38° C) are possible. Minima are quite warm, 60°–70° F (15°–21° C). During the dry season with no cloud cover, intense solar radiation in this tropical latitude can increase surface soil and rock temperature to as much as158° F (70° C).

The island has many endemics and unique growthforms. This area coincides with distribution of a major plant family, the Didiereaceae, and also with some significant *Euphorbia* species. Dominant vegetation is deciduous thorn forest that is green only after a rain. Dense thickets of succulents and thorn bushes up to 10 ft (3 m) high are mixed with taller tree succulents of Didieraceae and other families 33–50 ft (10–15 m) tall. Groundcover is generally sparse, depending on density of forest and amount of light transmitted. Annuals and grasses are few, and geophytes are almost absent.

Adaptations to the arid environment include green bark or leaf-like shoots that continue photosynthesis after leaves have fallen. Most plants have small leaves, especially many tree and bush euphorbias. Many plants have thorns, which are modified shoots or leaves, notably *Alluaudia, Pachypodium, Mimosa,* and *Didieria* species. Several types of succulence are common. Most impressive is the stem succulence of plants collectively called bottle trees—baobab (*Adansonia madagascariensis*), bottle tree (*Moringa drouhardi*), *Commiphera,* and *Pachypodium lamerei*—the trunks or stems of which can be 6 ft (1.8 m) in diameter. Other genera have smaller caudices, or basal trunks. Two major genera of leaf succulents are *Aloe* and *Kalanchoe,* some which are tree like and others part of the shrub layer or undergrowth. Most dwarf species in the undergrowth are leaf succulent euphorbias, such as *Euphorbia cylindrifolia* and *E. francoisii.* Root succulence is also common in several euphorbia species, especially *E. Cap-Saintemariensis* and *E. francoisii.* Most plants utilize the CAM method of photosynthesis.

Although many distinct communities form on different substrate and localities on the island, they are consistent in that the tree layer is sparse, the shrub layer can be a dense thicket, and the ground layer is sparse or nonexistent. While the tree layer is dominated by only two families, Didiereaceae and Euphorbiaceae, several families occur in the shrub layer, including begonia, mallow, Pedaliaceae, and Caesalpiniaceae.

No large animals are found here, but ostriches have been extinct only since colonization. Six species of primate, such as ring-tailed lemur (also called maki) and

Verreaux's sifaka (also a lemur), are found in the dense spiny thickets. They represent four of the five endemic families.

Endemism of both plants and animals is high, almost one-half the genera and 95 percent of the species. All the dominant forest species in the Didieraceae family, including *Didieria, Alluaudia*, and *Alluaudiopsis*, are endemic. Many reptiles and birds are also endemic or near endemic, including two nocturnal geckos, the radiated tortoise, spider tortoise, and a boa. Endemic birds include two couas and two vangas, among others. Several genera of lemurs are endemic. Many of the endemics are localized and rare.

Information on biota is limited, and the forests are rapidly disappearing due to wildfires, woodcutting for charcoal and construction, and clearing for agriculture or grazing. Problems have developed with the introduction of invasive plants like prickly pear cactus and the collection of plants for commercial trade.

Further Readings

Books

Constant, Pierre. 1997. *The Galapagos Islands: A Natural History Guide.* Lincolnwood, IL: Passport Books.

Cowling, Richard, and Shirley Pierce. 1999. *Namaqualand: A Succulent Desert.* Vlaeberg, South Africa: Fernwood Press.

Internet Sources

Charleston County School District (South Carolina) Can Do Project. n.d. "Exploring the Atacama." http://www.musc.edu/cando/geocam/atacama/atacama.html.

Dillon, Michael O. n.d. "South America: Lomas Formations of the Atacama Desert, Northern Chile." Smithsonian Institution. http://botany.si.edu/projects/cpd/sa/sa43.htm.

Dillon, Michael O. n.d. "South America: Lomas Formations Peru." Smithsonian Institution. http://botany.si.edu/projects/cpd/sa/sa42.htm.

Extreme Science. n.d. "Atacama Desert." http://www.extremescience.com/DriestPlace.htm.

San Diego Natural History Museum. n.d. "Ocean Oasis Field Guide: Vizcaino Desert." http://www.oceanoasis.org/fieldguide/vizcainodesert.html.

South African National Biodiversity Institute. n.d. "Welcome to PlantZAfrica.com." http://www.plantzafrica.com.

Appendix

Biota of the West-Coast Fog Desert Biome (arranged geographically)

North American Fog Deserts

Some Characteristic Plants of the Vizcaino Desert	
Trees	
Elephant tree	*Bursera* spp.
Torote	*Pachycormus* spp.
Shrubs	
Bursage	*Ambrosia camphorata*
Magdalena bursage	*Ambrosia magdalenae*
Saltbush	*Atriplex* spp.
Allscale	*Atriplex polycarpa*
Bush buckwheat	*Eriogonum fasciculatum*
Boojum or Cirio	*Fouquieria columnaris*
Ocotillo	*Fouquieria diguetii*
Ocotillo	*Fouquieria splendens*
Palmer's frankenia	*Frankenia palmeri*
Creosote bush	*Larrea tridentata*
Boxthorn	*Lycium decumens*
Ice plant	*Mesembryanthemum crystallinum*[a]
Jojoba	*Simmondsia chinensis*
San Diego goldeneye	*Viguiera laciniata*
Large leaf succulents	
Agave	*Agave avellanidens*
Blue agave	*Agave cerulata*
Desert mescal	*Agave deserti*
Maguey	*Agave shawii*

(*Continued*)

Dudleya or Siempreviva	*Dudleya* spp.
Datillo	*Yucca valida*
Cactus	
Barrel cactus	*Ferocactus* spp.
Senita	*Lophocereus schottii*
Pitaya agria	*Machaerocereus gummosus*
Cholla	*Opuntia prolifera*
Cardon	*Pachycereus pringlei*
Grasses and forbs	
Sand verbena	*Abronia villosa*
Three-awn grass	*Aristida* spp.
Daisy	*Dyssodia anthemidifolia*
Wooly plantain	*Plantago insularis*
Lichens and bromeliads	
Niebla (Fruticose lichen)	*Niebla* spp.
Ramalina (Fruticose lichen)	*Ramalina* spp.
Roccella (Fruticose lichen)	*Roccella* spp.
Ball moss (Bromeliad)	*Tillandsia recurvata*

Note: [a]Introduced.

Some Characteristic Animals of the Vizcaino Desert

Herbivores	
San Quintin kangaroo rat	*Dipodomys gravipes*
Merriam's kangaroo rat	*Dipodomys merriami*
Vizcaino kangaroo rat	*Dipodomys peninsularis*
Black-tailed jackrabbit	*Lepus californicus*
White-throated woodrat or Packrat	*Neotoma albigula*
Baja California rock squirrel	*Spermophilus atricapillus*
Carnivores	
Coyote	*Canis latrans*
Kit fox	*Vulpes macrotis*
Birds	
Burrowing Owl	*Athene cunicularia*
Cactus Wren	*Campylorhynchus brunneicapillus*
Gilded Flicker	*Colaptes auratus*
California Quail	*Lophortyx californicus*
Gila Woodpecker	*Melanerpes uropygialis*
Harris Hawk	*Parabutea unicinctus*
Bendire's Thrasher	*Toxostoma bendirei*
Reptiles and amphibians	
Zebra-tailed lizard	*Callisaurus draconoides*
Orange-throated whiptail lizard	*Cnemidophorus hyperythrus*

Coastal whiptail lizard	*Cnemidophorus tigris multiscutatus*
Banded gecko	*Coleonyx variegatus*
Red diamond rattlesnake	*Crotalus rubes*
Desert iguana	*Dipsosaurus dorsalis*
Desert horned lizard	*Phrynosoma platyrhinos*
Regal horned lizard	*Phrynosoma solare*

South American Fog Deserts

Some Characteristic Plants of the Sechura Desert

Trees	
Palo verde	*Cercidium praecox*
Honey mesquite	*Prosopis juliflora*
Willow	*Salix* spp.
Cactus	
Armatocereus	*Armatocereus cartwrightianus*
Monvillea	*Monvillea diffusa*
Monvillea	*Monvillea maritima*
Neoraimondia	*Neoraimondia arequipensis*
Pilocereus	*Pilocereus tweedyanus*
Grasses and forbs	
Saltgrass	*Distichlis spicata*
Glasswort	*Salicornia fruticosa*
Dropseed grass	*Sporobolus* spp.
Bromeliad	
Tillandsia	*Tillandsia* spp.

Some Characteristic Animals of the Sechura Desert

Herbivores	
Southern vizcacha rat	*Lagidium viscacia*
Guanaco	*Lama guanaco*
Sechura rat	*Phyllotis gerbillus*
Carnivores	
Argentine gray fox	*Pseudolopex griseus*
Sechura fox	*Pseudolopex sechurae*
Birds	
Cactus Canastero	*Asthenes cactorum*
Burrowing Owl	*Athene cunicularia*
Turkey Vulture	*Cathartes aura*

(*Continued*)

Inca Tern	*Larosterna inca*
Gulls	*Larus* spp.
Brown Pelican	*Pelecanus occidentalis*
Oasis Hummingbird	*Rhodopis vesper*
Peruvian Sheartail Hummingbird	*Thaumastura cora*
Blue-black Grassquit	*Volatinia jacarina*
Reptiles and amphibians	
Roedinger's lancehead viper	*Bothrops roedingeri*
Chilean lizard	*Callopistes maculatus*
Lava lizard	*Tropidurus peruvianus*
Lava lizard	*Tropidurus theresiae*
Lava lizard	*Tropidurus thoracicus*

Some Characteristic Plants of the Peruvian-Chilean Desert

Subtrees and shrubs	
Long-spine acacia	*Acacia macracantha*
In the Pea family	*Caesalpinia* spp.
Paloverde	*Cercidium praecox*
In the Euphorbia family	*Croton* spp.
Cactus	
Armatocereus	*Armatocereus procerus*
Candelabra cactus	*Browningia candelaris*
Old man of Peru	*Epostoa melanostele*
Haagocereus	*Haagocereus aureispinus*
Melocactus	*Melocactus trujilloensis*
Neochilenia	*Neochilenia* spp.
Neoraimondia	*Neoraimondia arequipensis*
Pygmaeocereus	*Pygmaeocereus rowleyanus*
Trichocereus	*Trichocereus chiloensis*
Lichens and bromeliads	
Cladonia (Fruticose lichen)	*Cladonia* spp.
Telochistes (Fruticose lichen)	*Telochistes* spp.
Tillandsia (Bromeliad)	*Tillandsia latifolia*

Some Characteristic Animals of the Peruvian-Chilean Desert

Herbivores	
Southern vizcacha rat	*Lagidium viscacia*
Guanaco	*Lama guanaco*
Leaf-eared mouse	*Phyllotis limatus*
Carnivores	
Argentine gray fox	*Pseudolopex griseus*
Sechura fox	*Pseudolopex sechurae*

Birds	
Burrowing Owl	*Athene cunicularia*
Turkey Vulture	*Cathartes aura*
Tamarugo Conebill	*Conirostrum tamarugense*
Chilean Woodstar	*Eulidia yarrellii*
Thick-billed Miner	*Geositta crassirostris*
Coastal Miner	*Geositta peruviana*
Inca Tern	*Larosterna inca*
Gulls	*Larus* spp.
Brown Pelican	*Pelecanus occidentalis*
Oasis Hummingbird	*Rhodopis vesper*
White-throated Earthcreeper	*Upucerthia albigula*
Blue-black Grassquit	*Volatinia jacarina*
Slender-billed Finch	*Xenospingus concolor*
Rufous-collared Sparrow	*Zonotrichia capensis*
Reptiles and amphibians	
Chilean lizard	*Callopistes maculatus*
Lava lizard	*Tropidurus peruvianus*
Lava lizard	*Tropidurus theresiae*
Lava lizard	*Tropidurus thoracicus*

Some Characteristic Plants of the Atacama Desert

Shrubs	
Rock purslane	*Calandrinia grandiflora*
Ephedra	*Ephedra* spp.
Euphorbia	*Euphorbia lactiflua*
In the Nightshade family	*Nolana mollis*
In the Iceplant family	*Tetragonia maritima*
Cactus	
Copiapoa	*Copiapoa* spp.
Eriosyce	*Eriosyce taltalensis*
Eriosyce	*Eriosyce rodentiophila*
Eulychnia	*Eulychnia iquiquensis*
Eulychnia	*Eulychnia saint-pieana*
Neochilenia	*Neochilenia* spp.
Opuntia	*Opuntia* spp.
Bromeliads	
Deuterocohnia	*Deuterocohnia chrysantha*
Puya	*Puya boliviensis*
Tillandsia	*Tillandsia geissei*
Bulbs and rhizomes	
Peruvian lily	*Alstroemeria* spp.
Lily	*Argylia radiata*
American amaryllis	*Hippeastrum ananuca*

Grasses and forbs	
In the Borage family	*Cryptantha parviflora*
Lupine	*Lupinus* spp.
Violet	*Viola polypoda*

Some Characteristic Animals of the Atacama Desert

Herbivores	
Southern vizcacha rat	*Lagidium viscacia*
Guanaco	*Lama guanaco*
Darwin's leaf-eared mouse	*Phyllotis darwini*
Carnivores	
Argentine gray fox	*Pseudolopex griseus*
Birds	
Burrowing Owl	*Athene cunicularia*
Turkey Vulture	*Cathartes aura*
Inca Tern	*Larosterna inca*
Gulls	*Larus* spp.
Brown Pelican	*Pelecanus occidentalis*
Oasis Hummingbird	*Rhodopis vesper*
Rufous-collared Sparrow	*Zonotrichia capensis*
Blue-black Grassquit	*Volatinia jacarina*
Reptiles and amphibians	
Chilean lizard	*Callopistes maculatus*
Lava lizard	*Tropidurus peruvianus*
Lava lizard	*Tropidurus theresiae*
Lava lizard	*Tropidurus thoracicus*

Southwest African Fog Deserts

Some Characteristic Plants of the Namib Desert

Trees	
Camel thorn	*Acacia erioloba*
Mustard tree	*Salvadora persica*
Salt cedar or Tamarisk	*Tamarix usneoides*
Tree succulents and caudiciforms	
In the Bursera family	*Commiphora* spp.
In the Grape family	*Cyphostemma* spp.
Euphorbia	*Euphorbia guerichiana*
African moringa	*Moringa ovalifolia*
Shrubs	
Nara	*Alcanthosicyos horrida*
Milkbush	*Euphorbia gregaria*

In the Morning glory family	*Merremia multisecta*
Resurrection plant	*Myrothamnus flabellifolia*
In the Iceplant family	*Othonna lasiocarpa*
In the Geranium family	*Pelargonium* spp.
In the Goosefoot family	*Salsola nollothensis*
In the Goosefoot family	*Salsola zeyheri*
In the Geranium family	*Sarcocaulon mossamedense*
Sea purslane	*Sesuvium* spp.
Welwitschia	*Welwitschia mirabilis*
Dollar plant	*Zygophyllum stapfii*
Small leaf succulents	
Living stones	*Lithops rushiorum*
Stem succulents (not cacti)	
Hoodia	*Hoodia* spp.
Grasses and forbs	
Lovegrass	*Eragrostis spinosa*
Tobacco	*Nicotania glauca*[a]
Stipagrostis grass	*Stipagrostis obtusa*
Stipagrostis grass	*Stipagrostis subacaulis*
Alkali blite	*Suaeda fruticosa*
Lichens	
Wandering lichen	*Omphalodium convolutum*
Parmelia (Fruticose)	*Parmelia* spp.
Ramalina (Fruticose)	*Ramalina* spp.
Telochistes (Fruticose)	*Telochistes capensis*
Usnea (Fruticose)	*Usnea* spp.
Xanthoparmelia (Foliose)	*Xanthoparmelia hyporbytida*

Note: [a]Introduced.

Some Characteristic Animals of the Namib Desert

Herbivores	
Springbok	*Antidorcas marsupialis*
Black rhino	*Diceros bicornis*
Hartman's zebra	*Equus zebra hartmanni*
Dune hairy-footed gerbil	*Gerbillurus paeba*
Setzer's hairy-footed gerbil	*Gerbillurus setzeri*
Giraffe	*Giraffa camelopardalis*
Cape porcupine	*Hystrix africaeaustralis*
Desert elephant	*Loxodonta africana*
Kirk's dik-dik	*Madoqua kirkii*
Gerbil mouse	*Malacothrix typica*

(*Continued*)

Pygmy mouse	*Mus minutioides*
Klipspringer	*Oreotragus oreotragus*
Gemsbok or Oryx	*Oryx gazella*
Vlei rat	*Paratomys littledalei*
Springhare	*Pedetes capensis*
Hyrax or Dassy	*Procavia capensis*
Common duiker	*Sylvicapra grimmia*
Ground squirrel	*Xerus inauris*
Carnivores	
Saddle-backed jackal	*Canis mesomelas*
Common mole rat	*Cryptomys hottentotus*
Golden mole	*Eremitalpa granti namibensis*
Brown hyena	*Hyaena brunnea*
Short-eared elephant shrew	*Macroscelides proboscideus*
Bat-eared fox	*Otocyon megalotis*
Lion	*Panthera leo*
Meerkat or Suricate	*Suricata suricatta*
Birds	
Namib Desert Lark	*Ammomanes grayi*
Karoo Lark	*Certhilauda albescens*
Pied Crow	*Corvus albus*
Cinderella Waxbill	*Estrilda thomensis*
Ruppell's Korhaan or Ruppell's Bustard	*Eupodotis rueppellii*
Rock Kestrel	*Falco tinnuculus*
Ostrich	*Struthio camelus australis*
Reptiles and amphibians	
Sand plated lizard or Desert plated lizard	*Angolosaurus skoogi*
Peringuey's adder	*Bitis peringueyi*
Spiny lizards	*Cordylus* spp.
Mountain tortoise or Leopard tortoise	*Geochelone pardalis*
Namba padloper tortoise	*Homopus bergeri*
Wedge-snouted sand lizard	*Meroles cuneirostris*
Cape cobra	*Naja nivea*
Web-footed gecko	*Palmatogecko rangei*
Southwestern shovel-nose snake	*Prosymna frontalis*
Karoo sand snake	*Psammophis notostictus*

Some Characteristic Plants of the Succulent Karoo

Trees	
Sweet thorn	*Acacia karoo*
Smelly shepherds tree	*Boscia foetida*
African olive	*Oleo europaea africana*
Cape ebony	*Euclea pseudebenus*

Wild peach	*Kiggelaria africana*
Namaqua resin tree	*Ozoroa dispar*
Sumac	*Rhus horrida*
Sumac	*Rhus undulata*
Cape willow	*Salix capensis*
Salt cedar or Tamarisk	*Tamarix usneoides*
Tree succulents and caudiciforms	
Quiver tree or Kokerboom	*Aloe dichotoma*
Pearson's aloe	*Aloe pearsonii*
Bustard quiver tree	*Aloe pillansii*
Maiden's quiver tree	*Aloe ramosissima*
In the Bursera family	*Commiphora* spp.
Halfmen	*Pachypodium namaquanum*
Botterboom	*Tylecodon paniculatus*
Nonsucculent shrubs	
Nara	*Alcanthosicyos horrida*
Wild rosemary	*Eriocephalus africanus*
Euryops daisy	*Euryops multifidus*
African daisy	*Osteospernum crassifolium*
In the Sunflower family	*Pentzia spinescens*
In the Sunflower family	*Pteronia rhigozum*
In the Sunflower family	*Pteronia pallens*
Saltbush	*Salsola nollothensis*
In the Goosefoot family	*Salsola zeyheri*
In the Sunflower family	*Stoebe plumosa*
Succulent shrubs	
In the Sunflower family	*Didelta carnosa*
Iceplant or Dewplant	*Drosanthemum luderitzii*.
Euphorbia	*Euphorbia gummifera*
In the Sunflower family	*Othonna* spp.
In the Geranium family	*Pelargonium ramossissimum*
Elephant's foot	*Portulacaria armiana*
Elephant's foot	*Portulacaria pygmaea*
Shrubby iceplant	*Ruschia* spp.
In the Geranium family	*Sarcocaulon spinosum*
In the Iceplant family	*Stoeberia frutescens*
In the Iceplant family	*Tetragonia* spp.
In the Iceplant family	*Tetragonia fruticosa*
Botterboom	*Tylecodon* spp.
Tortoise bush	*Zygophyllum morgsana*
Dollar plant	*Zygophyllum stapfii*
Small leaf succulents	
In the Iceplant family	*Amphibolia hutchinsonia*
In the Portulaca family	*Anacampseros* spp.

(*Continued*)

In the Iceplant family	*Arenifera* spp.
Iceplant	*Carpobrotus* spp.
In the Iceplant family	*Cheiridopsis* spp.
In the Iceplant family	*Conophytum* spp.
In the Jade plant family	*Crassula* spp.
Baby's toes	*Fenestraria* spp.
In the Asphodel family	*Haworthia* spp.
Stone plant	*Lithops* spp.
In the Iceplant family	*Oophytum* spp.
In the Iceplant family	*Phyllobolus digitatus*
Stem succulent (not cactus)	
Euphorbia	*Euphorbia virosa*
Bulbs and rhizomes	
Amaryllis family	Amaryllidaceae
In the Iris family	*Babiana* spp.
In the Asphodel family	*Bulbine* spp.
In the Amaryllis family	*Haemanthus* spp.
Hyacinth family	Hyacinthaceae
Iris family	Iridaceae
In the Hyacinth family	*Lachenalia* spp.
Lily family	Liliaceae
In the Iris family	*Moraea* pp.
Oxalis family	Oxalidaceae
Grasses and forbs	
Cladoraphis grass	*Cladoraphis cyperoides*
African daisy	*Dimorphotheca* spp.
Zulu fescue	*Fingerhuthia africana*
Stipagrostis grass	*Stipagrostis ciliata*
Stipagrostis grass	*Stipagrostis obtusa*
Lichens	
Telochistes (Fruticose)	*Telochistes capensis*
Xanthoparmelia (Foliose)	*Xanthoparmelia hyporbytida*
Orange lichen (Foliose)	*Xanthoria turbinata*

Some Characteristic Animals of the Succulent Karoo

Herbivores	
Springbok	*Antidorcas marsupialis*
Dune hairy-footed gerbil	*Gerbillurus paeba*
Cape porcupine	*Hystrix africaeaustralis*
Cape hare	*Lepus capensis*
Gerbil mouse	*Malacothrix typica*
Kirk's dik-dik	*Modoqua kirkii*

Klipspringer	*Oreotragus oreotragus*
Gemsbok or Oryx	*Oryx gazella*
Brant's whistling rat	*Paratomys brantsii*
Vlei rat	*Paratomys littledalei*
Springhare	*Pedetes capensis*
Warthog	*Phacoecerus aethiopicus*
Hyrax or Dassy	*Procavia capensis*
Steenbok	*Raphicerus campestris*
Meerkat or Suricate	*Suricata suricatta*
Common duiker	*Sylvicapra grimmia*
Ground squirrel	*Xerus inauris*
Carnivores	
Saddle-backed jackal	*Canis mesomelas*
Caracal	*Caracal caracal*
Common mole rat	*Cryptomys hottentotus*
Yellow mongoose	*Cynictis penicillata*
African wildcat	*Felis sylvestris lybicus*
Brown hyena	*Hyaena brunnea*
Short-eared elephant shrew	*Macroscelides proboscideus*
Honey badger	*Mellivora capensis*
Aardvark	*Orycteropus afer*
Bat-eared fox	*Otocyon megalotis*
Chacma baboon	*Papio cynocephalus*
Aardwolf	*Proteles cristatus*
Birds	
Karoo Lark	*Certhilauda albescens*
Pied Crow	*Corvus albus*
Rock Kestrel	*Falco tinnuculus*
Ostrich	*Struthio camelus australis*
Reptiles and amphibians	
Namaqua dwarf adder	*Bitis schneideri*
Boulenger's short-headed frog	*Breviceps macrops*
Namaqualand short-headed frog	*Breviceps namaquensis*
Frog	*Bufo robinsoni*
Spiny lizards	*Cordylus* spp.
Mountain tortoise or Leopard tortoise	*Geochelone pardalis*
Richtersveld dwarf leaf-toed gecko	*Goggia gemmula*
Namaqualand speckled padloper	*Homopus signatus signatus*
Cape cobra	*Naja nivea*
Geometric tortoise	*Psammobates geometricus*
Karoo tent tortoise	*Psammobates tentorius*
Calvinia thick-toed gecko	*Pachydactylus labialis*

(*Continued*)

Southwestern shovel-snout snake	*Prosymna frontalis*
Karoo sand snake	*Psammophis notostictus*

Some Characteristic Plants of the Nama-Karoo

Nonsucculent shrubs	
Boxthorn	*Lycium* spp.
In the Sunflower family	*Pentzia spinescens*
In the Trumpet creeper family	*Rhigozum trichotomum*
Sumac	*Rhus undulata*
In the Goosefoot family	*Salsola* spp.
Succulent shrubs	
Shrubby iceplant	*Ruschia ferox*
Grasses and forbs	
Three-awn grass	*Aristida congesta*
Lovegrass	*Eragrostis lehmanniana*
Dropseed grass	*Sporobolus* spp.
Stipagrostis grass	*Stipagrostis* spp.

Some Characteristic Animals of the Nama-Karoo

Herbivores	
Springbok	*Antidorcas marsupialis*
Burchell's zebra	*Equus burchelli*
Cape porcupine	*Hystrix africaeaustralis*
Cape hare	*Lepus capensis*
Kirk's dik-dik	*Madoqua kirkii*
Gerbil mouse	*Malacothrix typica*
Klipspringer	*Oreotragus oreotragus*
Gemsbok or Oryx	*Oryx gazella*
Vlei rat	*Paratomys littledalei*
Springhare	*Pedetes capensis*
Warthog	*Phacoecerus aethiopicus*
Hyrax or Dassy	*Procavia capensis*
Steenbok	*Raphicerus campestris*
Meerkat or Suricate	*Suricata suricatta*
Common duiker	*Sylvicapra grimmia*
Ground squirrel	*Xeros inauris*
Carnivores	
Saddle-backed jackal	*Canis mesomelas*
Caracal	*Caracal caracal*
Common mole rat	*Cryptomys hottentotus*
Yellow mongoose	*Cynictis penicillata*
African wildcat	*Felis sylvestris lybicus*

Brown hyena	*Hyaena brunnea*
Short-eared elephant shrew	*Macroscelides proboscideus*
Honey badger	*Mellivora capensis*
Aardvark	*Orycteropus afer*
Bat-eared fox	*Otocyon megalotis*
Chacma baboon	*Papio cynocephalus*
Aardwolf	*Proteles cristatus*
Birds	
Karoo Lark	*Certhilauda albescens*
Pied Crow	*Corvus albus*
Rock Kestrel	*Falco tinnuculus*
Ostrich	*Struthio camelus australis*
Reptiles and amphibians	
Spiny lizards	*Cordylus* spp.
Mountain tortoise or Leopard tortoise	*Geochelone pardalis*
Southwestern shovel-snout snake	*Prosymna frontalis*
Karoo sand snake	*Psammophis notostictus*

Small Fog Deserts

Some Characteristic Plants of the Galapagos Islands Desert

Trees	
Palo santo	*Bursera graveolons*
Jerusalem thorn	*Parkinsonia aculeata*
Shrubs	
Galapagos acacia	*Acacia rorudiana*
Croton	*Croton scouleri*
Honey mesquite	*Prosopis juliflora*
Cactus	
Lava cactus	*Brachycereus nesioticus*
Candelabra cactus	*Jasminocereus* spp.
Giant prickly pear	*Opuntia echios*
Prickly pear	*Opuntia helleri*

Some Characteristic Animals of the Galapagos Islands Desert

Small animals	
Bat	*Lasiurus* spp.
Galapagos rice rat	*Oryzomis* spp.
Birds	
Warbler Finch	*Certhidea olivacea*
Waved Albatross	*Diomedia irrorata*

(*Continued*)

Frigatebird	*Fregata* spp.
Large Ground Finch	*Geospiza magnirostris*
Gull	*Larus* spp.
Galapagos Mockingbird	*Nesomimus longicaudatus*
Galapagos Penguin	*Spheniscus mendiculus*
Boobies	*Sula* spp.
Galapagos Dove	*Zenaida galapagoensis*
Reptiles and amphibians	
Marine iguana	*Amblyrhnchus cristatus*
Giant tortoise	*Geochelone elephantopus*
Land iguana	*Conolophus* spp.
Lava lizard	*Tropidurus* spp.

Some Characteristic Plants of Socotra

Trees	
Christ's thorn jujube	*Ziziphus spina-christi*
Tree succulents or caudiciforms	
Adenium or Desert rose	*Adenium socotranum*
In the Bursera family	*Commiphora* spp.
Dragon's blood tree	*Dracaena cinnabar*
Euphorbia	*Euphorbia arbuscula*
Cucumber tree	*Dendrosicyos socotranus*
Shrubs	
Croton	*Croton socotranus*
In the Euphorbia family	*Jatropha unicostata*

Some Characteristic Animals of Socotra

Small animals	
Bat	*Rhinopoma* spp.
Shrew	*Suneus* spp.
Birds	
Socotra Sunbird	*Nectarinia balfouri*
Socotra Starling	*Onychognathus frater*
Socotra Sparrow	*Passer insularis*
Socotra Golden-winged Grosbeak	*Rhynchostruthus socotranus*

Some Characteristic Plants of the Madagascar Desert Scrub

Trees succulents and caudiciforms	
Madagascar baobab	*Adansonia madagascariensis*
In the Didieria family	*Alluaudia* spp.

In the Didieria family	*Alluaudiopsis* spp.
In the Bursera family	*Commiphora* spp.
Didieria	*Didieria* spp.
Euphorbia	*Euphorbia stenocladia*
Bottle tree	*Moringa drouhardii*
In the Dogbane family	*Pachypodium lamerei*
Leaf succulents	
Aloe	*Aloe* spp.
In the Jade plant family	*Kalanchoe* spp.
Shrubs	
Euphorbia	*Euphorbia cylindrifolia*
Euphorbia	*Euphorbia francoisii*
Euphorbia	*Euphorbia Cap-Saintemariensis*

Some Characteristic Animals of the Madagascar Desert Scrub

Small animals	
Fat-tailed dwarf lemur	*Cheirogaleus medius*
Ring-tailed lemur	*Lemur catta*
White-footed sportive lemur	*Lepilemur leucopis*
Gray mouse lemur	*Microcebus murinus*
Forked-marked lemur	*Phaner furcifer*
Verreaux's sifaka	*Propithecus verreauxi*
Birds	
Red-shouldered Vanga	*Calicalicus rufocarpalis*
Running Coua	*Coua cursor*
Verreaux's Coua	*Coua verreauxi*
Lafresnaye's Vanga	*Xenopirostris xenopirostris*
Reptiles and amphibians	
Boa	*Acrantophis dumerilii*
Nocturnal gecko	*Ebanavia maintimainty*
Madagascar radiated tortoise	*Geochelone radiata*
Nocturnal gecko	*Matoatoa brevipes*
Spider tortoise	*Pyxis arachnoides*

Glossary

Adiabatic. Process in physics whereby air warms due to compression and cools due to expansion, with no gain or loss of energy.

Advection. Horizontally moving air, wind.

Aestivation. Drop in metabolism, such as heartbeat and respiration, and need for energy. Used by animals to avoid an unfavorable season. May be triggered by high temperatures or scarce food resources.

Albedo. Reflectivity of a surface; refers to how much solar radiation is reflected.

Allelopathy. Process whereby plants exude toxins that prevent germination of competitors.

Alluvial Fan. Gentle slope of alluvium extending downward from a mountain into a desert valley.

Alluvium. Sediment of any size (clay, silt, sand, gravel, cobbles) carried by and deposited by running water.

Annual. A plant that completes its life cycle in one year or one growing season.

Aridisol. Desert soil showing little development due to lack of water.

Aspect. Direction toward which a slope faces. Also known as exposure.

Bajada. Gentle slope of alluvium created by merged alluvial fans.

Behavioral. Refers to activities or behavior of animals.

Biome. A large region with similar vegetation, animal life, and environmental conditions.

Biota. The combined flora and fauna, all the plants and animals in an area.

Browser. Herbivore that feeds on twigs and leaves rather than on grass. *Browse* refers to that kind of food.

Bulb. An enlarged root that stores nutrients and energy.

Caliche. Accumulation of calcium carbonate below the surface of desert soils. Hardpan, calcrete.

CAM (crassulacean acid metabolism). A form of photosynthesis used by plants to conserve water.

Caudiciform. Plant with an enlarged stem, base, or root that stores moisture. Swollen part is called a caudex.

Cenozoic. A recent geologic time period, roughly 65 million years ago to the present.

Chenopod. Member of the Chenopodiacea, or goosefoot family. Usually xerophytic or halophytic shrubs.

Climate. Typical weather patterns (especially temperature and precipitation) during a normal year that are experienced over decades or centuries. Weather refers to the conditions of the atmosphere at any given moment.

Community. The plants and animals assembled in a given area. Sometimes refers to only a subset of these organisms, such as the plant community or the bird community.

Continental Glaciation. Condition of massive ice sheets that covered much of North America and Eurasia during the Pleistocene.

Continentality. The effect a large landmass has on seasonal temperature variations. Continental areas are warmer in summer and colder in winter. *See also* **Maritime**.

Continental Shield. Hard rock, permanent core of a continent as opposed to sedimentary rock covers that are deposited and worn away over geologic time.

Convection. Warm air that rises. May cause convectional rain or thunderstorms.

Convergent Evolution. The process whereby unrelated plants (or animals) have evolved similar adaptations or appearance in response to similar environmental conditions.

Cover. The proportion of a surface on which vegetation occurs, usually measured as a percent.

Crepuscular. Refers to an animal being active at dawn and dusk.

Cretaceous. A geological time period from roughly 145 million years ago to 65 million years ago.

Crustose (lichen). Crust like. *See also* **Foliose; Fruticose**.

Cushion Plant. A multistemmed plant that grows as a dense mound.

Cyclonic Storm. Type of weather that results when cold air comes in contact with warm air in the mid-latitudes. It usually causes precipitation.

Deciduous. Refers to plants, usually trees and shrubs, that drop their leaves during non-growing seasons.

Desert Pavement. Hard-packed mosaic of stones on desert surfaces caused by wind blowing away finer sand and silt.

Diurnal. Change from day to night. Also refers to an animal active during the day.

Drought Deciduous. Plant that drops leaves in response to drought.

Dwarf Shrub. Small shrub with branches less than 12 in (30 cm) high.

Ectothermic. Animals in which body temperature is controlled by the environment. Cold-blooded.

El Niño. Event in the Pacific Ocean when warm water replaces the cold current off the coast of South America. Changes weather patterns in South America and affects weather worldwide.

Endemic. Originating in and restricted to a particular geographic area.

Endothermic. Animals in which body temperature is internally controlled. Warm-blooded.

Entisol. Recently developed soils that have no differentiated horizons or layers.

Ephemeral. Referring to short life span, such as annual plants or streams that have water infrequently.

Epiphyte. Plant that needs no soil, growing on other plants only for support.

Erg. Expanse of sand dunes.

Evaporative Cooling. Because evaporation requires energy, it is a cooling process.

Evapotranspiration. The combined processes of adding water vapor to the atmosphere through evaporation from the soil and bodies of water and from the passage of water out of plants through the stomata in their leaves.

Evergreen. Refers to plants, usually trees or shrubs, which maintain leaves all year. Leaves may be replaced throughout the year or in a flush during a single season, but the plant is never without live foliage.

Fault Block Mountain. Mountain caused by faulting, usually abrupt with no foothills.

Fauna. All the animal species in a given area.

Flora. All the plant species in a given area. *See also* **Vegetation**.

Floristic Province. A region with related plants that evolved in that area. Also called floristic realm.

Fog Drip. Moisture from fog that is deposited on the ground or on plants.

Foliose (lichen). Leaf like in appearance. *See also* **Crustose; Fruticose**.

Forb. A broadleaved, green-stemmed, nonwoody plant. One type of herb.

Free Water. Liquid water available for drinking, such as in rivers or as dew.

Fruticose (lichen). Shrubby, upright in appearance. *See also* **Crustose; Foliose**.

Garua. Fog in Peru formed by moisture-laden wind moving upslope.

Genus (plural = genera). A taxonomic unit composed of one or more closely related species.

Geophyte. Plant, such as a bulb, that holds its regenerating point below ground.

Gibber Plain. Gravelly desert pavement in Australia.

Growthform. The appearance or morphology of a plant that is adapted to particular environmental conditions. Examples include tree, shrub, and forb.

Habitat. The place where a species lives and the local environmental conditions of that place.

Halophyte. Plant adapted to growing on salty soil.

Hammada. Bare rock surface.

Herb. A nonwoody or soft, green-stemmed plant that dies down each year. May be annual or perennial. Broadleaved herbs are called forbs. Grasses and sedges are called graminoids.

Herbaceous. Nonwoody plant that dies back every year.

Hibernation. Refers to when an animal's body temperature is reduced to that of the environment, resulting in a decrease in metabolism and need for energy. Used by animals to avoid a cold season.

High Pressure. Air that is heavier than the normal 14.7 pounds per square inch. High-pressure air will sink.

Humidity. A measure of the amount of water vapor in the air.

Inceptisol. Developing soil that has least one distinctive horizon or layer.

Indicator Plant. A plant typical of a biome (or subdivision) that can be used to delimit the biome's extent in the absence of climatic data. Also called signature plant.

Inflorescence. Flower stalk.

Infrared Radiation. Energy that comes from the Earth. Also called long-wave radiation or terrestrial radiation.

Interior Drainage. Refers to regions where rivers flow to the interior of the landscape instead of emptying into the ocean.

Introduced (species). A species transported accidentally or deliberately by humans beyond its natural distribution area. Also called alien.

Inversion. Air is warmer with increasing elevation, instead of the normal lapse rate of cooler temperatures.

Karoo. Afrikaans word referring to shrubs or shrubland.

Koeppen. A climate classification system based on temperature and precipitation.

Lapse Rate. Decrease in temperature as elevation increases. Averages 3.5° F per 1,000 ft (1° C per 100 m) but is variable.

Latitude. Distance north or south of the Equator, measured in degrees. The Equator is 0° latitude. Low latitudes lie between 0° and 30° north and south; mid-latitudes between 30° and 60°, and high latitudes between 60° and 90°.

Lichen. A form of life composed of a fungus and an alga joined in a symbiotic relationship and classified as a single organism.

Lifeform (Raunkiaer's). A category of plant life based upon morphology and the position of the renewal bud.

Loess. Wind-blown dust that often develops into deep, fertile soil.

Loma. Hill or valley in coastal Peru or Chile where fog is trapped.

Low Pressure. Air that is lighter than the normal 14.7 pounds per square inch. Low-pressure air will rise.

Maritime. The effect large bodies of water have on moderating seasonal temperature variations. Maritime climates do not have extremes of temperature. *See also* **Continentality**.

Mesa. Flat-top mountain with steep sides, usually in sedimentary rocks.

Mesembryanthemaceae (mesembs). Large and unique family of succulent plants endemic to southern Africa. Ice plant family. Called vygies in Afrikaans.

Metabolic Water. Water that is manufactured within an animal's body from the food it eats.

Microclimate. Small area with climate conditions different from the general climate of the area.

Microhabitat. A tiny nook or habitat with specific environmental conditions that differ from that of the larger habitat in which it occurs.

Monsoon. Continental-scale wind-reversal system, primarily affecting Asia. Cold, dry winds blow from the continent in winter, reversing to warm, wet winds from the oceans in summer.

Morphology. Form and structure, size and shape of an organism. General appearance of an organism.

Nebka. Small sand hill where shrubs trap wind-blown sand.

Nocturnal. Refers to an animal being active at night.

Nurse Plant. Tree or shrub that provides shade and protection to a seedling beneath its canopy.

Orographic Precipitation. Precipitation that falls on the windward side of a mountain as air is forced to rise and cool.

Parent Material. Sediment or rock from which soil is developed. Contributes mineral component of the soil.

Parthenogenesis. Reproduction by females without male sperm.

Perennial. Refers to a plant that lives for several years and undergoes active growth each year.

PET (potential evapotranspiration). The amount of water that could be evaporated if it were available.

Photoperiod. Number of hours of daylight.

Photosynthesis. The process by which green plants convert oxygen and carbon dioxide in the presence of sunlight to sugars. Energy in the form of visible light is transformed into chemical energy that can be used by living organisms.

Phreatophyte. Plant with deep roots that obtain moisture from deep underground water sources.

Physiological Drought. Condition where even though water is available, it cannot be used by plants. Ice and salty soils are examples.

Physiology. The metabolic functions and processes of organisms.

Playa. Dry lake bed, with a clay or salt surface.

Pleistocene. Geologic time period when glaciers covered much of North America and Eurasia, from approximately 1.6 million to 10,000 years ago. Also called the Ice Age.

Psammophyte. Plant adapted to living in sand.

Rainshadow. The lee side of a mountain, opposite the windward side, that receives little precipitation. *See also* **Orographic Precipitation**.

Reg. Gravel surface, similar to desert pavement.

Reradiation. The sun's energy received during the day that is radiated back to the atmosphere at night. Also called infrared radiation.

Rhizome. A horizontal root structure that lies just below the surface of the soil.

Riparian. Refers to areas along rivers and other water courses where groundwater may be present. Also refers to vegetation in those areas.

Rosette. A growthform characterized by a basal whorl of leaves around a central stem or renewal bud. Can be flat to the ground or taller.

Sclerophyllous. Refers to leaves that are thick or waxy to prevent water loss.

Scrub. A vegetation type characterized by sparse, small shrubs.

Seasonality. Difference in temperature or precipitation between winter and summer.

Sexual Reproduction. The formation of new individuals by the fusion of gametes (ova) and pollen in plants; egg and sperm in animals.

Shrub. Woody plant with several branches growing from the base, as opposed to a tree with one main stem or trunk.

Soil. The uppermost layer on land. Composed of a mixture of mineral and organic materials in which plants grow.

Soil Horizon. A layer within the soil which is fairly distinct in terms of its chemistry, texture, and color.

Solar Radiation. Energy that comes from the sun, also called short-wave radiation or insolation.

Species. A group of sexually reproducing individuals that can produce viable offspring. The fundamental unit of classification in taxonomy.

Steppe. Semiarid grasslands.

Substrate. Surface material in which plants grow, including rock, soil, or sediments.

Subtree. Short, scrubby tree.

Subtropical High-Pressure Cells. Prominent areas of high-pressure centered on 25–30° north and south latitude.

Succulent. A growthform that has specialized tissue in the stem, leaves, or an underground organ for the storage of water.

Sun Angle. How high the sun is in the sky during the day and a major factor in temperature. Higher sun angle imparts more warmth; lower sun angle, less.

Symbiotic Relationship. Mutually beneficial for both organisms.

Taproot. A root that extends deep into the ground that provides access to water.

Taxonomy. The science of describing, classifying, and naming organisms.

Temperate. Refers generally to the temperature patterns of the mid-latitudes, the temperate zone, where summers are warm to hot and winters are mild to cool. Not too cold or too hot.

Tertiary. A recent geologic time period, from approximately 1.6 million to 65 million years ago.

Tolerance Limits. Refers to the extremes of environmental factors, such as cold, heat, drought, and snow depth, beyond which an individual species cannot survive.

Torpor. Reduction in an animal's body temperature for a short period of time, allowing the animal to avoid an unfavorable environmental period. The animal becomes torpid. Not true hibernation because body temperature is not reduced to that of the environment.

Tropics. The parts of Earth that lie between 23½° N and 23½° S or between the Tropic of Cancer and the Tropic of Capricorn. Subtropics refer to the regions slightly poleward.

Tussock. A growthform of grasses and sedges in which individuals grow as tufts or clumps and form conspicuous hummocks on the ground.

Ungulate. Any hoofed mammal, such as a cow, elk, or springbok.

Vascular Plant. Any plant with conducting vessels that move nutrients and water between roots and leaves. Includes flowering plants and ferns.

Vasoconstriction. Constriction of blood vessels that decreases blood flow and retains heat.

Vasodilation. Dilation of blood vessels that increases blood flow and dissipation of heat.

Vegetation. The general plant cover of an area, defined according to the appearance of the plants (grass, forest, shrubs) rather than the actual species present. *See also* **Flora**.

Vegetative Reproduction. The formation of new plants from pieces of the parent plant such as fragments of leaves, roots, stems, or rhizomes. Also called asexual reproduction. Includes cloning.

Veld. Afrikaans word meaning shrubby or grassy landscape.

Ventifact. Rock that has been faceted by wind-blown sand.

Virga. Rain that evaporates into dry air before reaching the ground. Can sometimes be seen as dark streaks extending down from a cloud.

Vygie. Afrikaans word for mesemb.

Wash. Dry stream bed in deserts that only holds water occasionally. Also called wadi or arroyo.

Window Plants. Plants with translucent pigment that allows sunlight to penetrate deep into the cells.

Windward. The side of a mountain in the path of prevailing winds that receives precipitation. Opposite of rainshadow or lee side.

Xerophyte. Plant that is adapted to arid conditions.

Yardang. Large rock outcrop shaped by wind-blown sand.

Bibliography

General

Page, Jake, and the editors of Time-Life Books. 1984. *Arid Lands.* Planet Earth Series. Alexandria, VA: Time-Life Books.

Schmidt-Nielsen, Knut. 1964. *Desert Animals: Physiological Problems of Heat and Water.* Oxford: Clarendon Press.

University of Michigan Museum of Zoology. n.d. "Animal Diversity Web." http://animaldiversity.ummz.umich.edu.

Walton, Kenneth. 1969. *The Arid Zones.* Chicago: Aldine Publishing Co.

Wang, Lawrence C. H., ed. 1989. *Advances in Comparative and Environmental Physiology, Vol. 4: Animal Adaptation to Cold.* New York: Springer-Verlag.

Weatherbase. n.d. http://www.weatherbase.com.

World Wildlife Fund. n.d. "Terrestrial Biomes." http://www.worldwildlife.org/wildworld/profiles.

Warm Deserts

Abd el Rahman, A. A. 1986. "The Deserts of the Arabian Peninsula." In *Hot Deserts and Arid Shrublands,* ed. Michael Evenari, Imanuel Noy-Meir, and David W. Goodall, 29–54. Ecosystems of the World, 12B. Amsterdam: Elsevier.

Ayyad, Mohamed A., and Samir I. Ghabbour. 1986. "Hot Deserts of Egypt and the Sudan." In *Hot Deserts and Arid Shrublands,* ed. Michael Evenari, Imanuel Noy-Meir, and David W. Goodall, 149–202. Ecosystems of the World, 12B. Amsterdam: Elsevier.

Barbour, Michael G., and William Dwight Billings, eds. 2000. *North American Terrestrial Vegetation,* 2nd ed. Cambridge: Cambridge University Press.

Bender, Gordon L., ed. 1982. *Reference Handbook on the Deserts of North America.* Westport, CT: Greenwood Press.

Breeding Centre. n.d. "Breeding Centre for Endangered Arabian Wildlife." http://www.breedingcentresharjah.com.

Brown, David E., ed. 1982. *Biotic Communities of the American Southwest—United States and Mexico.* Special Issue of *Desert Plants* 4 (1–4): 1–342. Tucson: University of Arizona Press, for Boyce Thompson Southwestern Arboretum.

Gupta, R. K. 1986. "The Thar Desert." In *Hot Deserts and Arid Shrublands,* ed. Michael Evenari, Imanuel Noy-Meir, and David W. Goodall, 55–99. Ecosystems of the World, 12B. Amsterdam: Elsevier.

Jaeger, Edmund C. 1957. *The North American Deserts.* Stanford, CA: Stanford University Press.

LeHouerou, Henri Noel. 1986. "The Desert and Arid Zones of Northern Africa." In *Hot Deserts and Arid Shrublands,* ed. Michael Evenari, Imanuel Noy-Meir, and David W. Goodall, 101–147. Ecosystems of the World, 12B. Amsterdam: Elsevier.

MacMahon, James A. 2000. "Warm Deserts." In *North American Terrestrial Vegetation,* 2nd ed., ed. Michael G. Barbour and William Dwight Billings, 285–322. Cambridge: Cambridge University Press.

Mares, Michael A. 2002. *A Desert Calling: Life in a Forbidding Landscape.* Cambridge, MA: Harvard University Press.

Mares, M. A., J. Morello, and G. Goldstein. 1985. "The Monte Desert and Other Subtropical Semi-arid Biomes of Argentina, with Comments on their Relation to North American Arid Areas." In *Hot Deserts and Arid Shrublands,* ed. Michael Evenari, Imanuel Noy-Meir, and David W. Goodall, 203–237. Ecosystems of the World, 12B. Amsterdam: Elsevier.

MacMahon, J. A., and F. H. Wagner. 1985. "The Mojave, Sonoran, and Chihuahuan Deserts of North America." In *Hot Deserts and Arid Shrublands,* ed. Michael Evenari, Imanuel Noy-Meir, and David W. Goodall, 105–202. Ecosystems of the World, 12B. Amsterdam: Elsevier.

McGinnies, Willam G. 1981. *Discovering the Desert: Legacy of the Carnegie Desert Botanical Laboratory.* Tucson: University of Arizona Press.

Morcombe, Michael K. 1980. *Australia's Living Deserts.* Sydney: Ure Smith.

Orians, Gordon H., and Otto T. Solbrig, eds. 1977. *Convergent Evolution in Warm Deserts: An Examination of Strategies and Patterns in Deserts of Argentina and the United States.* Dowden. (US/IBP synthesis series 3). Stroudsburg, PA: Hutchinson & Ross, Inc.

Orshan, G. 1985. "The Deserts of the Middle East." In *Hot Deserts and Arid Shrublands,* ed. Michael Evenari, Imanuel Noy-Meir, and David W. Goodall, 1–26. Ecosystems of the World, 12B. Amsterdam: Elsevier.

Sowell, John. 2001. *Desert Ecology: An Introduction to Life in the Arid Southwest.* Salt Lake City: University of Utah Press.

Sutton, Ann, and Myron Sutton. 1966. *The Life of the Desert.* Our Living World of Nature Series. New York: McGraw-Hill.

Swift, Jeremy, and editors of Time-Life Books. 1975. *The Sahara.* The World's Wild Places Series. Amsterdam: Time-Life International.

Williams, O. B., and J. H. Calaby. 1985. "The Hot Deserts of Australia." In *Hot Deserts and Arid Shrublands,* ed. Michael Evenari, Imanuel Noy-Meir, and David W. Goodall, 269–312. Ecosystems of the World, 12B. Amsterdam: Elsevier.

Cold Deserts

Barbour, Michael G., and William Dwight Billings, eds. 2000. *North American Terrestrial Vegetation,* 2nd ed. Cambridge: Cambridge University Press.

Bender, Gordon L., ed. 1982. *Reference Handbook on the Deserts of North America.* Westport, CT: Greenwood Press.

Soriano, Alberto. 1983. "Deserts and Semi-deserts of Patagonia." In *Temperate Deserts and Semi-Deserts,* ed. Neil E. West, 423–460. Ecosystems of the World, 5. Amsterdam: Elsevier.

Walter, H., and E. O. Box. 1983. "The Deserts of Central Asia." In *Temperate Deserts and Semi-Deserts,* ed. Neil E. West, 193–236. Ecosystems of the World, 5. Amsterdam: Elsevier.

Walter, H., and E. O. Box. 1983. "The Karakum Desert, an Example of a Well-studied Eu-Biome." In *Temperate Deserts and Semi-Deserts,* ed. Neil E. West, 105–159. Ecosystems of the World, 5. Amsterdam: Elsevier.

Walter, H., and E. O. Box. 1983. "Middle Asia Deserts." In *Temperate Deserts and Semi-Deserts,* ed. Neil E. West, 79–104. Ecosystems of the World, 5. Amsterdam: Elsevier.

West, Neil E. 1983. "Overview of North American Temperate Deserts and Semi-deserts." In *Temperate Deserts and Semi-Deserts,* ed. Neil E. West, 321–330. Ecosystems of the World, 5. Amsterdam: Elsevier.

West, Neil E. 1983. "Great Basin-Colorado Sagebrush Semi-desert." In *Temperate Deserts and Semi-Deserts,* ed. Neil E. West, 331–349. Ecosystems of the World, 5. Amsterdam: Elsevier.

West, Neil E. 1983. "Western Intermontane Sagebrush Steppe." In *Temperate Deserts and Semi-Deserts,* ed. Neil E. West, 351–374. Ecosystems of the World, 5. Amsterdam: Elsevier.

West, Neil E. 1983. "Intermontane Salt-desert Shrubland." In *Temperate Deserts and Semi-Deserts,* ed. Neil E. West, 375–397. Ecosystems of the World, 5. Amsterdam: Elsevier.

West, Neil E. 1983. *Temperate Deserts and Semi-Deserts.* Ecosystems of the World, 5. Amsterdam: Elsevier.

West-Coast Fog Deserts

Acocks, J. P. H. 1975. "Veld Types of South Africa." *Memoirs of the Botanical Survey of South Africa* 40: 1–128.

Amiran, David H. K., and Andrew W. Wilson. 1973. *Coastal Deserts: Their Natural and Human Environments.* Tucson: University of Arizona Press.

Constant, Pierre. 1997. *The Galapagos Islands: A Natural History Guide.* Lincolnwood, IL: Passport Books.

Cowling, Richard, and Shirley Pierce. 1999. *Namaqualand: A Succulent Desert.* Vlaeberg, South Africa: Fernwood Press.

Logan, Richard F. 1960. *The Central Namib Desert: South West Africa.* Publication 758. Washington, DC: National Academy of Sciences, National Research Council.

Milius, Susan. October 27, 2001. "Torn to Ribbons in the Desert, Botanists Puzzle Over One of Earth's Oddest Plants." *Science News* 160: 266–268.

Rauh, Walter. 1985. "The Peruvian-Chilean Deserts." In *Hot Deserts and Arid Shrublands,* ed. Michael Evenari, Imanuel Noy-Meir, and David W. Goodall, 239–267. Ecosystems of the World, 12B. Amsterdam: Elsevier.

Rauh, W. 1986. "The Arid Region of Madagascar." In *Hot Deserts and Arid Shrublands,* ed. Michael Evenari, Imanuel Noy-Meir, and David W. Goodall, 361–377. Ecosystems of the World, 12B, Amsterdam: Elsevier.

Schulz, Rudolf, and Attila Kapitany. 1996. *Copiapoa in Their Environment.* Teesdale, Victoria, Australia: Southbank Book.

Walter, H. 1986. "The Namib Desert." In *Hot Deserts and Arid Shrublands,* ed. Michael Evenari, Imanuel Noy-Meir, and David W. Goodall, 245–282. Ecosystems of the World, 12B. Amsterdam: Elsevier.

Werger, M. J. A. 1986. "The Karoo and Southern Kalahari." In *Hot Deserts and Arid Shrublands,* ed. Michael Evenari, Imanuel Noy-Meir, and David W. Goodall, 283–359. Ecosystems of the World, 12B. Amsterdam: Elsevier.

Index

The letter *f* following a page number denotes a figure. The letter *t* following a page number denotes a table

About the Author

JOYCE A. QUINN retired from California State University–Fresno as professor emerita after twenty-one years of teaching a variety of courses in physical geography and mapping techniques. She earned an M.A. from the University of Colorado and a Ph.D. from Arizona State University, specializing in the effect of climate on the distribution of plants. Travel throughout the United States, Latin America, Europe, northern and southern Africa, Uzbekistan, Nepal, China, Southeast Asia, Micronesia, and elsewhere allowed her to experience several biomes firsthand. She is a member of the Cactus and Succulent Society of America and maintains a collection of cacti and succulents representative of many of the world's deserts.